In this volume . . .

YOUR AUTOMATIC WASHER is a complex machine combining precise machinery, plumbing, and electronic controls. You can pin down malfunctions and make many repairs yourself. See the step-by-step troubleshooting charts starting on page 3258.

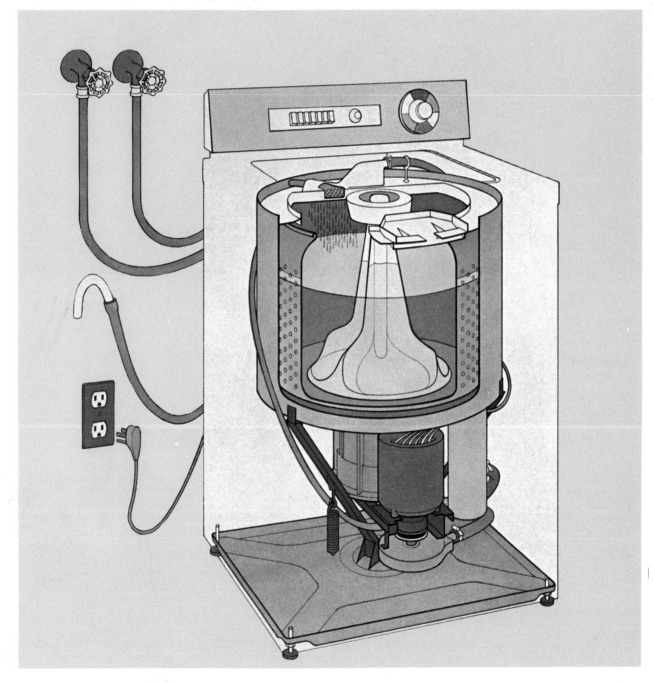

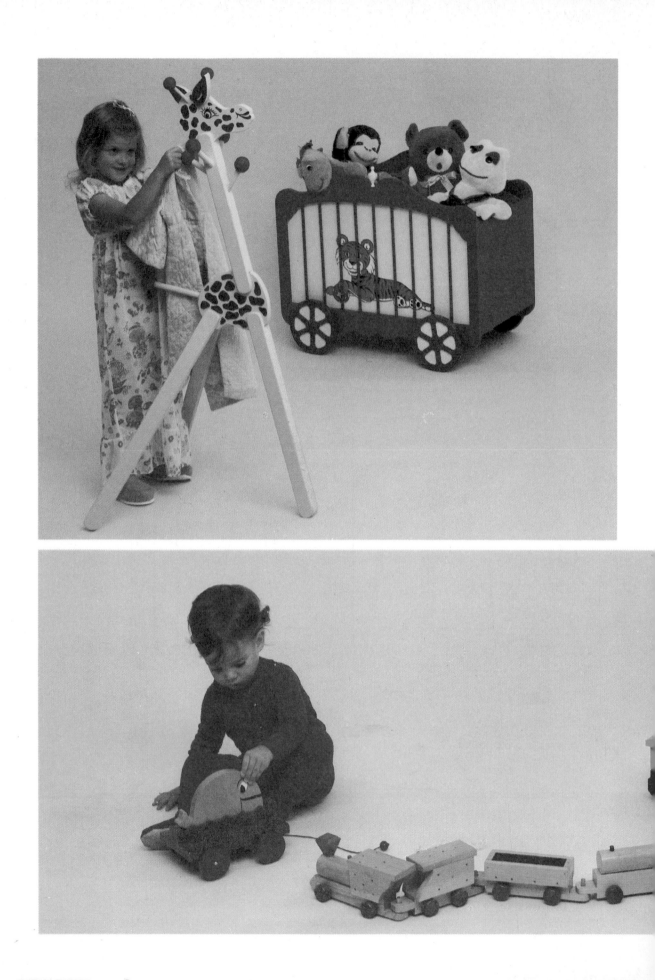

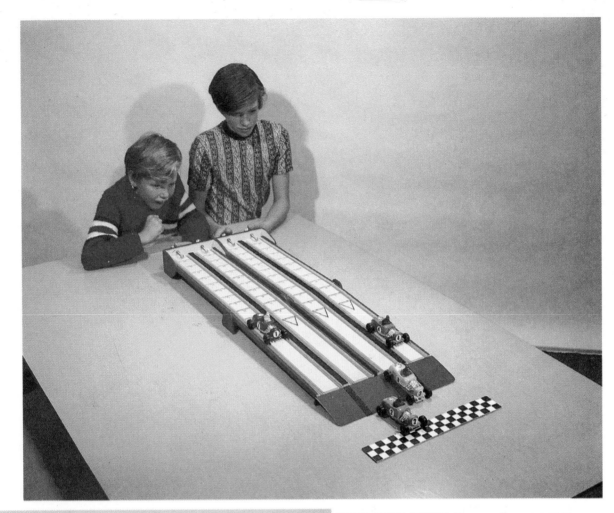

HERE THEY COME! Four racing cars roar down the track to an exciting finish. You can make this handsome toy yourself, mostly from scraps you'll find around the house. The plastic cars are available at toy stores. See complete plans on page 3100.

THESE BEAUTIFULLY DESIGNED toys not only are fun to play with, they're fun to make. They include a circus-wagon toy box, a giraffe clothes tree, a gobbling whale, a classic wood-block train, and a separate engine that puff-puffs as it's pulled across the floor. We know that *you* know certain children who'd love to have these special toys. Plans start on page 3088.

HOW DO YOU CHOOSE the right tree for your yard? It should be handsome in winter as well as summer, clean, and do its job well, whether that job is shading your home, decorating a patio, or providing a privacy screen. Find tips on selecting trees on page 3154.

WHEN IS A BOX not a box? When it becomes a work of art. This box started out as an ordinary box that held after-shave lotion. It's decorated with bits and parts from hobby stores and souvenir stands. With some imagination, you too can create a miniature masterpiece. For other examples, turn to page 3163.

Popular Mechanics
do-it-yourself encyclopedia

in 18 volumes

a complete how-to guide for the homeowner. the hobbyist—
and anyone who enjoys working with mind and hands!

All about:

home maintenance

home-improvement projects

wall paneling

burglary and fire protection

furniture projects

finishing and refinishing furniture

outdoor living

home remodeling

solutions to home problems

challenging woodworking projects

hobbies and handicrafts

model making

weekend projects

workshop shortcuts and techniques

hand-tool skills

power-tool know-how

shop-made tools

car repairs

car maintenance

appliance repair

boating

hunting

fishing

camping

photography projects

radio, TV and electronics know-how

clever hints and tips

projects just for fun

volume 17

Popular Mechanics, 250 W. 55th St., New York, NY 10019

ISBN 0-910990-68-9
Library of Congress Catalog Number 77 84920

Printed in the United States of America

Contents

What hand tools do you need?

Experienced craftsmen often began with a basic tool kit and added units as skills developed. Householders and budding crafters can save money following this procedure

By W. CLYDE LAMMEY

■ EVERY HOUSEHOLD HAS NEED for a small kit of tools for practical applications and the simple joys of using them for repair and maintenance of the home. Over a period of time the savings of doing-it-yourself can add up to an impressive figure in which the tool kit will have long since paid for itself. But sooner or later the beginner becomes a craftsman, planning projects of his own design—a special table, fireside bench, cabinet, or perhaps a reproduction of a cherished antique, using the methods and procedures of the craftsmen of old. It is then that his tool needs expand.

Any listing of basic tools is never really complete or all-inclusive. This is true of the lists given here. The household kit is quite complete for most home-repair jobs and such simple joinery as one might do at the bench, but there are

HOUSEHOLD KIT

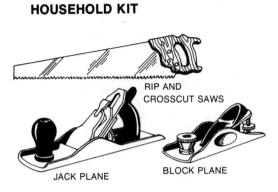

RIP AND
CROSSCUT SAWS

JACK PLANE

BLOCK PLANE

Nail hammer, curved claw, 10 or 16-oz. head
Hand crosscut saw, 12 point
Hand ripping saw, 5 point
Jack plane, 14 in.
Block plane, 6 in.
Ratchet brace, 8 or 10-in. sweep
Auger bit set, ¼ to 1 in. by 16ths
Screwdrivers, 4 and 8-in. blades
Tape rule, or folding rule, as desired
Combination square, 12-in. blade
Combination pliers
Soldering gun, or propane torch, or both
Solder, nonacid and acid core
Adjustable wrenches, sizes as needed
Pipe wrenches, 10 and 14-in. sizes
Hand drill, with fluted bits
Carpenter's level
C-clamps, sizes as needed
Nailset
Files, single and double-cut
Putty knife

HOME-SHOP KIT

All the above and the following:

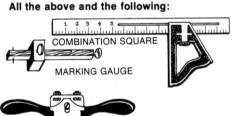

COMBINATION SQUARE

MARKING GAUGE

SPOKESHAVE (STRAIGHT)

Steel square, 24 in.
Twist-drill set, 1/16 to ¼ in.
Tinsnips, plain or duckbill type, or both
Cold chisels, ¼, ⅜ and ½ in.
Marking gauge
Scratch awl
Knife, retractable blade, or pocket knife
Bar clamps, pair, 24 or 36 in. or both sizes
Adjustable clamps, 2 to 8 in.
Miterbox with backsaw
Rose countersink
Combination oilstone
Wood chisels, butt or mortising type, or both
Dowel centers
Miter clamp
Spokeshave, straight blade
Magnetic brad driver "Pop" rivet tool, rivets

many hand tools that might be added to the list as you will see from the homeshop kit and the cabinetmaker's kit. Both the latter are suggested for the convenience and information of the more advanced craftsman.

There are, of course, alternate choices. For example, in the homeshop kit you will see a 24-in. steel square listed, but in the household kit a combination square with 12-in. blade. The former may be more suited to your immediate needs but the latter is also useful in a wide range of applications. In time you will likely find need for both, yet in the beginning the combination square is probably the better choice.

Likewise, in the cabinetmaker's kit there is listed the choice of a "soft" hammer or a wooden mallet. Most advanced craftsmen prefer the soft hammer for working a chisel when

CABINETMAKER'S KIT
All the above and the following:

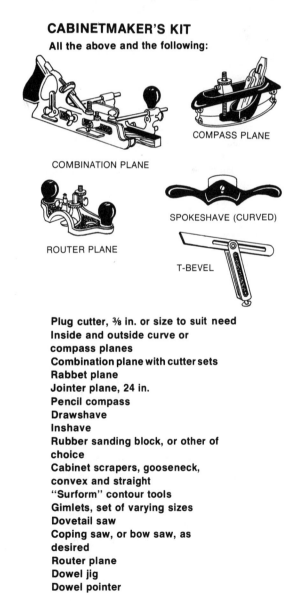

COMPASS PLANE

COMBINATION PLANE

ROUTER PLANE

SPOKESHAVE (CURVED)

T-BEVEL

Plug cutter, ⅜ in. or size to suit need
Inside and outside curve or
compass planes
Combination plane with cutter sets
Rabbet plane
Jointer plane, 24 in.
Pencil compass
Drawshave
Inshave
Rubber sanding block, or other of
choice
Cabinet scrapers, gooseneck,
convex and straight
"Surform" contour tools
Gimlets, set of varying sizes
Dovetail saw
Coping saw, or bow saw, as
desired
Router plane
Dowel jig
Dowel pointer

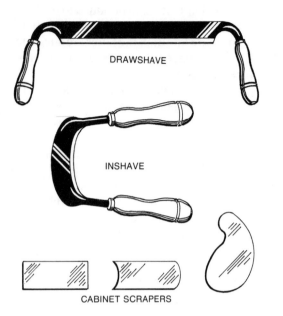

DRAWSHAVE

INSHAVE

CABINET SCRAPERS

Gouges, ¼, ½, and ¾ in.
Tap and die, ¾ or 1 in., for wood threads
Sloyd knife
Trammel points, for fitting on hardwood strip
Band clamp
Flexible ruler, for drawing curves
Stapler, with staple assortment
Universal woodworker's vise
Burnisher
Miter clamp
Pad saw
Spokeshave, curved
"Soft" hammer, plastic faces, or wood mallet
T-bevel
Wood rasps
Denim, canvas, or leather apron

HOME PLUMBING KIT

In addition to adjustable wrenches, pipe wrenches listed above:
Plumber's force cup
Closet-bowl auger, 5½ ft. length
Graphited packing, for faucets, still cocks
Pipe-joint compound
Faucet washers, assorted sizes
Seat reamer

CAULKING AND GLAZING KIT

Caulking gun, with spare cartridges
Wire brush with attached scraper
Glass cutter, with diamond point
Glazier's points (box)
Linseed oil, 1 pint
Glazier's putty, 1 to 5 lbs.
Yardstick, for measuring and cutting glass

GENERAL SUPPLIES

White polyvinyl glue
Epoxy glue
Household cement
Assorted stove bolts and small machine screws
Assorted wood screws, ½ in. #4 through 2-in. #10
Mending plates, corner braces
Screweyes, screw hooks, picture hangers
Tacks, brads, common and finishing nails, 2d to 8d
Assorted wall fasteners, plastic or lead anchors
Extra casters, furniture glides
Pressure-sensitive mending tape
Masking tape, ½ and 1-in. widths

chop-cutting a mortise, for example. The plastic faces of the soft hammer deliver a blow without upsetting and eventually damaging the chisel handle. Yet others, equally skilled, would choose the wood mallet for this purpose. However, in the end the soft hammer is perhaps the better choice as it has a somewhat wider application, such as tapping out dents in sheet metals.

For beginning craftsmen it's usually best to choose only a few tools, such as a hammer, saws, a plane, brace and bits, pliers, whatever is immediately needed and then add to the kit as tool requirements develop. In this way you avoid a high initial investment, gradually build a kit of the most useful units, eliminate those of only marginal use and save some money in the end. The more inclusive homeshop kit and the cabinetmaker's kit are, of course, for those who acquire skills and who wish to go all-out in build-

ing a more nearly complete set of hand tools.

For beginners certain of these may be more or less unfamiliar in type and application. The compass plane, combination plane, router plane and inshave are specialized tools used in advanced cabinet work; in chair-making and in making shallow bowls and trays where it is necessary to work concave and curved edges and surfaces. Here one uses the compass plane—which is made in "inside" and "outside" types—for working curved edges.

The router plane is, as its name suggests, for the purpose of making dadoes and grooves of limited lengths. The combination plane comes with an array of cutters designed for making beading, sash moldings and for grooving in various widths and depths. The inshave is used by chairmakers for working chair seats and by tray and bowl makers for the necessary concavities.

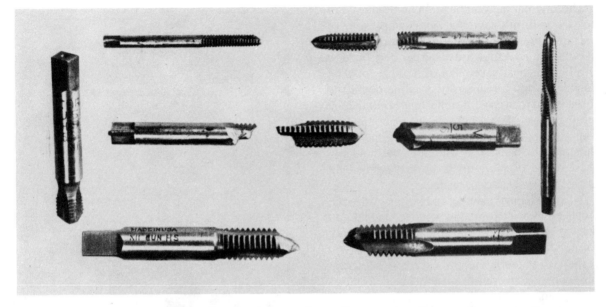

Make tools from broken taps

By WALTER E. BURTON

■ WHEN YOU BREAK a tap trying to thread a hole, don't be hasty in mourning its loss—perhaps you can convert what's left into a useful tool.

All it takes is a bit of grinding to transform a damaged tap (usually the shank end, including some of the threaded portion) into a metalcutting

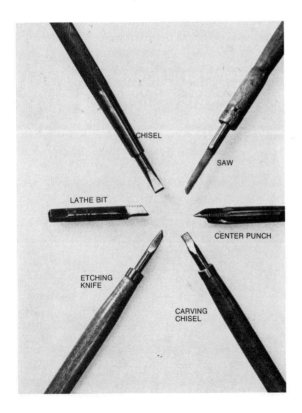

CHISEL

SAW

LATHE BIT

CENTER PUNCH

ETCHING KNIFE

CARVING CHISEL

chisel, center punch, scriber, carving tool for wood and plastic, tiny "saw," etching knife, engraving tool, screwdriver blade, lathe bit, turning chisel, reamer or thread-cleaning tool—to name a few.

The tap may be either high-speed steel or carbon-tool steel. Often, this makes little or no difference. High-speed steel makes durable lathe bits, cold chisels and the like. Carbon steel is likely to hold a keener edge and, therefore, is more suitable for etching knives, carving tools and wood chisels.

For chisels, punches and similar percussion tools, or lathe bits and other tools where high brittleness might be a hazard, the original tap hardness may be too great. This can be reduced by tempering. (Heat the steel until a polished area turns purple, then quench in water.)

When grinding, avoid "burning" (letting the steel get so hot that discoloration shows). If you do overheat carbon steel and thus reduce hardness, you can reharden and temper it satisfactorily enough for most purposes. High-speed alloys, on the other hand, usually require special hardening and drawing techniques.

SEE ALSO

The original tap combination sometimes can be used to form a new tool. For example, one of the tap flutes can form the top surface of a woodcarving gouge. A four-fluted tap can be ground to fit a Phillips-head screw slot. A tap also could be converted into a reamer by grinding down the threads and then grinding relief angles behind the cutting edges. For a lathe bit to fit a standard toolpost holder, you may have to grind some flats on the shank so it will enter the holder—these will also square-up the bit so it can be held at the proper side-rake angle.

To make a tiny "saw," grind the tap into a thin single-edge blade (or a double-edge blade if you started with a two or four-flute tap) with teeth formed by the original tap threads. Unless you reshape each tooth, the saw will cut with a scraping action, and therefore is useful for such chores as cleaning out slots and squaring internal corners of relatively soft materials. By grinding bevels, such a blade also can be converted into a serrated-tooth knife.

You can use an etching knife having a skewer-type blade for the retouching of photographic negatives and prints. Of course, you also can make knives and chisels in many other special shapes for etching, engraving and carving. The efficiency of such tools depends on their sharpness. After grinding, work up a keen edge on a medium or fine stone, then give the bevels several swipes on a very fine oilstone (such as an

GRINDING WHEEL chucked into drill press offers easy method of grinding taps. A cloth protects the vise.

Arkansas stone). For some work, such as print retouching, a faint wire edge may be desirable. Other tools, such as a dissecting knife for use in a biology lab, may work better if left with a "saw-tooth" edge.

SIMPLE SAW is ideal for squaring notches in soft materials, such as this short length of plastic pipe.

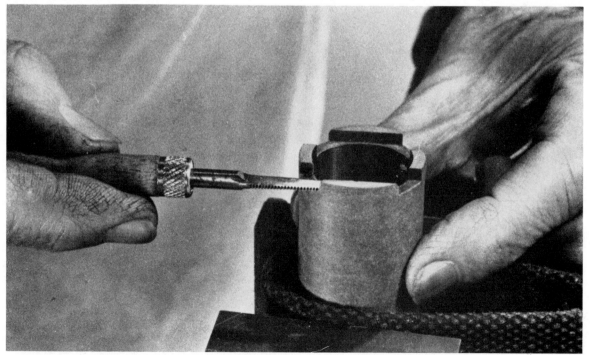

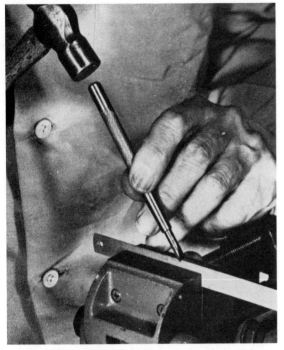

NEAT MODELMAKER'S SAW can be made by using a sharp chisel to notch a strip of carton-binding steel.

ETCHING KNIFE shaped from a tap makes it easy to lighten photographs by shaving off silver deposits.

Although you can mount broken-tap tools in a pin vise for easy manipulation, a permanent handle usually is desirable. Several of the tools in the photos were equipped with handles made from ⅜-in. maple dowels about 5 in. long. Each handle is tapered at the blade end by filing or sanding, then a hole is drilled in the end to receive the bit in a tight drive fit. To discourage splitting, a ferrule of thin-walled steel should be forced over the tapered end of each handle.

HIGH-SPEED STEEL taps can be used for lathe bits. Carbon steel bits are used for soft materials only.

Perfect cuts with torch attachments

By KENNETH B. LITTLEFIELD

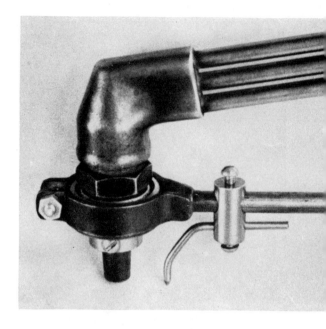

■ THE OXYACETYLENE torch is probably the handiest and fastest working tool when it comes to cutting steel. But unfortunately, considerable skill and practice are needed—both of which the infrequent do-it-yourself user seldom acquires.

Consistently good results with a cutting torch *can* be assured, however, simply by using the torch attachments shown. The cutting of circles, straight lines, bevels and other unusual shapes simply becomes a matter of setting up a guide, then fitting and adjusting the proper attachment for the job.

Since the tip is held at a fixed distance from the work, the preheat action of the torch is highly efficient and reduces the chances of excessive melting.

To obtain the best results with these attachments, however, some deviation from standard practice is necessary. First lay out the work with scribed lines. Then measure the distance from

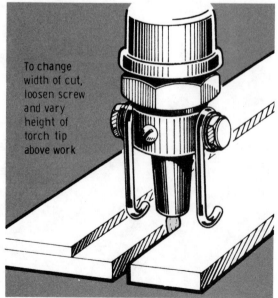

STRAIGHT CUTS and moderate curves are easy to cut with this attachment. The two legs assure exact 90° cuts, while the height is easily adjusted to suit the length of preheat flames and width of the cut.

To change width of cut, loosen screw and vary height of torch tip above work

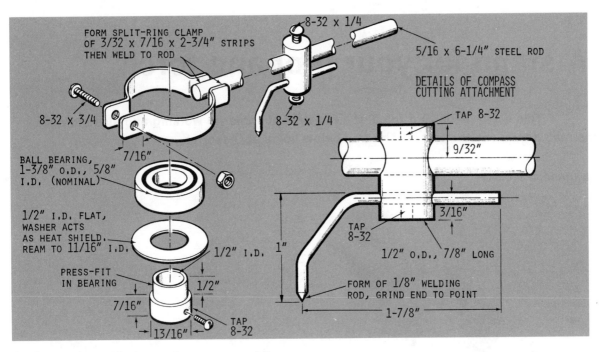

FORM SPLIT-RING CLAMP OF 3/32 x 7/16 x 2-3/4" STRIPS THEN WELD TO ROD

8-32 x 1/4

8-32 x 1/4

5/16 x 6-1/4" STEEL ROD

8-32 x 3/4

BALL BEARING, 1-3/8" O.D., 5/8" I.D. (NOMINAL)

7/16"

1/2" I.D. FLAT, WASHER ACTS AS HEAT SHIELD. REAM TO 11/16" I.D.

PRESS-FIT IN BEARING

1/2" I.D.

1/2"

7/16"

13/16"

TAP 8-32

DETAILS OF COMPASS CUTTING ATTACHMENT

TAP 8-32

9/32"

3/16"

TAP 8-32

1/2" O.D., 7/8" LONG

1"

FORM OF 1/8" WELDING ROD, GRIND END TO POINT

1-7/8"

the jet to the guide leg and set up a guiding straight-edge the same distance away from the scribed lines. Thus, as you start moving the burning torch evenly along the guiding edge, a clean, uniform cut will appear on the scribed line.

For an inside cut, a small hole (at least ⅛-in.) should be drilled in the work as a starting and ending point—while cutting circles with the compass attachment requires a centerpunched hole and a similar ⅛-in. hole to start the cut.

WHEN MAKING beveled cuts, first make a trial cut in a piece of scrap to determine the exact distance from the straightedge to the cutting jet. Then clamp or weight the straightedge to the work.

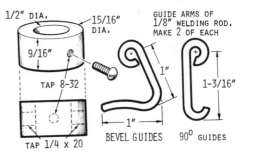

1/2" DIA.

9/16"

TAP 8-32

TAP 1/4 x 20

15/16" DIA.

GUIDE ARMS OF 1/8" WELDING ROD. MAKE 2 OF EACH

1"

1-3/16"

1"

BEVEL GUIDES   90° GUIDES

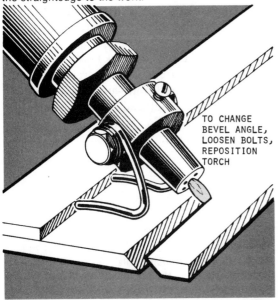

TO CHANGE BEVEL ANGLE, LOOSEN BOLTS, REPOSITION TORCH

A stand for your propane torch

This stand holds your torch at a convenient angle for working and also storage. It is constructed from one-inch stock. The tray below holds accessories

By HAROLD JACKSON

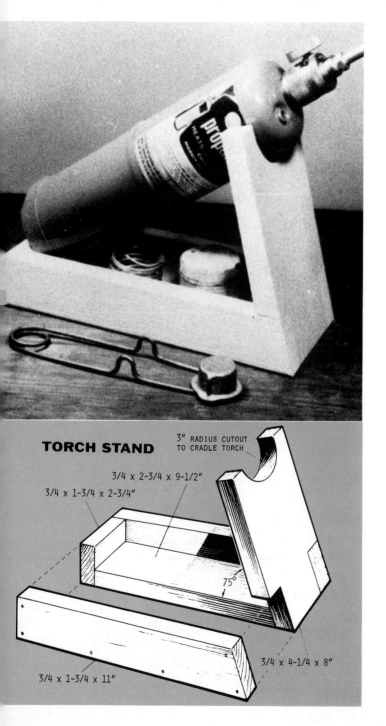

TORCH STAND

3" RADIUS CUTOUT TO CRADLE TORCH

3/4 x 2-3/4 x 9-1/2"

3/4 x 1-3/4 x 2-3/4"

75°

3/4 x 4-1/4 x 8"

3/4 x 1-3/4 x 11"

■ A PROPANE TORCH has an important place in every home workshop, but I've found that it is easily tipped over and presents a constant hazard once it is lit. To remedy this, I constructed the simple rack at left. It holds the torch at a convenient angle and leaves both hands free. In addition, when the torch is not in use it can remain in the stand for storage. The torch can be readily lifted out when desired and the tray in the base provides handy storage for the lighter, solder, flux and other torch-related items.

All parts of nominal one-inch stock and assembly is with glue and 4d finishing nails. You may want to build several stands, altering the angle of the rest so that the torch can be used for special jobs. If you decide to make a rest that will hold the torch nearer to the vertical, I recommend that you notch the small board at the other end in order to cradle the tank bottom securely.

If desired, you can add a torch stand as a permanent fixture to your workbench by attaching it with a large flathead screw. You can turn stand to whatever direction is most convenient for the job at hand.

SEE ALSO

Arbor presses . . . Bench anvils . . . Cutoff machines . . . Hydraulic presses . . . Machining . . . Power hacksaws . . . Sheet metal

COLORS THAT have been mixed often dry somewhat lighter or darker than they appear in the paint can. A wet dab placed on a white blotter "dries" quickly to give you an idea of the exact hue.

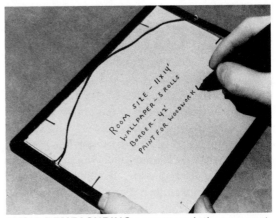

AVOID REMEASURING a room each time you get ready for new wallpaper with this trick. Put all of the data on the back of a wall-hung picture in the room—and the information will always be at hand.

PLACE A JAR LID under each leg of a chair or table to keep them from sticking to newspapers spread on the floor. When the newly painted furniture dries, simply roll up the papers and lids and throw away.

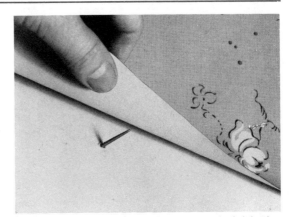

NEXT TIME you wallpaper, insert a toothpick in the hole as you remove each picture hook from the wall. Toothpicks, left in place, will protrude through the new paper, making hook replacement easy.

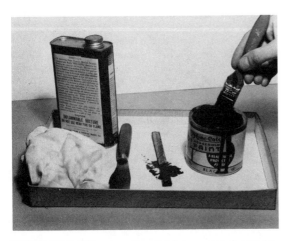

WHEN YOU DO a small paint job, a good way to keep paint and other equipment together is to place them in a cardboard box cover. All is handy, and you'll save steps going for forgotten items.

USE A DISC of wire screen cut slightly smaller than the diameter of your paint can to save yourself the trouble of straining lumpy paint. The round pieces of screen takes the lumps with it as it sinks.

You should own a torque wrench

By ROBERT TAYLOR and CURT WOLFE

■ WHETHER YOU ARE a beginner or an advanced do-it-yourselfer, you should have a torque wrench.

For some reason, a torque wrench is the tool most Saturday mechanics and even professional mechanics put off buying. It's haste, perhaps, that leads to tightening nuts and bolts by "feel."

Various problems arise when fasteners are not torqued to specification, and some of them can relate to safety and involve major repair. More oil leaks, for example, are caused by overtightening than by fasteners that are too loose.

The prime example is leaky valve cover gaskets. Many of these gaskets allow leaks only because the screw or bolt holding the cover is too tight. The gasket itself is fine.

It's not exaggeration when one torque wrench manufacturer described his wrench as a gauge tool that can be compared with a micrometer, dial indicator, level and many other precision instruments. It's that important to torque fasteners to spec.

You can find a torque wrench for almost any size job. They range from the very large to the very small.

Some manufacturers make torque wrenches that have built-in sensory devices so you can feel when the specified torque value has been reached. You preset the specified value before you start work. You feel a click when you reach the right torque.

Many of these types also use direct reading scales so you can use it either as a direct reading or sensory model.

On the beam type torque wrench, a pointer moves across the scale as you apply force to the handle. You stop when the pointer hits the torque value you want.

Torque is based on the law of the lever. Distance multiplied by force equals the torque around a point. The distance between the centerline of the drive square and the centerline of

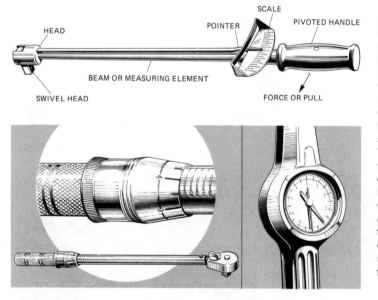

SCALE

HEAD

POINTER

PIVOTED HANDLE

BEAM OR MEASURING ELEMENT

SWIVEL HEAD

FORCE OR PULL

ROUND-BEAM TYPE of torque wrench is shown at left (top). This is the common automotive torque wrench available in standard foot-pound models or metric, meter-kilogram models. The round-beam torque wrench is also available in various ranges: zero to 100 foot-pounds, for example, for cars and small engines. Most have ⅜-inch square drives for use with your socket set. Prices range from $10 to $20. The scale on the round-beam type indicates torque when the pointer is deflected in either direction. Other types are shown at left. At far left is the micro-adjusting type which can be set to a specified torque: A click indicates when you reach the preset torque. Near left is the dial used on many commercial heavy-duty types. Most have memory pointers, read up to 250 foot-pounds.

the force being applied at the handle is the lever length of the torque wrench.

Most torque wrenches are made with a male driver or square at the end. The drive is used to fasten various attachments to the end of the wrench. For automotive work, the ⅜-inch or ½-inch-square drive is most common.

Attachments can be divided into several classifications—extensions, sockets and adapters. Typical attachments are for slots, gears, shafts, drive pins, screwdrivers and various size sockets, of course.

The popular pivoted handle, sometimes called a floating handle, is designed so that your hand will fit around it a certain way: This positions the pulling force at a fixed point on the wrench.

There are times when you'll be using a torque wrench right up to its limits for measuring foot-pounds. Other times you'll be using it at the low end of the scale. Still, you should select the wrench best for you, in terms of size and range, by considering the particular application you'll use it for. Always check the service manual for your car to see the specified torque values for the jobs you'll be doing most. Then select a torque wrench with a capacity so that the working range you most often use will be within the mid two-quarters of the scale.

Through the use of planetary gears, a torque multiplier will boost torque and at the same time allow a shorter lever length to be used.

The most popular torque multipliers use a gear ratio of 4 to 1. You can multiply the torque for a given leverage length and force by four. Or you can use one-fourth of the lever length.

adapters, attachments, extensions

Adapters and extensions can make a torque wrench multirange and multipurpose. For instance, an adapter equal to the lever length of the torque wrench will multiply the torque by two. Therefore a 100-foot-pound torque wrench can be used to tighten bolts up to 200 foot-pounds.

You'll encounter special jobs where conventional adapters, attachments and/or extensions still make it awkward or almost impossible to reach the work. For very special applications, you'll find that irregularly shaped and designed accessories are available.

Special attachments are relatively expensive, and you shouldn't invest in them until you know you're going to need them. What you do need before you can even accurately tighten your sparkplugs the next time you replace them is a torque wrench!

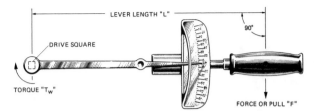

TORQUE LAW is based on the lever principle. You multiply force by lever length to get torque. Torque is measured in foot-pounds (or inch-pounds at smaller values) or in meter-kilograms if the scale is in metric. A standard round-beam type with a 0-100 foot-pound range is best for automotive use. However, before buying a torque wrench, check the range of torque values specified for the various parts of your car.

Some of the fasteners on your car that should be torqued

BODY
Engine compartment hood mounting bolts
Radiator mounting bolts
Shock absorber mounting bolts
Wheel-to-drum mounting bolts (front and rear)
Front-wheel-bearing adjusting nut (both sides)
Door-to-body mounting bolts (front and/or rear)
Trunk-to-body mounting bolts
Body-to-frame mounting bolts
Bumper-bracket-to-frame mounting bolts (front and rear)

ENGINE
Sparkplugs
Engine head bolts and pan bolts
Valve-cover screws
Main-bearing cap bolts and connecting rod cap bolts
Carburetor to intake manifold stud nuts
Fuel-pump attaching bolts
Alternator/generator bracket to engine bolts
Starter attaching bolts
Airconditioner mounting bolts
Power steering mounting bolts
Flywheel-to-crankshaft mounting bolts
Motor-mounts-to-engine bolts
Motor-mounts-to-cross member bolts
Transmission-to-engine mounting bolts
Distributor-to-engine mounting bolts
Exhaust manifold(s) to engine mounting bolts

POWER TRAIN
Front U-joint yoke to transmission mounting bolts (some cars)
Rear U-joint yoke to third member attaching nuts or bolts
Third member to differential housing mounting bolts

CIRCUS-WAGON TOY BOX

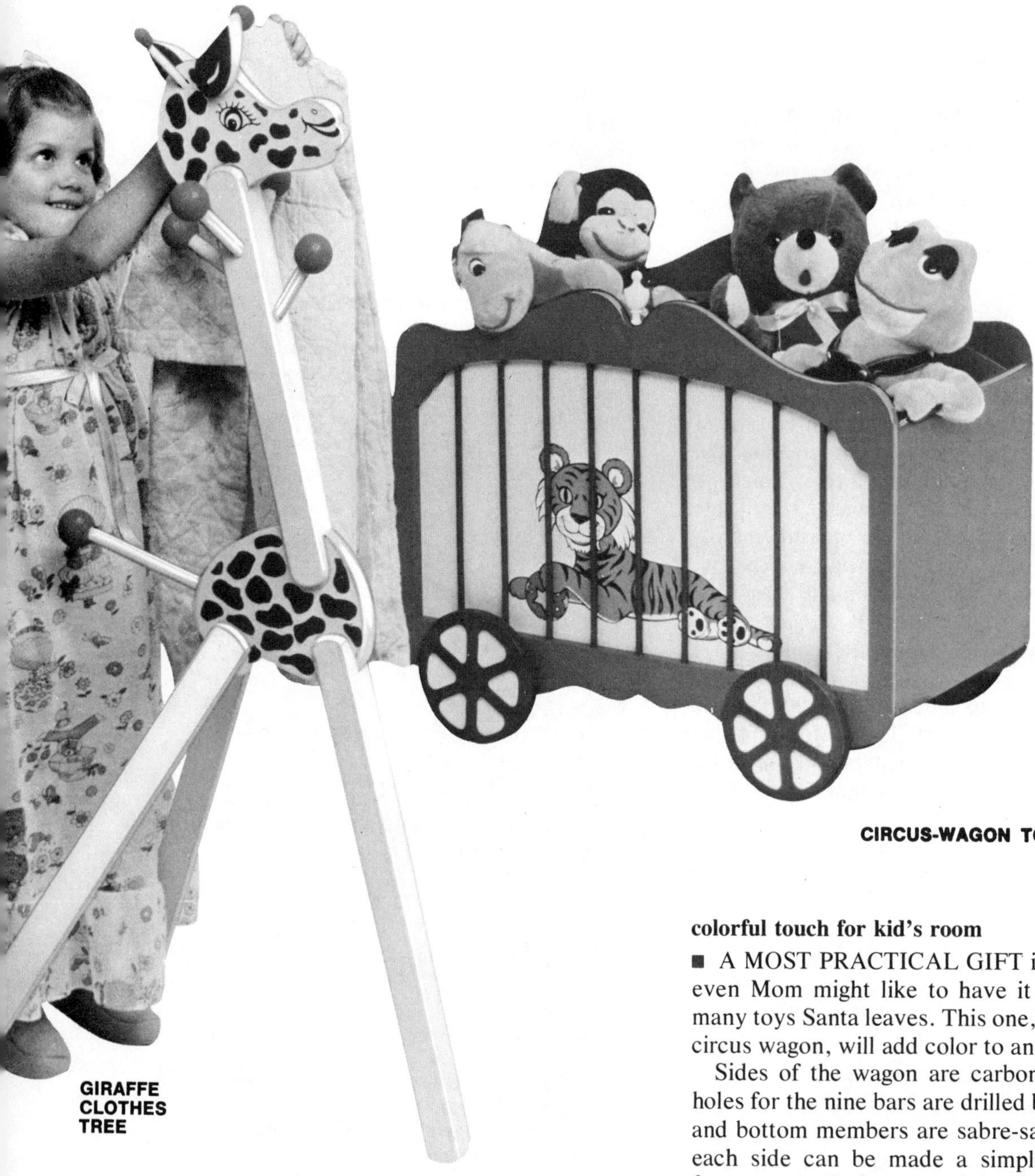

GIRAFFE CLOTHES TREE

It's fun to make toys

SEE ALSO

Children's furniture . . . Desks, children's . . . Games . . . Gifts, Christmas . . . Playhouses . . . Pull toys . . . Puzzles . . . Weekend projects

colorful touch for kid's room

■ A MOST PRACTICAL GIFT is a toy box—even Mom might like to have it to corral the many toys Santa leaves. This one, a classy little circus wagon, will add color to any kid's room.

Sides of the wagon are carbon copies. The holes for the nine bars are drilled before the top and bottom members are sabre-sawed. In fact, each side can be made a simple rectangular frame to start before any of the pieces are bored and sawed. If you have a doweling jig, use it to bore mating holes dead-center and 3 in. apart. Make a full-size pattern from the half pattern given and trace the curves on your wood. For perfect alignment, drill the holes for the ¾-in. dowel axles through both side assemblies at one time. Enlarge the holes slightly with a round file or sandpaper wrapped around a dowel.

The 7-in. wheels consist of two plywood discs and a hub. The spokes are jigsawed first, then the ¼-in. thickness is glued to the ½ in. and both are sawed round as one. The hubs are centered and glued to the wheels, then ¾-in. holes are bored through both hub and ½-in. disc.

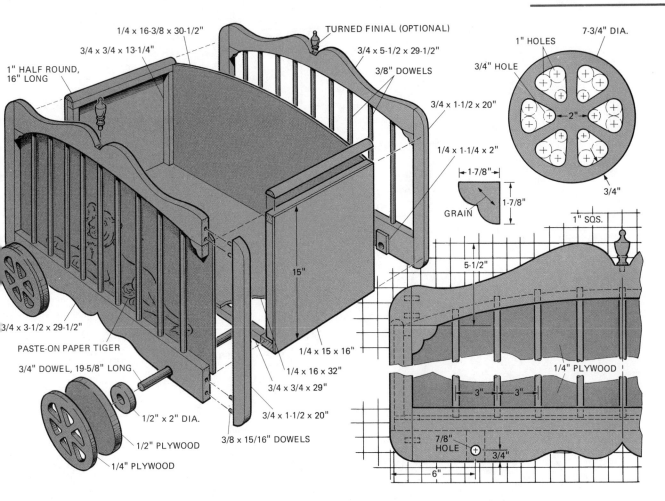

1/4 x 16-3/8 x 30-1/2"

3/4 x 3/4 x 13-1/4"

1" HALF ROUND, 16" LONG

TURNED FINIAL (OPTIONAL)

3/4 x 5-1/2 x 29-1/2"

3/8" DOWELS

3/4 x 1-1/2 x 20"

1/4 x 1-1/4 x 2"

GRAIN

1-7/8"

1-7/8"

1" HOLES

3/4" HOLE

7-3/4" DIA.

2"

3/4"

15"

1/4 x 15 x 16"

3/4 x 3-1/2 x 29-1/2"

PASTE-ON PAPER TIGER

3/4" DOWEL, 19-5/8" LONG

1/2" x 2" DIA.

1/2" PLYWOOD

1/4" PLYWOOD

1/4 x 16 x 32"

3/4 x 3/4 x 29"

3/4 x 1-1/2 x 20"

3/8 15/16" DOWELS

1" SQS.

5-1/2"

1/4" PLYWOOD

3" 3"

7/8" HOLE

3/4"

6"

ADJUSTABLE DOWELING JIG simplifies drilling and aligning the mating dowel holes in the upper and the lower side members of the wagon.

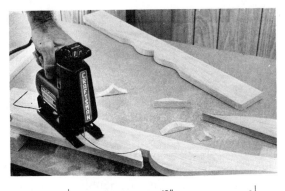

AFTER HOLES are bored, the curves in the top and the bottom members are then cut with a sabre saw. With dowel bars in place, the ends are added.

Cutting layout

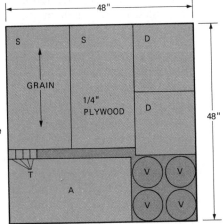

48"

S   S   D

GRAIN

1/4" PLYWOOD

D

T

A

V V

V V

48"

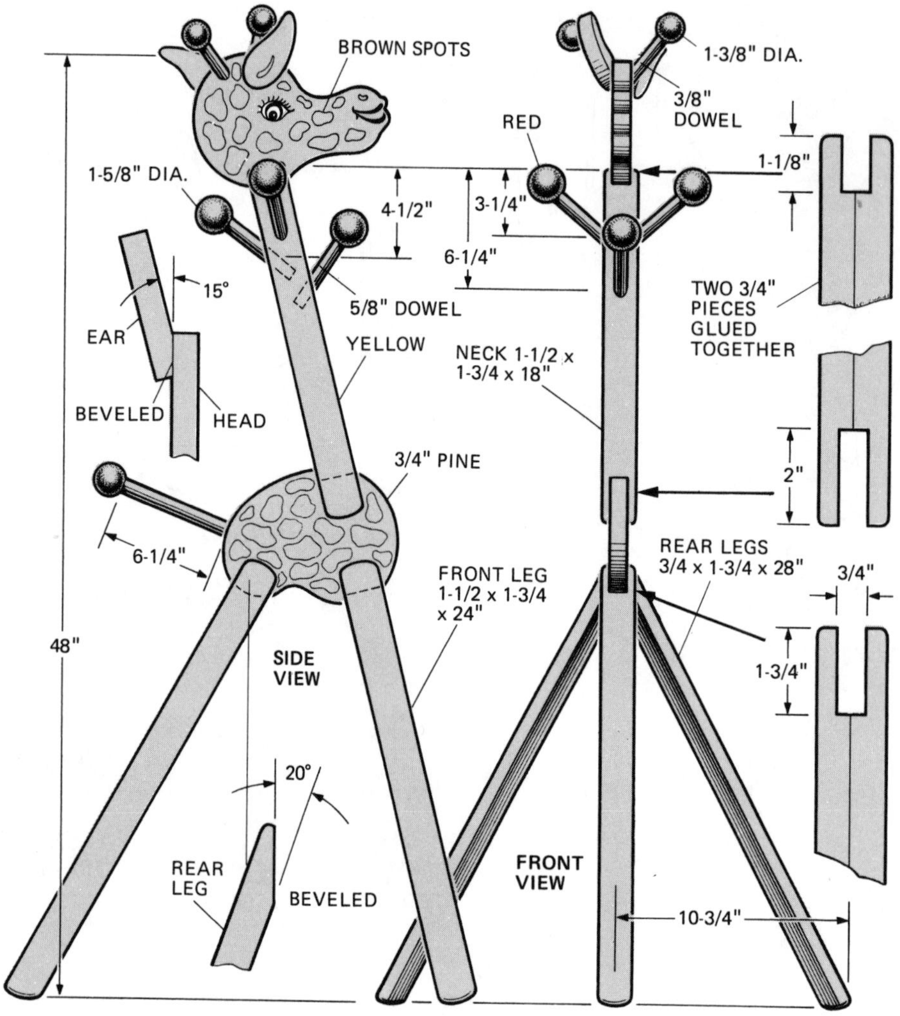
BROWN SPOTS
1-3/8" DIA.
3/8" DOWEL
RED
1-1/8"
1-5/8" DIA.
4-1/2"
3-1/4"
6-1/4"
15°
5/8" DOWEL
TWO 3/4" PIECES GLUED TOGETHER
EAR
YELLOW
NECK 1-1/2 x 1-3/4 x 18"
BEVELED
HEAD
3/4" PINE
2"
6-1/4"
REAR LEGS 3/4 x 1-3/4 x 28"
FRONT LEG 1-1/2 x 1-3/4 x 24"
3/4"
48"
SIDE VIEW
1-3/4"
20°
REAR LEG
BEVELED
FRONT VIEW
10-3/4"

GIRAFFE CLOTHES TREE

The completed sides are glued to a simple ¼-in. plywood box and the cutting layout shows how the five parts can be laid out economically on a 4x4-ft. panel with wood to spare for the wheels. They are glued to ¾-in.-square members which are placed inside the ends and under the bottom. Sides of the cage are finally glued to the box; then panels S are painted white, and the paper tigers are attached with rubber cement and finally nailed in place behind the bars. Wheels are glued to the dowel axles to complete the project.

he'll hold their clothes

You'll be surprised how this long-necked, three-legged fellow can get little ones to hang up their clothes. Sawing the head, body and ears is hardest; the rest is easy. Ears are beveled on the inside to point outward when glued in place. Front leg and neck are two 1x2 pieces notched at ends, then glued together. Balls on ends of the pegs are wood finials you'll find at lumberyards and craft centers. Note that the top balls are

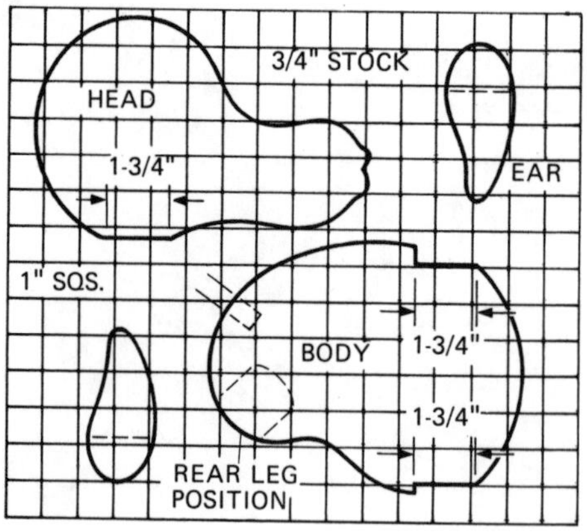
3/4" STOCK
HEAD
EAR
1-3/4"
1" SQS.
BODY
1-3/4"
1-3/4"
REAR LEG POSITION

smaller than others. Paint him yellow and add brown spots to make him look like a giraffe.

any little girl's favorite

Next to a doll, a dollhouse is perhaps the most wanted gift for any little girl. On the following page is a simple one Dad can make in a weekend. It's designed by Mary Schreck, dollhouse furniture designer, after an early 19th century English

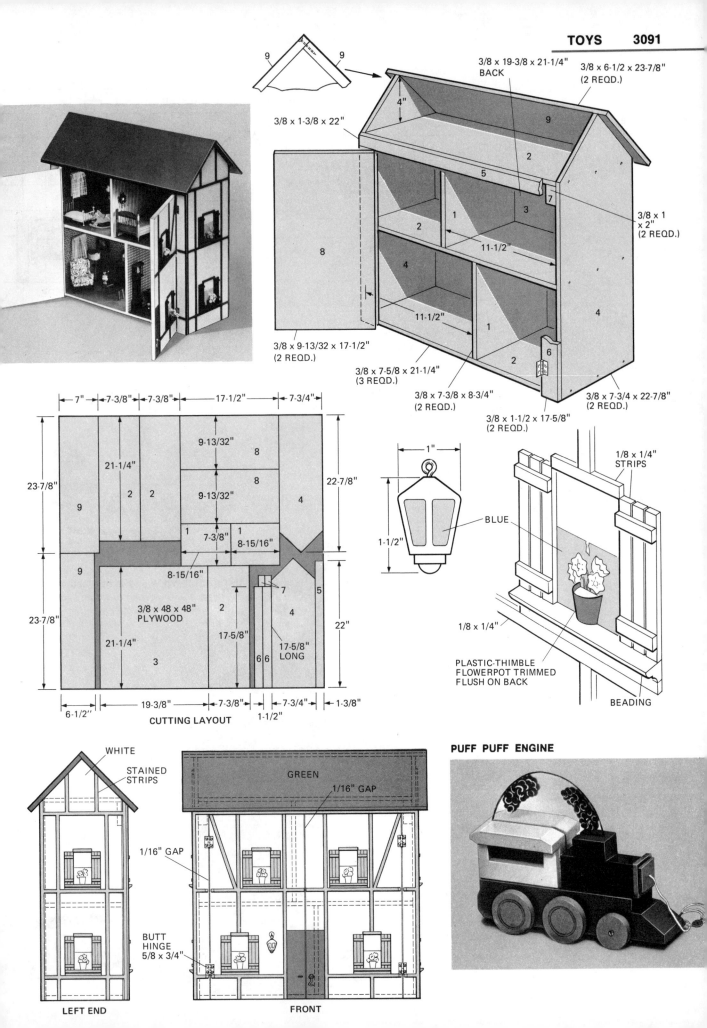

9   9

3/8 x 19-3/8 x 21-1/4"
BACK

3/8 x 6-1/2 x 23-7/8"
(2 REQD.)

3/8 x 1-3/8 x 22"

4"

9

2

5

9

3

7

3/8 x 1
x 2"
(2 REQD.)

8

2

1

2

11-1/2"

4

4

1

4

11-1/2"

6

2

3/8 x 9-13/32 x 17-1/2"
(2 REQD.)

3/8 x 7-5/8 x 21-1/4"
(3 REQD.)

3/8 x 7-3/8 x 8-3/4"
(2 REQD.)

3/8 x 1-1/2 x 17-5/8"
(2 REQD.)

3/8 x 7-3/4 x 22-7/8"
(2 REQD.)

CUTTING LAYOUT

7"   7-3/8"   7-3/8"   17-1/2"   7-3/4"

23-7/8"

9-13/32"   8

21-1/4"   2   2

8
9-13/32"

22-7/8"

9   1   1   4

7-3/8"

8-15/16"

8-15/16"

23-7/8"

9

3/8 x 48 x 48"
PLYWOOD

2

7

5

21-1/4"   3   17-5/8"   4

17-5/8"
LONG

22"

6 6

6-1/2"   19-3/8"   7-3/8"   7-3/4"   1-3/8"

1-1/2"

CUTTING LAYOUT

1"

1-1/2"

BLUE

1/8 x 1/4"
STRIPS

1/8 x 1/4"

PLASTIC-THIMBLE
FLOWERPOT TRIMMED
FLUSH ON BACK

BEADING

WHITE

STAINED
STRIPS

GREEN

1/16" GAP

1/16" GAP

BUTT
HINGE
5/8 x 3/4"

LEFT END

FRONT

PUFF PUFF ENGINE

B 1/2" BLIND HOLE EACH SIDE FOR LEAD SHOT

GRAY

3/4" PINE

1/4 x 2 x 9"

7/8" THICK

3/4"

WASHER

RH SCREW

3/4 x 1-1/2 x 5-3/8"

B

3/4 x 2-1/4 x 9"

1/2" DOWEL

1/16" WASHER

1/2" HOLE

1/2 x 2-1/2" WHEELS

1/4 x 1-1/2 x 1-3/4" AXLE BRACKET

RUBBER BAND

CAM
1/2 x 1-1/2" DIA.

1/2" HOLE

2-1/4"

1/2"

BLUE

RED

A

3/4"

7/8"

STATIONARY JAW AND END BLOCK

HALE THE WHALE

1/16" THICK EYE

1" SQS.

3" RAD.

1-1/4" RAD.

A

1-3/16"

WOOD BEAD

PULL CORD

3/4"

END VIEW
(BLOCK A REMOVED)

SIDE VIEW

UNDERSIDE VIEW shows how cam on dowel axle opens and closes the whale's mouth.

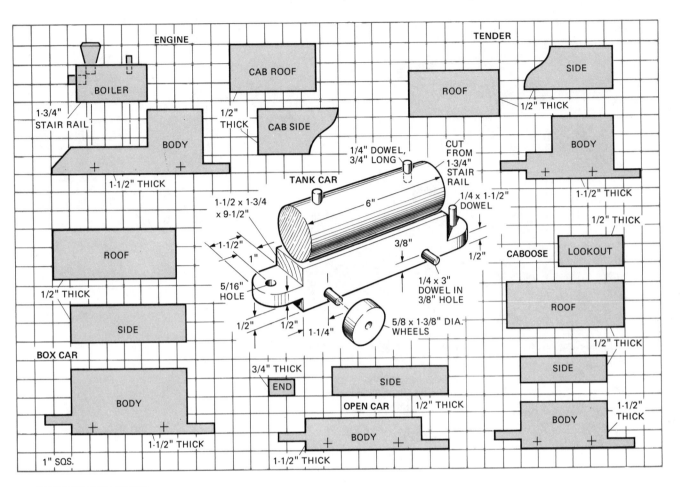

ENGINE — BOILER, CAB ROOF, CAB SIDE, BODY, ROOF, SIDE (BOX CAR), TANK CAR, TENDER, CABOOSE, OPEN CAR

1-3/4" STAIR RAIL
1/2" THICK
BODY 1-1/2" THICK
ROOF 1/2" THICK
SIDE
BOX CAR
BODY 1-1/2" THICK
1" SQS.

1-1/2 x 1-3/4 x 9-1/2"
1-1/2"
1"
5/16" HOLE
1/2"   1/2"   1-1/4"

1/4" DOWEL, 3/4" LONG
CUT FROM 1-3/4" STAIR RAIL
3/8"
1/4 x 1-1/2" DOWEL
1/2"
1/4 x 3" DOWEL IN 3/8" HOLE
5/8 x 1-3/8" DIA. WHEELS

3/4" THICK
END
SIDE 1/2" THICK
OPEN CAR
BODY 1-1/2" THICK

TENDER — SIDE 1/2" THICK, ROOF, BODY 1-1/2" THICK, 1/2" THICK
CABOOSE — LOOKOUT, ROOF 1/2" THICK, SIDE, BODY 1-1/2" THICK

WOOD-BLOCK TRAIN

farmhouse. The front opens wide to provide full access to four rooms.

The 17 parts can be cut from a 4x4-ft. piece of ⅜-in. plywood. Follow the diagram when laying out the parts, but follow the dimensions when cutting.

Start assembly by nailing and gluing the three floors to one end, inserting partitions as you go. Then add the second end and the back. Glue parts 7 next, then part 5, and parts 6. Hinge panels 8 to the front and add the roof.

Paint the house white; then decorate ends and front with stained wood strips as shown in front and end views. Paint on windows and doors and fit them with shutters, window boxes and plastic thimble flowerpots.

'smokes' as it rides along

Puff puff engine is a toy which puffs "smoke" as it is pulled along. The illusion is created by a 7-in. clear plastic disc which rests on two inner wheels and turns clockwise when the wheels turn. Four "puffs" of blue tape are stuck to each side of the plastic disc at 12, 3, 6 and 9 o'clock, and a ⅛-in. wire shaft in an elongated center hole holds the disc in place.

The body is a sandwich of five layers, two ¾-in. thick, two ½-in. and one ¼ in. Spacers A and B form the ¼-in.-wide slot for the disc. The ½-in. pieces are made right and left hand, and the cab's roof is slotted for the disc. Blind holes are made in the four drive wheels and the wheels glued to their axles.

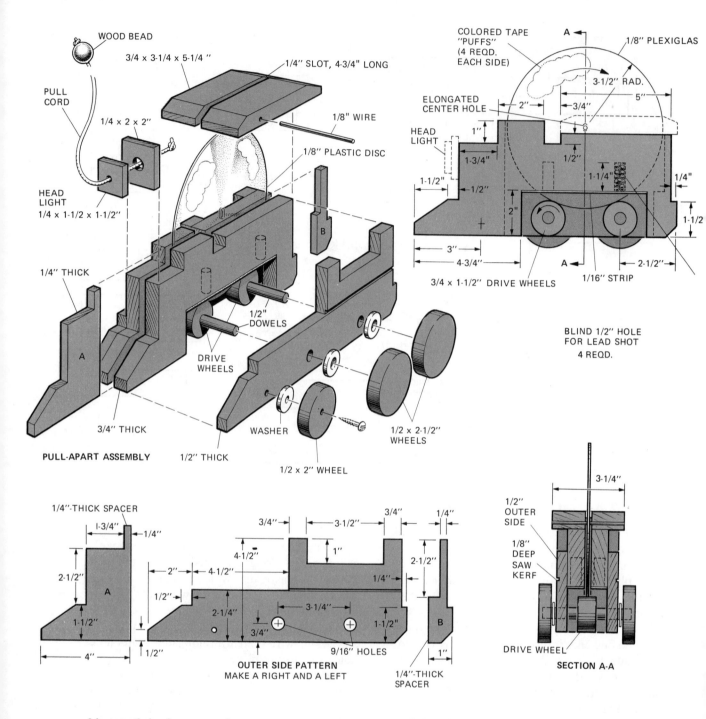

WOOD BEAD

PULL CORD

3/4 x 3-1/4 x 5-1/4 ''

1/4" SLOT, 4-3/4" LONG

1/8" WIRE

1/8" PLASTIC DISC

1/4 x 2 x 2''

HEAD LIGHT
1/4 x 1-1/2 x 1-1/2''

1/4'' THICK

B

A

3/4'' THICK

DRIVE WHEELS

1/2'' DOWELS

WASHER

1/2'' THICK

1/2 x 2'' WHEEL

1/2 x 2-1/2'' WHEELS

PULL-APART ASSEMBLY

COLORED TAPE "PUFFS" (4 REQD. EACH SIDE)

1/8" PLEXIGLAS

3-1/2'' RAD.

ELONGATED CENTER HOLE

HEAD LIGHT

1''

2''

3/4''

5''

1-3/4''

1/2''

1-1/2''

1/2''

1-1/4''

1/4''

2''

3''

4-3/4''

2-1/2''

1-1/2''

3/4 x 1-1/2'' DRIVE WHEELS

1/16'' STRIP

BLIND 1/2'' HOLE FOR LEAD SHOT 4 REQD.

1/4''-THICK SPACER

1-3/4''

1/4''

2-1/2''

1-1/2''

4''

1/2''

A

2''

4-1/2''

1/2''

2-1/4''

3/4''

3-1/2''

3/4''

1''

1/4''

2-1/2''

1/4''

1-1/2''

3-1/4''

9/16'' HOLES

B

1''

OUTER SIDE PATTERN
MAKE A RIGHT AND A LEFT

1/4''-THICK SPACER

1/2'' OUTER SIDE

1/8'' DEEP SAW KERF

3-1/4''

DRIVE WHEEL

SECTION A-A

his mouth is always moving

Opening and closing his mouth as he swims along at the end of a string, Hale the Whale is an irresistible toy small fry will go for in a big way. A wood cam between the front wheels works the mouth up and down as the toy is pulled; ⅞-in. spacer blocks A and B allow free movement for the ¾-in. pivoted body.

A circle cutter in a drill press will cut the ½-in.-thick plywood wheels quickly. Round-head screws serve as axles for the rear wheels; blind holes in the front wheels fit the dowel axle

and the wheels are glued on. Enlarge holes in the brackets slightly so the axle turns freely.

fast freight from scrap wood

Little guys always like trains for Christmas. The wood-block freight train can be made from scrap found in your woodbox. If you plan to make several as gifts, it will pay you to buy a length of 1⅜-in. wood closet pole and slice the ¾-in. wheels from it. Likewise a length of 1¾-in. stair rail will save time in making several engine boilers and tanks for tank cars.

Frosty metal door

The door to my patio from the family room is metal framed. When cold, it's covered with frost. During the day this often melts and runs down on the floor. The moisture is on the inside. How does it get in and how can I prevent it from forming the frost?—T.R., Ky.

It doesn't "get in," as you put it. It's already inside the room. You're looking at condensate that forms on the surface of the metal that's at a lower temperature than the air with which it is in contact; so much lower that frost forms on cold days and nights.

I assume the door is weatherstripped and closes tightly. A tight-fitting storm door would probably minimize the formation of condensate to the point where it is no longer damaging. Some homeowners with this trouble on both metal sashes and doors apply adhesive tape to the exposed metal frames. This usually prevents the trouble. Even colored tape does not enhance the appearance of window sashes or doors but perhaps it is better than mopping water off the floor.

If your home is heated by a gas-fired furnace, especially one of the floor type, make sure it is adequately vented to prevent excessive moisture inside the house. Other sources of moisture are uncontrolled furnace humidifiers, boiling teakettles, frequent showering, unvented washers and dryers.

Replacing sash cord

I have old-type sash with cords and balancing weights. The cords need replacing. I can see how to replace them on the lower sash, but how do I replace those on the upper sash? That is, how is the upper sash removed?—C.R., Utah.

After you've removed the lower sash you have to pry out one of the two parting strips you'll see between the sashes. On an old window frame these strips may have been "painted in," and you'll have to proceed very carefully to get one out without breaking it or splintering the frame. Perhaps the best way is to break the paint seal on both sides of the strip by tapping the edge of a chisel in lightly at the point where the strip meets the sash frame. Do this at spaced intervals along the exposed length of the strip on both sides. Then tap the edge of the chisel into the strip and pry *very lightly* until it loosens at the lower end. Repeat this along the length until the strip loosens sufficiently for you to lift it out with your fingers. Be especially careful in this step not to break the strip or, worse, splinter the frame. Once the strip is out the sash can be lifted clear without removing the strip on the other side of the frame.

Basement wall 'leak'

I have an outside entrance to my basement. There are drops of water on the concrete-block wall near the floor—even when weather is dry. What could cause such a leak?—G.R. Waud, Elmira, N.Y.

I don't think it's a leak; I'm quite sure it's condensate. If you place your hand on the wet surface, you no doubt will find that it's noticeably cold. Moisture condenses here because of the variation in temperature. Though it is hard to diagnose from this distance, it is also possible that these drops of water are caused by sweating cold-water pipes overhead. If so, you can correct the problem by wrapping the pipes with a pipe insulation that comes in rolls, and is carried by well-stocked hardware stores.

Removing fabric stains

I spilled chocolate topping on my sofa, but didn't notice the stain until it had hardened. How can I remove it?—J. Hansen, Beatrice, Neb.

Since you didn't identify the fabric, I can't guarantee to give you the correct procedure. Generally, however, dry-cleaning fluids are safe on most common fabrics. Just twist a ball of cotton on the end of a small dowel—or handy stick or sliver of wood—and sponge the stain lightly. Follow with a warm, damp cloth, rubbing lightly away from the center. Repeat the procedure if necessary.

Pinpointing roof leak

Shingles on my home are laid over a low-pitch plywood deck. I've just discovered a leak and don't know how to locate it. About halfway down the ridge, it shows as a discoloration at a joint in the deck. How can I pinpoint it?—D.W., Nev.

It's going to take some rather blind sleuthing. You're reasonably certain that water is coming through at a point more or less directly above the discoloration at the joint in the plywood deck. You also know this point can't be more than 4 ft. above the stain. So, drive back the projecting ends of the roofing nails across the width of the plywood sheet directly above where the stain appears. Then go up on the roof and gently lift the loosened shingles until you locate the cause of the leak.

This may turn out to be a split or broken shingle tab, a bent nail hammered inadvertently through a shingle, a not-fully-seated nail, permitting rain to creep under a shingle, or other damage. Once you've found the cause, the remedy should be quite simple: replace a defective shingle or seal a break with roofing cement. Drive all nails back in place.

by W. Clyde Lammey

THE MINIATURE KITCHEN furniture consists of a two-door refrigerator, a sink with faucet, and a stove with play dials and an oven. All are constructed alike—¼-in. chipboard over ¾ x 1¼-in. framework. Appliances can be painted to match your full-size ones.

Small-fry kitchen appliances

What daughter or granddaughter wouldn't love these sturdy toy appliances made up to look just like full-size ones?

By TERENCE E. HOGAN

■ STURDY, REALISTIC-LOOKING and sure to please your little gal is this set of pint-sized kitchen appliances you can build in a weekend or two. Unlike the flimsy metal or corrugated cardboard counterparts available commercially, these scaled-down versions of major appliances have enough movable parts to keep the youngest lady of the house occupied for months.

Because the units are constructed of pine stock and skinned with ¼-in. chip and hardboard, they are light enough to be easily moved, yet rugged enough to take the punishment small fry can dish out. All units are assembled using glue as well as nails. To fasten the outer covering, also use white glue and ¾-in. finishing nails.

Since the three units are basically alike, you can save time by using jigs, gang-cutting and other production-line methods wherever possible. For example, after roughing out the hardboard and chipboard, all frame pieces of a given dimension can be clamped together and cut simultaneously on the table saw. To avoid confusion, mark all pieces as they are cut. With all pieces of the frames cut, these parts can be sanded and prime painted

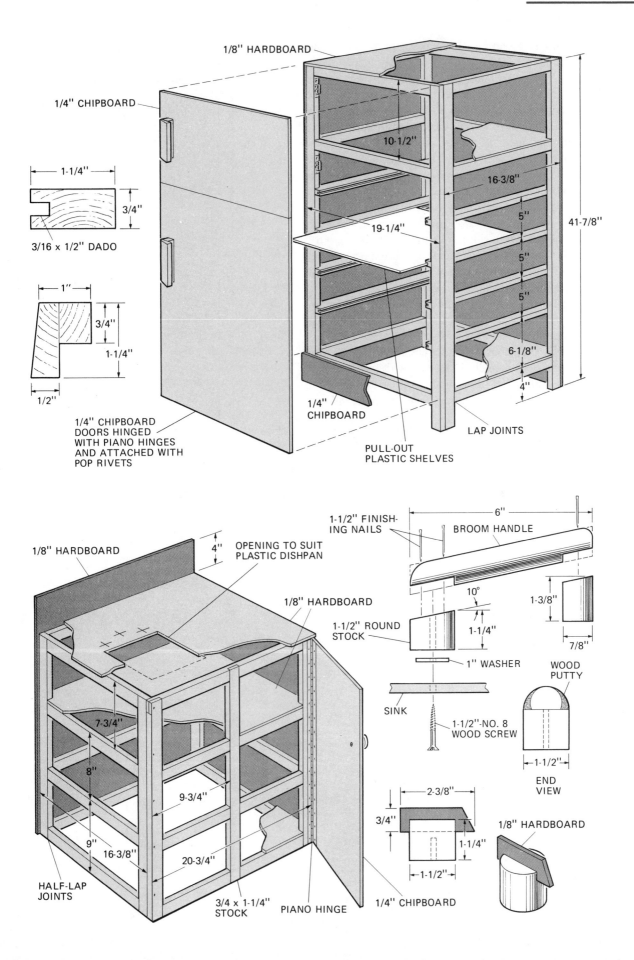

1/8'' HARDBOARD

1/4'' CHIPBOARD

1-1/4''

3/4''

3/16 x 1/2'' DADO

1''

3/4''

1-1/4''

1/2''

1/4'' CHIPBOARD
DOORS HINGED
WITH PIANO HINGES
AND ATTACHED WITH
POP RIVETS

10-1/2''

16-3/8''

19-1/4''

5''

5''

5''

41-7/8''

6-1/8''

4''

1/4''
CHIPBOARD

PULL-OUT
PLASTIC SHELVES

LAP JOINTS

1/8'' HARDBOARD

4''

OPENING TO SUIT
PLASTIC DISHPAN

1/8'' HARDBOARD

1-1/2'' FINISH-
ING NAILS

6''

BROOM HANDLE

1-1/2'' ROUND
STOCK

10°

1-1/4''

1-3/8''

7/8''

1'' WASHER

WOOD
PUTTY

SINK

1-1/2''-NO. 8
WOOD SCREW

1-1/2''

END
VIEW

7-3/4''

8''

9-3/4''

9''

16-3/8''

20-3/4''

2-3/8''

3/4''

1-1/4''

1-1/2''

1/8'' HARDBOARD

HALF-LAP
JOINTS

3/4 x 1-1/4''
STOCK

PIANO HINGE

1/4'' CHIPBOARD

prior to assembly. But make certain you do not prime those areas that will be glue-joined.

Range. To mark the range for the clocks and dials as shown, use a center punch to locate exact centers. After painting the front, the circles, clock dials and other details can be applied using India ink and an artist's brush. When this "artwork" is dry, apply clear varnish. The window on the chipboard door is simply a piece of plexiglass set in the rabbet with bathtub caulk.

Sink. On the unit shown, the sink is a 2¼ x 7½ x 7½-in. bowl that came with a 49-cent vegetable grater. Before cutting out your sinktop, have your "sink" on hand to assure a neat fit. The sink trim requires a little effort using a chisel and coping saw to do the notching. After assembling these parts, fill any voids with a wood filler and sand smooth. Trim can be finish-painted with aluminum paint for realism.

Refrigerator. This is the easiest unit to construct because it is really just a box with two doors. As with all units, sand all surfaces and edges absolutely smooth before applying a *nontoxic paint*.

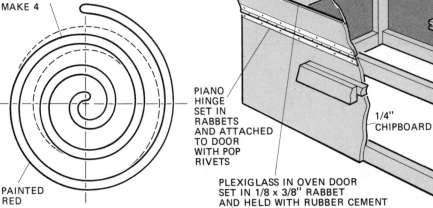

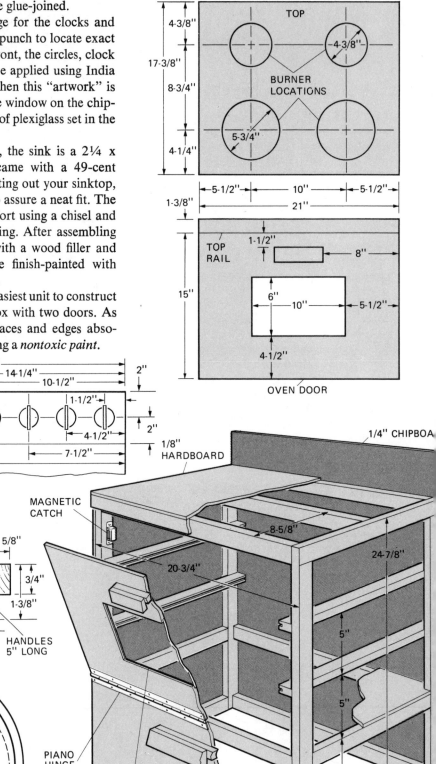

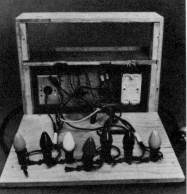

CHRISTMAS-TREE BULBS work perfectly in this switch-box toy. They are small and are available in many colors.

A switch toy for toddlers

By JAMES H. PICKERELL

■ SINCE HER FIRST BIRTHDAY, one of my daughter's favorite pastimes has been coaxing someone to lift her so that she could reach an electric switch and turn it on or off. Her curiosity is what prompted this toy project. While I was designing it, I decided to employ a variety of switches. For example, I used six different switches (one has two "on" positions), each wired to its own bulb.

The important design feature is to make certain that construction is such that the toddler can't possibly get to the wires. Use different color bulbs and you can also teach your toddler color recognition.

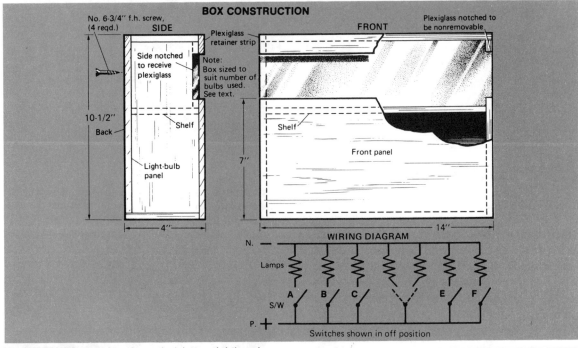

SIX SWITCHES used in schematic (above, right) and photo (top, left) are: A) wall-type push-button; B) doorbell button; C) push-type lamp; D) three-position rotary lamp; E) pull-chain and F) wall-type toggle. Types can be varied depending upon what switches you have on hand.

SEE ALSO

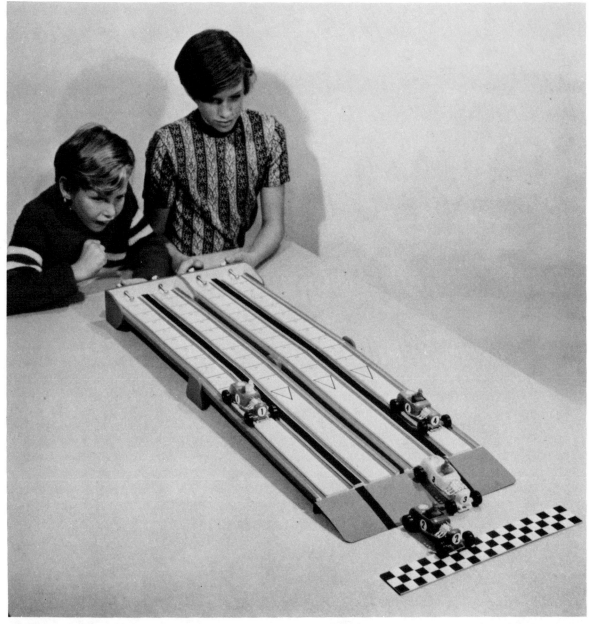

Toy racetrack

By NELLO J. ORSINI

■ HERE'S AN EXCITING toy that will provide youngsters with all the thrills of a real speedway. I call it the Derby Hill 500. Four plastic cars are sent roaring down the track by two or four "drivers," each pulling one or two spring plungers. The car that goes the farthest or crosses the checkered finish line first wins.

SEE ALSO
Games . . . Gifts, Christmas . . . Pull toys . . . Puzzles . . . Weekend projects

STOVEBOLT SLIPPED through coil spring and capped with drawer knob makes a plunger to propel the cars. Holes for plungers are centered in each track lane.

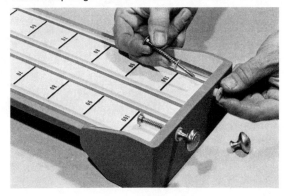

The four roadbed sections required can be placed either side by side or end to end to vary the fun. Placed in pairs side by side, the sections provide a four-track raceway 36-in. long. Hooked end to end, the sections provide a 6-ft.-long raceway. In the latter case, only two cars are driven and drivers are stationed at opposite ends, each taking turns racing his car down and up the inclined track. The driver who scores a total of 500 points first wins.

Each roadbed section measures 7-in. wide by 18-in. long and has four ½-in.-wide grooves spaced to suit the wheels of the particular plastic race cars used. The cars I used were purchased at Woolworth's and are about 6-in. long.

The drawings show how the roadbed sections are supported and how they hook together. Metal angles formed from sheet aluminum engage saw kerfs in the support blocks. The outboard end of the track hooks similarly into an open fold in the metal ramp.

Stick-on scoring numerals are used for marking the track, and ⅛-in. black matte charting tape (Prestype) is used to rule off scoring divisions.

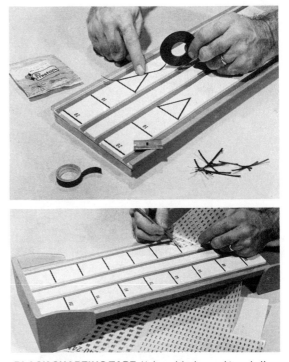

BLACK CHARTING TAPE, ⅛-in. wide, is used to rule lines on track surface (top). Green tape marks wheel channels; press-on numerals make neat numbering job.

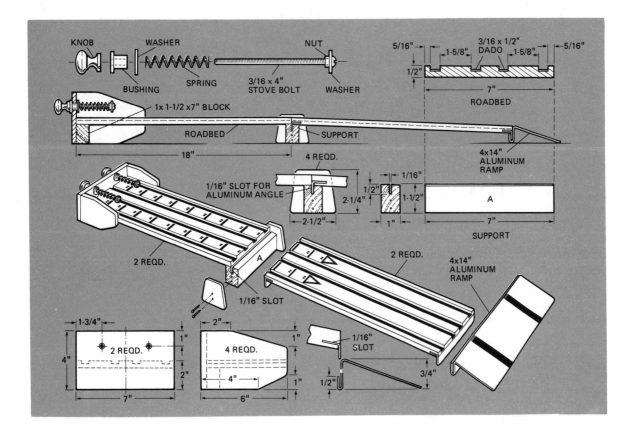

Build a fleet of blockmobiles

By WILLARD WALTNER

■ A FLEET of these classy blockmobiles will provide hours of fun for a 4-year-old, and they can be made for practically nothing from scraps of ¾ and 1½-in. pine found in your woodbox. They are also practically unbreakable.

All are made by first gluing up blocks of varying thicknesses after precutting them to shape. All fender "wells" are bored ½ in. deep with a 1⅜-in. spade power bit. Then ⁵⁄₁₆-in. holes are drilled from each side for free-turning axles of ¼-in. dowel rod.

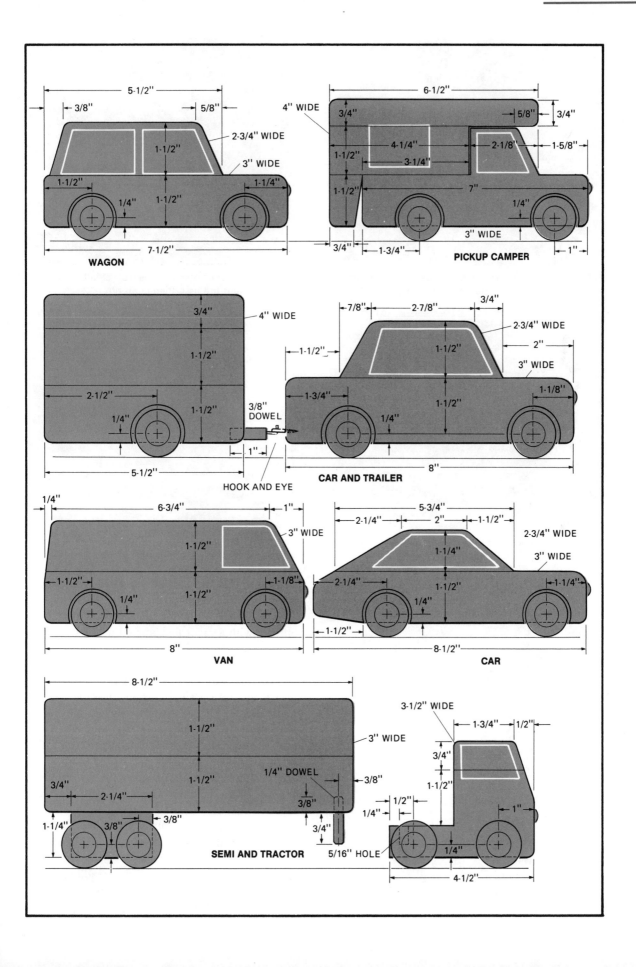

WAGON

PICKUP CAMPER

HOOK AND EYE

CAR AND TRAILER

VAN

CAR

SEMI AND TRACTOR

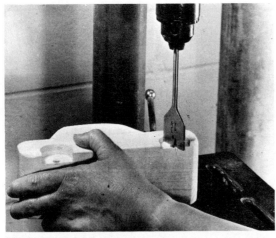

FENDER WELLS for wheels are made ½ in. deep with 1⅜-in. spade-type bit chucked in drill press.

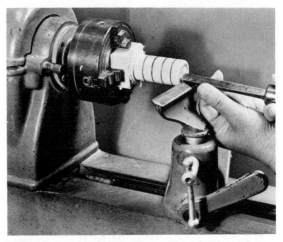

WHEELS are turned one at a time from chucked turning. Shape hub and tire first, then cut it off.

GLUE WHEELS to axles after inserting axles in their holes and slipping washers over the ends.

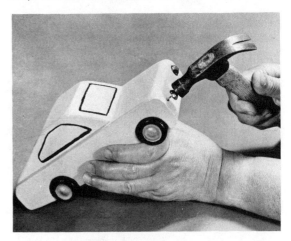

FANCY-HEAD upholstery nails make perfect headlights. Wooden screw-hole buttons, painted, can also be used.

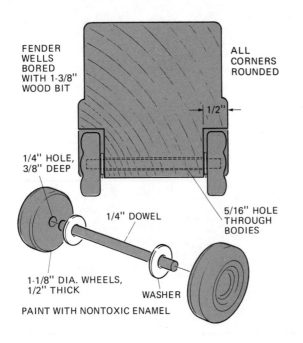

FENDER
WELLS
BORED
WITH 1-3/8"
WOOD BIT

ALL
CORNERS
ROUNDED

1/2"

1/4" HOLE,
3/8" DEEP

1/4" DOWEL

5/16" HOLE
THROUGH
BODIES

1-1/8" DIA. WHEELS,
1/2" THICK

WASHER

PAINT WITH NONTOXIC ENAMEL

The wheels are easy to make if you own a lathe, but there are other ways to make them. One way is with a hole cutter in a drill press; another is with a pivot jig clamped to the table of a disc sander. In a pinch, checkers could be used for wheels.

The best way to turn the wheels is to gang-turn them from a single turning as shown in the photo above. Here the wheels are cut off one by one after you form a hub on the face of the wheels and round the edges to form a tire. The wheels are glued onto the ends of the dowel axles after being drilled ⅜ in. deep from the inside. Washers keep the wheels from rubbing and sticking. It's best to paint the wheels beforehand.

It's important, of course, to round all sharp edges, sand the wood smooth and paint the vehicles with a *nontoxic* paint.

Upholstery tacks are used for headlights, and a small L-hook and screw eye are used as a hitch for the car and trailer.

Tracking—an Indian art that still saves lives

Today's tracker uses the oldest of tools and techniques—plus newest psychology—to track down the lost. Yet tracking is a skill every family camper, hunter and outdoorsman needs to practice. One day you may need this knowledge

By JAMES JOSEPH

BRUISED GRASS, blurred footprints, depth of impressions may be all that tell George Birdsell that a lost boy has passed.

■ DUSK HAS DARKENED your family campsite as tragedy threatens. Suddenly your wife asks, "Where's Bobby?" Your five-year-old is missing. Beyond the campfire lie miles of night woods, streams and jagged terrain. In your mind forms one of the ugliest four-letter words—LOST. Can you find Bobby, find him in time?

"You can—with a basic knowledge of *tracking,* and a good flashlight, in perhaps 30 minutes," declares George B. Birdsell, one of the nation's top "cold trail" trackers, a fast-vanishing breed.

Birdsell's specialty is among the rarest of tracking's lost arts. He can pick up a days-old "cold" trail. Thus has grown the Birdsell legend as a tracker of last resort. When others run out of

track and luck, it's Birdsell they often summon.

Ace tracker for the San Bernardino, CA, sheriff's department which patrols what may be the nation's largest and most rugged county, Birdsell has "cold trailed" after lost boys, campers, fugitives, hunters and wounded game. Seldom during the past 55 years and 130 major "tracks" have their trails—in dense forests, across sizzling deserts, through snow and sand hills—escaped his all-perceiving blue eyes.

And neither, with just a little insight, need a

SEE ALSO

Backpacking ... Binoculars ... Boat camping ... Campers ... Camping ... Clothing, winter ... Hunting ... Map reading ... Recreational vehicles

A LOST CHILD is apt to keep moving at night, to keep warm, and sleep during the daytime.

"lost trail" escape yours. If you camp, hunt or vacation anywhere outdoors, you owe it to your own and your family's safety to learn the ABCs of Indian tracking. Quickly picking up the trail of a family member, or retracing your own, can be the margin between life and death.

Fortunately the trail you will be following will usually be a "hot track" only minutes or perhaps a few hours old. Almost any camper, self-schooled in the basics, can follow a "hot track." How, then, would you find Bobby, your lost child? You've got three things going for you, analyzes Birdsell: *Time*—he's only been gone a short while; *intimate personal knowledge*—you know his weight, which can be important, his habits, and even the kind of shoes he's wearing. And, oddly, the *darkness*. Tracks "shadow" better by flashlight than by sunlight.

Quickly you'd circle your campsite's perimeter "cutting track"—to read the ground for tracks which, heading out and away, might be Bobby's. "Cutting track" is the expert's shortcut for finding a track fast, and establishing in which direction a lost person has gone. Birdsell contends that the test of a tracker is his skill in "placing the search" to put search parties on the right track. In cutting track, the tracker searches along an imaginary line around a campsite, along a ridge or parallel to an existing road or trail that he is sure the man or animal which he is following has crossed.

"A 'cut line' is best run some distance from local track congestion," explains Birdsell, "50 to 100 feet and all the way around a campsite, for example. Almost any track crossing and leading away from your cut line is a transient track worth closer study." But how can you be sure that one set of tracks crossing your cut line is Bobby's?

identifying the right tracks

First, by the kind of shoes, and wives more often than husbands know what shoes every family member is wearing. "The male species," shrugs the leader of a Nevada search-and-rescue team, "is clothes-blind." Recently the team found a member of a lost hunting twosome. Though one partner had camped for a week with his hunting buddy, he hadn't the foggiest notion whether his lost friend was wearing shoes, boots—or was barefoot. But the lost hunter's wife, 500 miles away in Los Angeles, knew when searchers phoned her. "John is wearing his old beat-up hunting boots with worn-down heels," she advised. Put on track, searchers quickly found their man.

Second, by depth and age of tracks. Youngsters under 10 tread lightly, but tend to drag their feet and their tracks may be elongated. Except for shallowness, these can be mistaken for a larger foot. Adults, until they tire, step more precisely. Footprint age is also telltale. Newmade prints (like Bobby's) will be dark and sharply defined when the foot has disturbed fresh moist earth. Within a few hours they begin to dry out and lighten.

Third, by width and length. To assure that the print is Bobby's, measure it. Birdsell uses straight twigs or sticks cut to heel-to-toe length and width. "Your measurements must be accurate to within a quarter inch at least," he explains. "Down trail another set of prints may intersect, but your length and width sticks tell you which to follow." Where dozens of prints converge in a camping area, Birdsell "measures" his way through, also checking print pattern, depth, and age.

"You'd also call Bobby's name," notes Birdsell, "but don't bet on his answering. At night, approaching lights terrify children and they may hide or actually run from searchers." For 11 days Kevin Dye, a 9-year-old epileptic, apparently played hide-and-seek with a 3000-man search force combing Wyoming's rugged Casper Mountains. When finally found, he was asleep on a knoll which had been searched repeatedly.

Obviously, there's more to tracking than tracks, and you need insight into what some call the "behavioral pattern of the lost." Lost children (and some adults) expect *you* to find *them*.

TRACKING ACE George B. Birdsell, a living legend in an almost lost art, has become known far beyond his San Bernardino Mountains. His six basic tools include a metal ski pole with basket removed, to use as a walking stick, scribe around tracks or ward off brush and rattlers. He also carries measuring sticks, pocketknife, canteen, widebeam searchlight to shadow footprints, and matches in a waterproof container. (A quick fire can warm searchers or help save the life of an exposure victim when the latter is found.)

Trackers tell of children huddling all night within sight of a rescue team's campfires, but never venturing close. Tracking a child and faced with two tracks, one headed uphill and the other down, the expert follows uphill. He knows that little ones nearly always go uphill; they find it easier to keep their balance while climbing, and also tend to go on a straight course.

Adults wander in circles, usually favoring the strongest leg. Right-handed (so presumably "right-legged") adults circle to the right. Lefties go the other way.

The lost person's mental and physical condition are often found in his tracks:

Panic is sometimes revealed by a "heel-and-toe" track as the lost alternately run, showing just toe marks, and then tire and walk with much weight on heels. A trail strewn with clothing by a panicking adult might indicate presence of mind in a child. Once, tracking a six-year-old girl, Birdsell suddenly found a second set of footprints joining the first. A more careful "reading" showed the little girl had removed her shoes to rid them of rocks and carefully put them back on—on the wrong feet.

Shock is often shown when a lost track unhesitantly crosses well-trodden trails. Dazed, the lost have been known to stumble past direction signs, ignore railroad tracks and cross busy highways without seeing them.

Exhaustion telltales itself in many ways, from a weaving stumbling gait to body-mark depressions when the lost, exhausted, have fallen or thrown themselves to the ground.

Trailing techniques and speed depend on track, terrain, the quarry and the weather. Where Bobby's trail, for example, is intermittently visible, you'd "skip-track," posting an "anchor man" to mark the last distinct track, and then moving ahead rapidly, skipping faint footprints.

If the terrain is steep and hard-packed or weather and time critical factors, trackers may "sweep" the trail. Half a dozen or more hold hands in roughest terrain or spread out about 15 feet apart to form a sweep line covering every inch of ground.

Might not helicopters, jeeps or bloodhounds track faster? Planes do spot the lost sometimes, but their usefulness is limited to fairly open terrain. Bloodhounds, if brought in early and given proper scent, have turned the trick. "The foot tracker," admits Birdsell, "is usually called after all the quick methods have failed."

Afoot in the desert, veterans—and even a "weekend tracker"—can make about 1½ miles an hour. In mountains where you must ferret out the track, half a mile an hour is likely. On one blistering desert track, Birdsell once led a search party 12 miles in 9 hours. On another he kept going 93 hours with only catnaps. His most dramatic recent track, following a man whose mental impairment kept him from speaking or calling for help, took less than three hours once Birdsell had pulled searchers off the wrong track they'd been following.

MEASURING STICKS or twigs, notched or broken to exact size, are Birdsell's key to footprint identity.

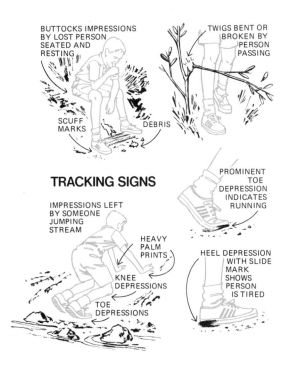

TRACKING SIGNS

BUTTOCKS IMPRESSIONS BY LOST PERSON SEATED AND RESTING

TWIGS BENT OR BROKEN BY PERSON PASSING

SCUFF MARKS

DEBRIS

IMPRESSIONS LEFT BY SOMEONE JUMPING STREAM

PROMINENT TOE DEPRESSION INDICATES RUNNING

HEAVY PALM PRINTS

KNEE DEPRESSIONS

TOE DEPRESSIONS

HEEL DEPRESSION WITH SLIDE MARK SHOWS PERSON IS TIRED

SLIGHTEST CLUE can tell searchers the age, weight, physical and even mental condition of a lost person, if they are on the right track, how long ago he had passed, and if he is now in danger of exhaustion.

"Night is probably the best time to track after kids like Bobby," says Birdsell. In the chill darkness kids tend to keep moving to stay warm. Come daylight they may curl up in some hard-to-find place and sleep. A moving target is easier to spot, and so are faint prints "shadowed" by a searchlight. Pursuing the same faint trail is often impossible during high-noon hours. Following fast on Bobby's hot track, chances are you'd find him within a quarter mile of camp. Lost children seldom travel very fast or far.

Neither may some adults, Birdsell learned when, as a California ranch kid of 16, he took part in his first search. An elderly neighbor, having bagged a buck, borrowed one of the Birdsell's burros to help fetch it. A day later when he hadn't returned, a posse was formed. The burro's tracks were easy to follow, but not until 3:00 a.m. did the posse find the burro hobbled to a tree on a trail high above a mountain stream. The deer lay nearby.

In the glare of lanterns, they read the story in the ground. The old man had tried to heft the heavy deer aboard the burro, had tired, and headed down to the stream. Lantern in hand, young Birdsell followed. Suddenly the tracks dead-ended at a log. "The old man's 'rest marks' with heels dug into the soil showed he sat there getting his wind." Beyond, the hill dropped 300 feet to the stream below. "Getting up to go," Birdsell diagnosed, "he stumbled. We'll find him down there somewhere." And they did: face up, half submerged in the stream, unconscious but alive.

Not all Birdsell tracks have ended so happily. Deep in the sweltering Mojave desert on a Marine Corps search, Birdsell gasped in 120° heat. A young marine had become lost the previous night. The track was distinctive with a right foot toed-in. Plain, too, was the evidence. Time and again the youth had tracked back from desert scrub and cactus. The quick reversals were all but time-clocked to the night's moonless hours. They also told that the youth had panicked, exhausted and scared with the coming of the day's furnace heat. "He was dead when we found him," Birdsell notes quietly, yet he might have saved his own life—as you can, should you become lost—by retracing his own tracks.

good practice—track yourself

Next time you're hiking or jogging, practice it: Retrace your own tracks for a quarter mile or so. "Backtracking teaches a man a lot about himself and about the fellow he may someday be tracking," says Birdsell.

Such insight led Birdsell in 1970 on one of his briefest, most publicized searches. Ten-year-old Marcell Strong, a mentally retarded boy, had wandered from his mountain campground. A 200-man party had searched 20 miles around for five days before Birdsell was called. Birdsell picked six men, including his 21-year-old expert son Bruce, gave them walkie-talkies, and began to cut trail a good mile away. Birdsell almost immediately picked up a track, recognized by its age, size, shallowness and beeline course that mentally retarded often walk. The trail led straight through heavy brush which had been thrashed aside, rather than parted by a more logical person. And at the edge of a canyon the trail went straight down 1200 feet to the bottom. There they found him huddled in an abyss so steep he had to be brought up (alive and surprisingly well) by litter basket. "Just 30 minutes after we'd cut his track, and not a mile from the campground," Birdsell recalls.

But the boy had more than youth and pluck going for him during his five-day survival. He had George B. Birdsell, a living legend among cold-trail trackers.

A FIVE OR SIX-INCH length of a broken hacksaw blade can be altered to give continued service as a deburring tool when you're working with plastics or aluminum. Simply grind a couple of 45° V-notches at the center about halfway up the blade-width as shown. After the ground notch is drawn across the workpiece, the edge will be left perfectly smooth.—*Ernie Wiezorek.*

CRAFTSMEN who are proud of their cabinetry always use glue blocks on the underside of furniture. A good way to make certain that these blocks stay where they are put is to kerf them in two or three places on each gluing surface. The kerf should not be more than 1/16 in. deep; they can be cut quickly with either a hand or table saw.—*Bob Brightman.*

HERE'S A QUICK WAY to improvise a snow shovel when your little guy wants to help. It consists of an old dustpan and the handle from a discarded broom. Shape the handle to force-fit the dustpan holder and attach it with a couple of sheet-metal screws. Drill a hole in the other end for hanging the shovel when not in use.—*Frank Shore.*

WHEN A TUNGSTEN-CARBIDE sanding strip (carbide grains bonded to a thin sheet of steel) becomes so gummed up that a bristle brush alone won't clean it, try using a solvent. In some cases, lighter fluid or lacquer thinner will work; in others, an oven-cleaning liquid. Apply, let soak, and then finish cleaning with stiff-bristle brush as shown.—*W. Ervin.*

YOU CAN QUICKLY plug in and remove three-wire tools with this setup—whether the plug has a pigtail (shown) or prong for grounding. Simply solder a length of insulated wire to the grounded outlet box and affix a small alligator clamp to the other end. Then, when plugging in the tool or adapter, attach the clamp to the ground connection.—*Harold T. Bodkin.*

Build a hydraulic lift for your tractor

By MAURICE ORLAREY

■ LIFTING A HEAVY bulldozer blade manually is for the birds even when it's only a fairly small one on a garden tractor. Pulling a lever to raise and lower the blade can make you arm-weary after only a few hours of grading or snow pushing. That's why I decided to do it the easy way and add a hydraulic lift-so a mere push of a button would lift and lower the blade. Now I feel like a big-time heavy-equipment operator!

The first step I took to add this pushbutton convenience was a trip to the local junkyard to pick up the power unit—a hydraulic system from the convertible top of a car. (The one I selected happened to be from an Oldsmobile.) At the time I built the lift, $10 purchased:

- Motor, pump, reservoir unit.
- Cylinder with bottom plate.

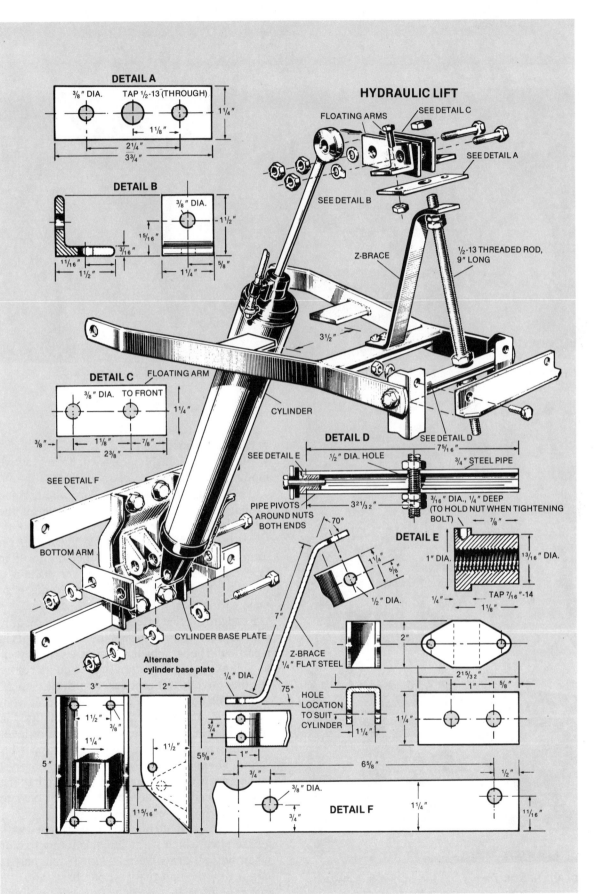

DETAIL A

$\frac{3}{8}$" DIA.   TAP $\frac{1}{2}$-13 (THROUGH)

$1\frac{1}{4}$"

$1\frac{1}{8}$"

$2\frac{1}{4}$"

$3\frac{3}{4}$"

DETAIL B

$\frac{3}{8}$" DIA.

$1\frac{1}{2}$"

$1\frac{5}{16}$"

$\frac{3}{16}$"

$1\frac{11}{16}$"

$1\frac{1}{2}$"

$1\frac{1}{4}$"

$\frac{5}{8}$"

HYDRAULIC LIFT

FLOATING ARMS

SEE DETAIL C

SEE DETAIL A

SEE DETAIL B

Z-BRACE

$\frac{1}{2}$-13 THREADED ROD, 9" LONG

$3\frac{1}{2}$"

DETAIL C   FLOATING ARM

$\frac{3}{8}$" DIA.   TO FRONT

$1\frac{1}{4}$"

$\frac{3}{8}$"

$1\frac{1}{8}$" $\frac{7}{8}$"

$2\frac{3}{8}$"

SEE DETAIL F

CYLINDER

SEE DETAIL D

DETAIL D

SEE DETAIL E $\frac{1}{2}$" DIA. HOLE

$\frac{3}{4}$" STEEL PIPE

$7\frac{5}{16}$"

PIPE PIVOTS AROUND NUTS BOTH ENDS

$3\frac{21}{32}$"

$\frac{3}{16}$" DIA., $\frac{1}{4}$" DEEP (TO HOLD NUT WHEN TIGHTENING BOLT)

$\frac{7}{8}$"

DETAIL E

70°

$1\frac{1}{4}$"

$\frac{5}{8}$"

$\frac{1}{2}$" DIA.

1" DIA.

$\frac{13}{16}$" DIA.

$\frac{1}{4}$"   TAP $\frac{7}{16}$"-14

$1\frac{1}{8}$"

BOTTOM ARM

CYLINDER BASE PLATE

7"

Z-BRACE $\frac{1}{4}$" FLAT STEEL

$\frac{1}{4}$" DIA.

75°

HOLE LOCATION TO SUIT CYLINDER

$1\frac{1}{4}$"

Alternate cylinder base plate

3"   2"

$1\frac{1}{2}$" $\frac{3}{8}$"

$1\frac{1}{4}$"

5"

$1\frac{1}{2}$"

$5\frac{5}{8}$"

$\frac{3}{4}$"

1"

$1\frac{15}{16}$"

2"

$2\frac{15}{32}$"

1" $\frac{5}{8}$"

$1\frac{1}{4}$"

$6\frac{5}{8}$"

$\frac{3}{4}$"

$\frac{3}{8}$" DIA.

$\frac{3}{4}$"

DETAIL F

$1\frac{1}{4}$"

$\frac{1}{2}$"

$1\frac{11}{16}$"

CYLINDER BOTTOM arms are attached to plate with a bolt and to cylinder with shaft, washer and cotter pin.

BLADE RESTING on ground exposes ½-in. threaded rod. Extended down, it allows room for adjustment.

• Hydraulic hose.
• Wiring and dashboard switch for above motor.

Since at this point I wasn't sure whether one cylinder would provide enough muscle for the job, I also bought the second cylinder (manufacturers use two per car) for an additional $2. As it turned out, one cylinder was sufficient. It will, in fact, effortlessly raise and lower the blade at a touch of the button, even with an average-size male sitting atop the blade.

Recognizing that prices can vary and probably will, depending upon the number of junkyards in a particular geographical location, a visit to your local junkyard for a materials price quote before starting the job is a practical approach.

Some changes on the manual lifting unit were necessary so that the cylinder could be fitted in place. First, I had to disassemble the lifting lever and linkage that connects it to the upper-lift frame. Then, using ¼ x 1¼ x 14¼-in. flat iron, I made a flat brace (Detail F) and fastened it to the tractor. Finally, I fastened the cylinder base to the upper and lower braces.

The cylinder that I bought came equipped with a base plate which was adaptable to my tractor when bottom arms were added. If this part is missing on the unit that you purchase, you can make the alternate base plate shown in the draw-

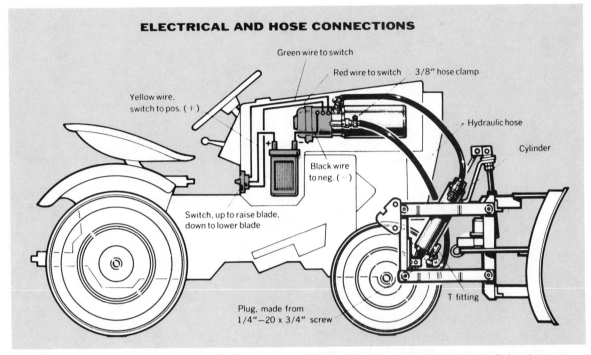

ELECTRICAL AND HOSE CONNECTIONS

Green wire to switch

Red wire to switch

3/8" hose clamp

Yellow wire, switch to pos. (+)

Hydraulic hose

Cylinder

Black wire to neg. (−)

Switch, up to raise blade, down to lower blade

T-fitting

Plug, made from 1/4"−20 x 3/4" screw

AFTER CUTTING HOSE to unused second cylinder, plug T-fitting with a ¼-in.-diameter bolt and a ⅜-in. clamp.

ings. With this version, the bottom arms can be eliminated since the cylinder-holding U-channel provides ample swing-clearance.

The motor-pump reservoir unit fits snugly under the tractor hood. On my rig it had to be positioned on the top left side of the engine between the air cleaner, gas tank and left headlight. To make room, it was necessary to move the air-cleaner cover slightly to the right.

Current draw is given at about 35 amps. which is no problem for my 12-v. heavy-duty battery. The "on" time is very short since the blade is lifted at a speed of roughly 2 in. per second. If your blade doesn't stay up, due to slow leakage through the pump, it can be corrected by stiffening the pivot points of the upper and lower frames by inserting spring lock washers under the bolt heads.

All of the dimensions shown were determined by trial-and-error fitting as I built the lift to suit the tractor (Sears 10-hp XL). For other makes I would recommend experimenting with cardboard and/or plywood templates to check for fit and clearance before cutting, shaping and welding the iron.

Working at a leisurely pace, I completed the setup in my spare time. I'm so pleased with the results that I feel it borders on understatement to say that my effort was worth every minute.

WITH THREADED ROD almost vertical, floating arm position indicates that the blade is free to float.

POWER UNIT fits neatly under hood on the engine's left side when the air cleaner was moved slightly.

Make a trailer for your garden tractor

By G. R. JOBE

■ YOU'LL HAVE A SURE CURE for those backaches caused by heavy back-yard chores with this functional utility trailer that can be constructed of common materials to fit most any make of garden tractor.

The versatility of the trailer is mainly a result of the flexible arrangement of interlocking slatted sides and a removable rear panel. The trailer can be used with its four slatted sides, or it can be converted quickly to a three or four-sided flatbed type.

Made of four horizontal and two vertical strips of ¾ x 2¾-in. fir, the slatted sides slip into retainers of 16-ga. cold-rolled steel (CRS) permanently mounted to the four side panels of ¾-in. exterior plywood. Attached to the top slats of each side are supports of 12-ga. CRS that hook onto each other and greatly strengthen the corner joints while allowing quick and easy removal of the sides without the need for any tools.

The main section of the trailer consists of a three-sided plywood enclosure mounted on a steel frame. The fourth side (rear panel) slips into the channel formed by the lengths of 1x1 and 2x2 angle that are screwed to the inner and outer surfaces of the side panels.

The frame or chassis of the trailer is made of 1⅛-in.-square steel bar, although steel pipe, square or round tubing, angle or channel also could be used. Regardless of which material you use, however, make certain that all joints are securely welded together with fillet welds.

Almost any type of pneumatic tire and wheel assembly can be used, as long as it is at least 12 in. in diameter. Suitable wheels often can be

SEE ALSO

Engines, small . . . Gardening . . . Mowers . . . Snowplows . . . Tractor lifts . . . Yard machines

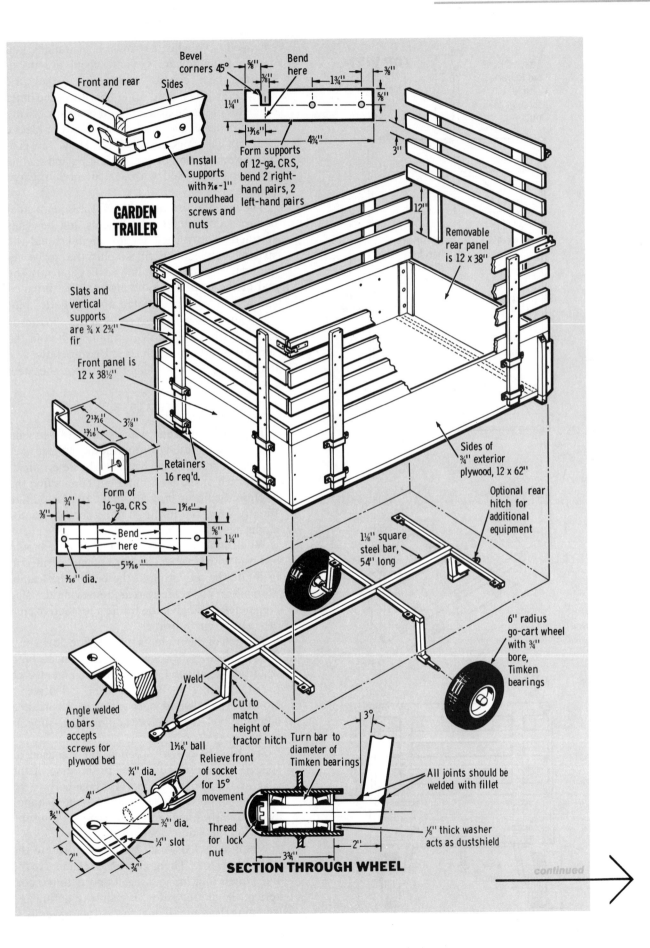

Front and rear

Sides

Bevel corners 45°

Bend here

Install supports with ³⁄₁₆-1" roundhead screws and nuts

Form supports of 12-ga. CRS, bend 2 right-hand pairs, 2 left-hand pairs

GARDEN TRAILER

1¼"
⅝"
³⁄₈"
1¾"
³⁄₈"
⅝"
1³⁄₁₆"
4¾"
3"

12"

Removable rear panel is 12 x 38"

Slats and vertical supports are ¾ x 2¾" fir

Front panel is 12 x 38½"

2¹³⁄₁₆"
1³⁄₁₆"
3⅞"

Retainers 16 req'd.

Form of 16-ga. CRS

Bend here

¾"
³⁄₈"
⅝"
1¼"
1⁹⁄₁₆"
5¹⁵⁄₁₆"
³⁄₁₆" dia.

Sides of ¾" exterior plywood, 12 x 62"

Optional rear hitch for additional equipment

1⅛" square steel bar, 54" long

6" radius go-cart wheel with ¾" bore, Timken bearings

Angle welded to bars accepts screws for plywood bed

Weld

Cut to match height of tractor hitch

Turn bar to diameter of Timken bearings

Relieve front of socket for 15° movement

1¹⁄₁₆" ball

¾" dia.

4"

¾"

¾" dia.

¼" slot

2"

¾"

Thread for lock nut

3°

All joints should be welded with fillet

⅛" thick washer acts as dustshield

2"

3¾"

SECTION THROUGH WHEEL

continued ➡

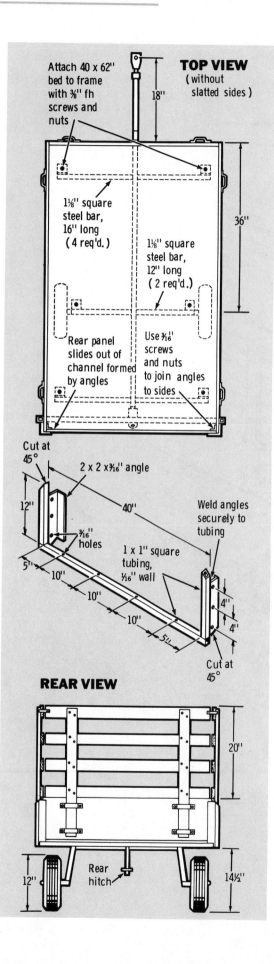

Attach 40 x 62" bed to frame with ⅜" fh screws and nuts

TOP VIEW
(without slatted sides)

18"

36"

1⅛" square steel bar, 16" long (4 req'd.)

1⅛" square steel bar, 12" long (2 req'd.)

Rear panel slides out of channel formed by angles

Use ³⁄₁₆" screws and nuts to join angles to sides

Cut at 45°

2 x 2 x³⁄₁₆" angle

12"

³⁄₁₆" holes

40"

Weld angles securely to tubing

5" 10"

1 x 1" square tubing, ¹⁄₁₆" wall

10"

10"

5"

4"

4"

Cut at 45°

REAR VIEW

20"

12"

Rear hitch

14½"

salvaged from wheelbarrows, boat trailers, golf carts or lawnmowers. Go-kart wheels are probably the best choice, especially if they are equipped with tapered roller bearings. The inner diameter of the bearings should be at least ¾ in.

Ball bearings (sealed or nonsealed) or sleeve bearings will work equally well. However, provisions must be made for lubricating and sealing any hubs not fitted with sealed, prelubricated bearings.

The spindles are turned from the square steel bar to accommodate the wheels and bearings selected. The turned length should equal the spacing between bearings, plus the space required for a grease seal, flat washer and nut. The end of the turned spindle also can be threaded and drilled for a castellated nut and cotter pin.

An alternative method to form the spindles is to weld a headless bolt in a hole drilled in the supporting arm of the chassis. Be sure, however, that the wheel will clear the arm of the steel chassis.

construction sequence

The steel frame and wheels should be assembled first, then fitted to your tractor so the proper vertical position of the hitch can be determined. The length of the horizontal bar connecting the hitch to the frame may also have to be modified slightly since the turning radius of your tractor might be smaller than that shown.

When completed and tested, the frame should be fitted with six short sections of angle drilled to facilitate the mounting of the bed to the frame. Then clean all welded areas, removing the slag completely, and give the frame a protective coat of zinc chromate primer.

The bed of the trailer is built upside down on a level surface. All joints should be made with waterproof glue and secured in alignment with 1¼-in. finishing nails. Then drill and drive in No. 8 1½-in. wood screws every 10 in. and allow the bed to dry before adding the U-support at the rear.

Six 3-in. blocks of scrap wood are used as spacers to insure the proper positioning of the slats on the vertical supports. Make certain the vertical supports are spaced the same distance away from the ends of the slats before gluing and screwing the sides together.

When all glued joints have dried, screw the bed to the frame. Then secure the retainers to the side panels and the locking supports to the corners of the slatted sides. Finish by painting and trimming the trailer to match the tractor's colors.

How to tow a trailer

By A. R. ROALMAN

■ "CARS PULLING TRAILERS were involved in four times as many single-vehicle rural highway accidents as the same number of cars without trailers," said the man sitting across a cluttered desk from me.

No ordinary sort, the man is one of the most knowledgeable traffic authorities in the country. He is J. Stannard Baker, former director of research for the highly regarded Traffic Institute of Northwestern University. When he says something about traffic safety, you can count on it being hard-nosed fact based on on-the-roadway sniffing and hunting he has done. He had just completed his share of a massive survey for the federal government, which, with the cooperation of the police of seven states from Illinois to California, had studied highway accidents on

"PEOPLE PULLING TRAILERS stop at a service station . . . find they have 25 or 26 pounds of pressure in their car tires and maybe as much in the trailer tires . . . and take off. Their chances of a trailer-tire blowout went up like a skyrocket." Best pressure for a heavy-duty trailer tire might be 50 pounds.

50 lbs   25 lbs   25 lbs

U. S. 66. Called "Single Vehicle Accidents on Route 66," Baker's report of this study at the annual meeting of the Highway Research Board told about the factors contributing to all single-vehicle accidents studied while the project was underway. In this report, which was not for publication, is a reference that anyone who pulls something—another car, boat, house trailer, camper, a rental trailer (every driver is likely to pull one of these units at some time during the next few years, considering the way trailer rental stations are mushrooming) or even a horse trailer—behind his car should know about. This small statistical tabulation entitled *Risk Index By Type of Vehicle,* also stated:

"If you are driving a standard-sized car, your 'risk index' is 4.57 if you have a trailer and 1.00 if you aren't pulling a trailer; if you have a compact car, your RI is 8.48 when you have a trailer behind and 2.23 when you don't; if you have a small car, the numbers are 14.47 with a trailer, 3.49 without.

In all cases, when you put a trailer behind your car the odds of your having a single-vehicle accident quadruple.

SEE ALSO

**Autos, safety . . . Night driving . . .
Recreational vehicles . . . Trailers, tent . . .
Winter driving**

Why? The odds were a little too much to allow to go unexplored. What steps can you take to reduce the odds against you? If you expect, during the next few years, to hook anything behind your car, what can you do to wipe out some of the specific dangers of trailer pulling?

As a veteran boat puller with a lot of hours chalked up to pulling mobile homes and rental units, I had had my share of close calls and hard-knock education, but I wanted to know what Baker, state police and manufacturers of trailer equipment, automobiles and trucks had to say.

be "sober and rested"

Let's assume that you're clean on two major causes of all accidents: Driving while sleepy and driving right after having a few drinks. These are cited most often as the major causes of single-car wrecks: going off the road, plowing into a big, immovable tree or a rock-hard concrete abutment, or flipping over. Let's assume that, when you hook up your trailer, you are sober and rested, and you're not going to push yourself so hard that you are likely to fall asleep at the wheel. What else can you do to reduce the possibility of having a trailer accident?

"Either have brakes or remember that you don't have brakes," said Baker, who pointed out that a lot of people who hook on a trailer forget they no longer have a normal braking situation. In all likelihood, the trailer—if it's small—will not have separate brakes. That, in itself, is dangerous. Here's why:

You're buzzing down a country road at 60 mph, come into a curve and suddenly see a cow 100 feet ahead. If you're like most drivers, you'll ram your foot down hard on the brake pedal. Good show, except that those brakes are only going to stop your car.

How about that 400 or 500 pounds of iron behind you? No brakes? It will tend to keep coming. And if it's at a slight angle to your car, it easily could swing right on around, pull the rear end of your car with it just as sweetly as you please, and dump the whole shebang against the nearest tree or concrete rail. Unexpected little problems like that make the odds against an accident about four to one worse with a trailer than without it.

So, okay, what do you do? You're without trailer brakes and have to get from where you are to where you want to be.

"Most people with trailers drive like they don't have trailers," said Baker. "That's foolish. They should slow down about 10 percent from their normal speed and give themselves plenty of room to stop without hitting their brakes suddenly and hard." Coming to a blind curve or intersection? Tail off on your speed and enter the potential danger spot with every chance to stop your car and the load behind it without violent braking.

The bigger the trailer load and the smaller the car, the more necessary it is to have brakes on the trailer. According to Baker, a rule of thumb is that if a loaded trailer weighs more than one-third the weight of the car, the trailer should have brakes.

"Tires are another problem," said Baker. "People pulling trailers stop at a service station to check their tires. They find they have 25 or 26 pounds of pressure in their car tires and maybe as much in the trailer tires. They think everything is okay, get back in and take off."

Their chances of trailer-tire blowout went up like a skyrocket because the recommended maximum air pressure in a heavy-duty trailer tire could be 50 pounds. Boom along on a hot summer day with 25 or 26 pounds in such tires, and you'll flex their side walls in the same way a piece of metal reacts when you bend it back and forth rapidly: Build up heat in it, cause it to grow weak, then break.

I drove the interstate highway system in Illinois, Wisconsin and Missouri to check on blown-out trailer tires. They were as common as dirty rags around a service station.

How do you beat this problem? Simply observe and follow the maximum tire pressure and maximum load ratings marked on your trailer tires. The load rating refers to the permissible

"COMING TO A BLIND CURVE or intersection? Tail off on your speed and enter the potential danger spot with every chance to stop your car and the load behind it without violent braking."

"**STICK YOUR HAND** against the trailer-wheel hub and feel how warm it is."

load at maximum pressure for one wheel; thus if the load rating is 1000 pounds and you have a two-wheel trailer, the tires can stand a total trailer load of 2000 pounds.

You don't *have* to carry maximum pressure if you have a light load, but you might as well. Many people underinflate their auto tires to get a softer, more comfortable ride, but a trailer load usually doesn't need such consideration.

If you have very old tires made before tires carried an inflation recommendation and load rating, ask a tire dealer to give you an estimate. Until you know for sure, don't drive for long periods above 45 miles per hour, and don't drive for more than an hour without going back to check the tires. If they feel hot, stop and let them cool off. Hot tires are getting ready to blow, and blown trailer tires cause problems.

Trailer wheels don't go sour only because of blown tires. Bearings are another problem. Usually, trailer wheels turn much faster than the

wheels of your car; they're smaller but still cover the same distance as the car. If the bearings aren't well protected by grease, they get chewed up in no time and you lose a wheel or a trailer . . . or a car . . . or your life.

Every time you stop at a service station and check the pressure of your trailer tires, stick your hand against the trailer-wheel hub and feel how warm it is. If it's hot enough to make you jerk your hand back, don't waste time. Ask the attendant to pull that wheel and glob the bearing with grease, after checking to make sure that the bearing housing is still intact.

"Loading is another factor," said Baker. He showed me how some drivers will load the tail end of a trailer with heavy furniture, thus lifting the rear end of the car until it has little rear-wheel braking ability.

Distribute the load evenly, with the heaviest pieces as close as possible to the area over the axle. Place those pieces as low in the trailer as you can, so they won't swing or fall and cause the load to shift. Put a little more weight ahead of the axle than behind it, so that 10 to 15 percent of the total weight is on the trailer hitch; if you need help to lift the hitch from the ground, you probably have too much in front. When that occurs, the *front* wheels of the towing car are lifted a bit and don't brake as well.

Proper loading doesn't solve everything. Winds, for example. Most trailer pullers aren't prepared for the effect of crosswinds, says Baker.

A high-sided rental unit, house trailer or camper has relatively little weight to hold it on the highway, when compared with their area exposed to crosswinds. A trailer emerging from a tunnel or shelter of a roadside hill may suddenly be hit by a crosswind that forces car and trailer off the road or into the incoming lane.

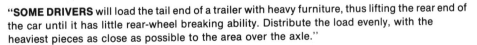

"**SOME DRIVERS** will load the tail end of a trailer with heavy furniture, thus lifting the rear end of the car until it has little rear-wheel breaking ability. Distribute the load evenly, with the heaviest pieces as close as possible to the area over the axle."

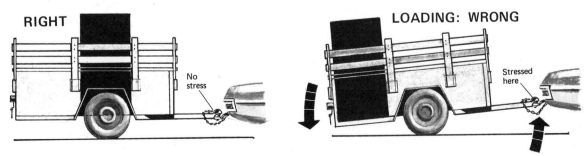

RIGHT   LOADING: WRONG

No stress   Stressed here

Come out of protected areas cautiously and slowly when you are pulling a trailer. If there's a stiff side breeze, roll along slowly. Park when wild winds blow. There's no way to drive a big-area trailer safely under strong side-wind conditions.

Safer when you're towing? Let's go to that little round ball where your trailer and car become one—the ball of the hitch. According to the Society of Automotive Engineers, there are four classes of trailers:

Class 1. Nonpassenger trailers with a loaded weight of 2000 pounds or less.

Class 2. Nonpassenger trailers with a gross weight of 2000 to 3500 pounds.

Class 3. Nonpassenger trailers with a gross weight of 3500 to 5000 pounds.

Class 4. Nonpassenger trailers that weigh more than 5000 pounds.

Why "nonpassenger?" Because common sense and state laws say carrying passengers in a moving trailer is wrong and dangerous, SAE people use the term "nonpassenger" trailer to remind everybody that trailers should never be used for hauling people.

According to the SAE, your trailer is a Class 1, 2, 3, or 4, depending upon the weight you are pulling. The coupling of your trailer should be stamped: "Meets SAE Standards for Coupling Designation No. _____." If that is not on the unit somewhere, and you can't get firm information about the class trailer the hitch is capable of hauling, don't use it.

SAE also points out you should have at least one welded-steel safety chain (wise heads in the trailer-pulling business use two) that has a breaking-test load equivalent to the maximum weight of your trailer when loaded. If you're buying a new rig, the selling company should be

HIGH WINDS

"A TRAILER EMERGING from a tunnel or shelter of a roadside hill may suddenly be hit by a crosswind that forces car and trailer . . . into the oncoming lane."

able to tell you the breaking-test load figure for its safety chain.

If you're buying safety chain for a used rig, be certain of the test load before you use it. Make sure your hitch is welded to the frame of your car by a first-class welder. Don't hook it to your bumper, which, in many instances, isn't held in place too firmly.

If you're renting a trailer, you'll be given a bolt-on hitch. Make sure the hitch is so well locked in place that you'll bet your life on it.

Friction causes balls to break off hitches. Be sure the socket is well lubricated with grease before you hook it in place over the ball.

Don't tow a rented trailer without brake and turn-signal lights on it. Not only are you a hazard on the highway but you may be legally responsible if rammed from behind. Be sure your rental agency hooks up the necessary lights.

Make sure your mirror gives you a clear view of following traffic. Most cab-over camper owners and house-trailer towers do have both right and lefthand outside mirrors so they can see cars approaching on either side. Some boat pullers do this, but not everyone pulling rental units does. If you have a trailer wider than your car, or if the trailer is so high it blocks the view on your inside rear-view mirror, you should rent extra clamp-on side mirrors.

If you haven't backed a trailer before, learn how before you pull onto the highway. Find yourself a parking lot and practice until you're a pro. You're bound to get into situations where you'll be glad you are.

"MOST CAB-OVER CAMPER owners . . . do have both right and left-hand outside mirrors so they can see cars approaching on either side."

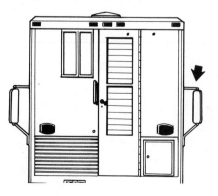

Stippling technique

Years ago I remember seeing a room with stippled walls. It was a beautiful job, and I'd like to know how it was done. The figure or texture was fine spots, or dots, in a uniform pattern over a lighter base color. I know it's old-fashioned, but I'd like to do a room or two in this manner. Can you tell me how?—Robert Catton, Tulsa, Okla.

This was a common mode of decoration for painted walls in the '30s and early '40s. Judging by your description, it was done with a natural sponge, trimmed to form one flat face, which was dipped in unthinned paint. This is tricky, but if you're careful to avoid producing the sponge pattern you can carry out the job neatly. It usually looks best when two or more colors that are just slightly different in value are used, with the lighter color treated as the background.

Condensation remedy

You and others make much talk about condensation but you never give the specific cure. Let's have the "specific" for a change. Come now, just what is it?—C.N., Ky.

There isn't any. What's "specific" for one instance isn't always so in another. The cause is built-in in nearly all new homes because they are more "airtight" than older structures. This is an oversimplification, but still it is basically the cause of troubles from excessive condensate as stated. Moisture trapped in newer homes cannot normally escape through walls and ceilings in sufficient amounts to prevent condensate from forming on surfaces having a lower temperature such as window panes, often doors and even walls. The only remedy is to reduce the moisture content of the air in the rooms. Some homeowners do this with an automatic dehumidifier, which is reported to give satisfactory results.

Oops . . . more stains

I spilled a small amount of ink on the seat of an upholstered chair. Can you tell me how to get out the stain?—John Weaver, Salem, Ore.

Ink removal—especially from any pile fabric—can be tricky. I'd try dry-cleaning fluid first, using just enough to cover the stain. Apply it with a ball of cotton, then blot it with a dry cloth, refolding the cloth after each blotting. This should get at least part of the stain. If not, apply ink eradicator (No. 1 solution) to *an inconspicuous place on the fabric as a test for color fastness.* If okay, apply it to the stain with an eyedropper and remove it with a blotter. Repeat until the blotter shows no stain, then rinse the fabric with cold water and let it air-dry.

Smaller, not weaker

If I plant miniature or dwarf roses this spring, will they live through the next winter in this climate? I'm told they will—and also that they won't. Who is right?—J. Edwardson, Carbondale, Ill.

Your "will-live" advisors should be right. Dwarf, or miniature, roses are normally hardy if cared for properly during the growing season. Supply them with adequate water and plant food, and protect them from winter kill just as you would the other varieties.

One-way lamp

Please tell me how to make my three-way lamp light three ways. Heretofore it's worked okay. But now the new bulb lights only once, on the second click of the switch. I did notice that the old bulb seemed to catch, did not turn out freely.—Mrs. Ted Willis, Tacoma, Wash.

In turning out the old bulb, you may have bent or otherwise damaged the center contact in the socket. First, *disconnect the lamp cord from the outlet.* Then remove the bulb and examine the center contact in the socket. If it is bent out of position or twisted, straighten it with pliers or a screwdriver and bend it back to the central position. The contact is delicate—be careful not to break it. Reassembled, the lamp should again light properly, on all three power levels.

Below-grade tile

I plan to retile a 14x30-ft. basement room where there is humidity and foundation moisture. After old tile is removed and adhesive scraped away, should I wash the floor with a cleaner such as trisodium phosphate for better adhesion? The old tile is asbestos and I intend to replace it with vinyl.—Bud Haak, West St. Paul, Minn.

I favor asphalt tile for installation on concrete floors below grade. It wears well and is less subject to harm caused by the moisture conditions found in most basements. But I know of asbestos-tiled basement floors—including one that has been flooded twice—that are 25 years old and still in good condition. In any case, you'll need to clean the floor thoroughly to remove all cement residues, dust and dirt before laying new tile. It must also be dry before you lay tile.

by W. Clyde Lammey

We built our own tent trailer

Camping can make for an inexpensive and interesting vacation. This four-sleeper tent trailer is just the thing for your next trip. You can build it yourself in your garage. It unfolds easily when you get to the campsite

By JAMES L. BENNETT

SEE ALSO

Campers . . . Camping . . . Recreational vehicles . . . Trailers

■ BECAUSE WE THINK camping is the best and least expensive way to take vacations, my wife and I decided to put together this tent trailer.

With an 8½-foot trailer, we thought we could take our two children and dog on fun trips for less money.

So with my wife's help, I built our first tent trailer. It took me four weekends and it cost $335—at the time we did it.

I purchased the open A-frame chassis for $145. You can build the whole tent trailer for about $250 if you make the chassis yourself. I decided to purchase the chassis because I am not that experienced in metalwork. But I do know woodworking.

I found that building the trailer box was simple once the plywood and lumber are cut to size. The plywood sections are so designed that you can use every bit of eight 4x8-ft. pieces of plywood. This means that you don't have extra bits and

pieces left over after construction. It also means that you will not have the expense of extra sheets of plywood.

To start, you need the trailer chassis. You can get this from a number of commercial metal works. Better still, you can scavenge it from an old beat-up trailer. Or you can build it from scratch—but you will need metalworking equipment.

Should you want to build the chassis, the materials you'll need include two 10½-foot sections of 2½-inch pipe. The trailer bed is 8 feet long, but you'll need an additional 2½ feet of length for the trailer tongue. Next, you need six 6½-foot

BUILD THE CHASSIS, then attach floor pieces. The trailer stands are attached to the forward portion.

FLOORING is laid on the joists. Attach floor and joists to angle iron with bolts or wood screws.

PREFABBING SIDES is a good idea. Note the position of the structural supports for cabinets.

pieces of angle-iron stringers. These must be welded to the piping. Suspension springs, brackets, axle and wheels come next. (See diagram.) Positioning of the axle is critical. You want the completed trailer to tow straight behind the car, and be so balanced that only 50 to 60 pounds of weight rests on the hitch. The trailer tires should be 4.80/4.00 x 8-in., which are rated to carry 1200-pound loads at 60 mph. You want to try to

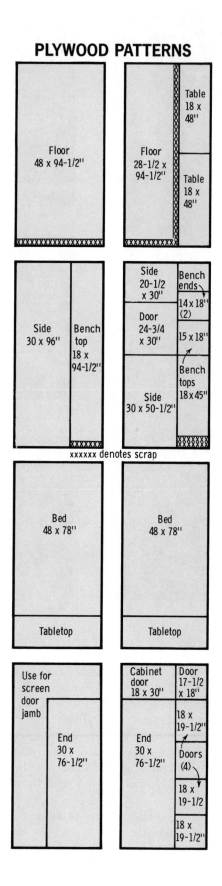

PLYWOOD PATTERNS

Floor
48 x 94-1/2"

Floor
28-1/2 x
94-1/2"

Table
18 x
48"

Table
18 x
48"

Side
30 x 96"

Bench
top
18 x
94-1/2"

Side
20-1/2
x 30"

Bench
ends
14 x 18"
(2)

Door
24-3/4
x 30"

15 x 18"

Side
30 x 50-1/2"

Bench
tops
18 x 45"

xxxxxx denotes scrap

Bed
48 x 78"

Bed
48 x 78"

Tabletop

Tabletop

Use for
screen
door
jamb

End
30 x
76-1/2"

Cabinet
door
18 x 30"

Door
17-1/2
x 18"

18 x
19-1/2"

End
30 x
76-1/2"

Doors
(4)

18 x
19-1/2

18 x
19-1/2"

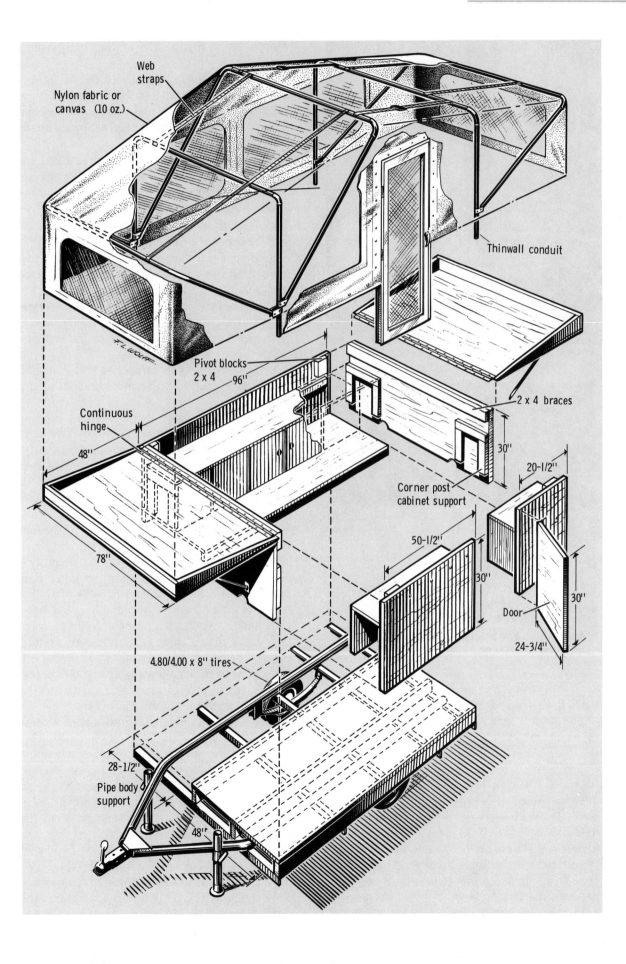

Web straps

Nylon fabric or canvas (10 oz.)

Thinwall conduit

Pivot blocks 2 x 4   96"

Continuous hinge

2 x 4 braces

48"

30"

Corner post cabinet support

20-1/2"

50-1/2"

30"

30"

78"

Door

24-3/4"

4.80/4.00 x 8" tires

28-1/2"

Pipe body support

48"

F.L. WOLFF.

A SCREEN DOOR can be mounted. This door is removed and laid on the floor when you collapse the trailer.

PIVOT BLOCKS AND BOLTS are necessary for tent pole. Note steel straps that attach oblique pole.

keep away from large tires as they call for wheel wells in the camper box for wheel clearance.

The trailer body is basically a box made of plywood with 2x4-in. lumber used as joists under the floor.

The floor should be of ⅝-in. plywood, while the trailer sides, top and cabinets can be of ⅝-in. or ½-in. Once you've cut all your wood, start by laying floors on joists and drilling through floor, joist and angle iron. Bolt together securely. Remember, this trailer will take a lot of bouncing.

To finish off the floor, it's a good idea to lay tile. Remember to arrange the tile so the joint between the two plywood floor sheets is covered. Also lay the tile before adding cabinets.

This avoids intricate tile cutting and assures proper fit.

For the cabinets, use strips of 1x3-in. lumber as supports and lengths of 2x2-in. as structural supports in the corners and at the ends. Cabinet doors can be covered with vinyl to spruce up the trailer interior.

For extra sleeping space, make the table so the support leg can be folded under and the table can be detached from trailer bracket. Then lay the tabletop across the cabinet tops or benches. This can make up into another bed.

Here are some other trailer building tips:

Remember to keep the door handle low enough so there is enough space for collapsed tent poles and canvas.

Use heavy 2½-in. continuous piano-type hinges to secure bedwings to the trailer box.

Use awning brackets as sockets for bedwing support rods.

Use pivot blocks in corners so tent poles fall within the trailer box. Use pivot bolts to secure poles.

Cement sponge-rubber weatherstripping around the top edge of the trailer box. When the trailer is closed in the travel position, this stripping will absorb shock and help keep road dust out.

Paint the chassis so it will not rust and so it can be hosed off after long, muddy trips.

Now you're ready for the tough part—the tent canvas.

It is possible that you may want some professional help on this important section. Few people have sewing machines capable of double stitching 10-oz. canvas. Rug-binding and hand awls may also present a problem to the average builder. A good awning and tentmaker can turn out a first-rate job for you when given the dimensions of your trailer. Remember, the tent poles, from pivot to peak, cannot be longer than the interior dimensions of the trailer box.

Electrician's thinwall conduit—about 9 cents a foot—can be used for tent poles and ribs. This material can be bent with a plumber's bending tool. Or you can have formed corners of ¹³/₁₆-in. bar inserted in saw-cut tubing ends. Wrap all joints with tape to prevent wear on canvas. Web luggage straps can serve to hold poles in the correct standing position.

There is a helpful source for those of you who might have trouble building the chassis and sewing the canvas. It's the Stratford Fabricating Co. in Bridgeport, CT. This firm manufactures the open A-frame chassis and the tent.

SUSPENDING a paintbrush in thinner without damaging the bristles is a problem that has inspired a number of solutions. The idea shown here is my particular favorite. Select a coffee can or pail that will accommodate your brush, and keep the brush vertical by clamping it to the container with a C-clamp. Pour in just enough solvent to reach the brush's ferrule. —*Andrew Vena.*

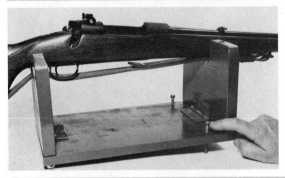

HERE'S AN ADJUSTABLE "no hands" support for sighting a rifle that can be made of scrap 1x8 stock. It consists of a base and two hinged arms with notches to cradle the gun stock. For elevation control, long ¼-in. machine bolts in undersized holes are used. With trigger guard against rear upright, rifle weight keeps assembly firm.—*Robert Hertzberg.*

A SLIDING GATE in our fenced-in rear yard is a convenience because it doesn't require any swinging room. But its considerable weight caused the inevitable sagging which made it hard to slide. The problem was permanently solved by mounting two pairs of wide-tread wheels on pipe "axles" and clamping them to the bottom rail on the outboard end.—*Norman Redding.*

IF YOU HOLD A FILE edge at 45° and draw it across the cutting edge of your tin snips, you'll give the tool a better bite. As a result, there is much less chance that the metal will crawl away from the jaws as you cut. This trick, of course, should be used on ordinary snips only; do not file special-purpose, serrated cutters.—*W. H. McClay.*

WHEN HEATING IRON or other metal on a gas stove, half of a clay flowerpot can be used effectively to confine the heat around the workpiece where it's wanted. To cut the pot, use a hacksaw, then place it over the burner. If you use both halves, one over the other as shown, you'll retain even more heat.—*Joe Chinclair.*

Build a simple transistor tester

By LARRY D. SMITH

One of the handiest gadgets any
electronics hobbyist can have is a transistor checker.
This inexpensive model checks a
transistor's gain, type and proper
functioning. It's easy to build yourself.
Here's how to construct and use it

■ IF YOU'RE A TYPICAL weekend electronic
genius, you need a transistor tester, both to expose bad transistors in devices you're trying to
fix, and to tell you the characteristics of the
transistors in your junk box. This little tester
does both, costs next to nothing and takes very
little time to build.

What the circuit does is measure emitter-
collector leakage and d.c. current gain (which is
usually quite close to the a.c. current gain, or
Beta). Switch one (S1) applies the correct battery polarity to the transistor. S2 opens to disconnect the base lead for leakage measurement,
or closes to connect the base lead to the collector
through resistor two (R2) for measuring gain. R1
is simply to protect the meter in case the transistor under test is shorted.

For d.c. gain measurement, a nine-volt battery
supplies a current of about .01 mA through the
emitter-base junction, that current being determined by the combined resistances of R2 (820K)
and the junction itself. D.c. current gain is the
ratio between the emitter-collector and the
emitter-base currents, which, in this case,
amounts to 100 times the emitter-collector current in mA.

If you already have a multimeter with a d.c.
mA range, you can keep the cost of the tester to a

USED WITH ANY D.C. milliammeter, this simple tester
tells you a transistor's gain, type (PNP or NPN),
and whether or not it's working properly.

minimum by providing test points instead of a
built-in d.c. milliammeter; if you prefer a self-
sufficient tester, you can build the meter in.
Either way, connect the meter correctly, as indicated on the schematic. Since Test Point 1 (TP1)

CONSTRUCTION IS ULTRASIMPLE; the size of the box
and layout aren't in the least critical.

SEE ALSO
Antennas . . . Electronics . . . Shortwave radio . . .
Stereo . . . Television

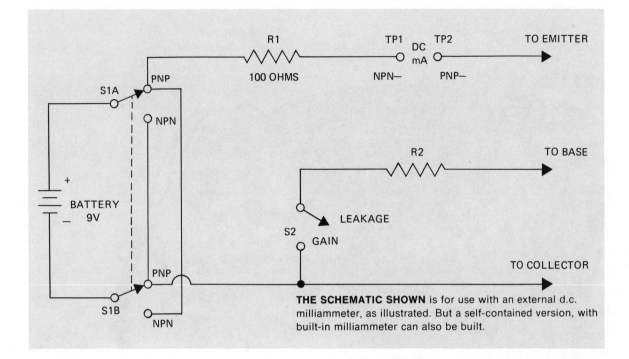

R1
100 OHMS

TP1   DC   TP2   TO EMITTER
       mA
NPN—   PNP—

S1A   PNP
       NPN

BATTERY
9V

R2   TO BASE

S2   LEAKAGE
      GAIN

PNP   TO COLLECTOR
S1B
NPN

THE SCHEMATIC SHOWN is for use with an external d.c. milliammeter, as illustrated. But a self-contained version, with built-in milliammeter can also be built.

is the negative terminal when testing NPN transistors, and TP2 is negative when testing PNPs, you'll have to switch leads to your external meter, or wire a second double-pole, double-throw (d.p.d.t.) switch to change the meter's polarity the same way S1 reverses the battery's. (A 4-p.d.t. switch would reverse both polarities at once.)

To use the tester, first set S1 to the correct position for the type of transistor (NPN or PNP) under test. Observing correct polarity, insert the milliammeter leads into TP1 and TP2. Connect the three small clip leads to their correct transistor terminals (color-coding the wires will help you keep them straight).

To read leakage, open S2. A good transistor will give you a very low reading, usually a few tenths of a milliampere or less. If you get a high leakage reading it indicates a partially or completely shorted transistor.

To read gain, close S2 and multiply the meter reading by 100.

If you get the same reading for both positions of S2, you may have set S1 for the wrong transistor type. If you get no reading for either position of S2, the transistor is open.

A RUBBER BAND, two bolts run through holes drilled in the cabinet, and four nuts hold the small 9-volt battery securely in place.

Parts list

S1—D.p.s.t. switch*
S2—S.p.s.t. switch
TP1, TP2—Insulated tipjacks to fit VOM or VTVM probes*
R1—100-ohm, ½-w. resistor
R2—820 k, ½-w. resistor
E1—9-v. transistor battery
Misc.—small utility box, 3 small, insulated alligator clips, wire battery lead.
Optional—a 4-p.d.t. switch and d.c. milliammeter may be substituted for the starred items above (see text).

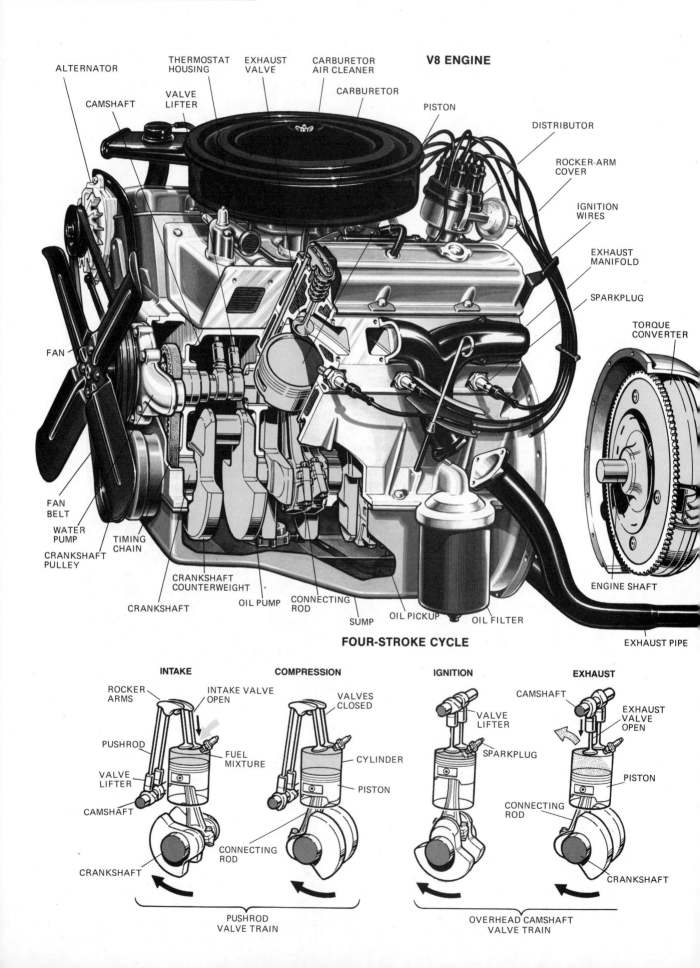

V8 ENGINE

ALTERNATOR

CAMSHAFT

THERMOSTAT HOUSING

VALVE LIFTER

EXHAUST VALVE

CARBURETOR AIR CLEANER

CARBURETOR

PISTON

DISTRIBUTOR

ROCKER-ARM COVER

IGNITION WIRES

EXHAUST MANIFOLD

SPARKPLUG

TORQUE CONVERTER

FAN

FAN BELT

WATER PUMP

CRANKSHAFT PULLEY

TIMING CHAIN

CRANKSHAFT

CRANKSHAFT COUNTERWEIGHT

OIL PUMP

CONNECTING ROD

SUMP

OIL PICKUP

OIL FILTER

ENGINE SHAFT

EXHAUST PIPE

FOUR-STROKE CYCLE

INTAKE

ROCKER ARMS

INTAKE VALVE OPEN

PUSHROD

FUEL MIXTURE

VALVE LIFTER

CAMSHAFT

CRANKSHAFT

COMPRESSION

VALVES CLOSED

CYLINDER

PISTON

CONNECTING ROD

IGNITION

VALVE LIFTER

SPARKPLUG

EXHAUST

CAMSHAFT

EXHAUST VALVE OPEN

PISTON

CONNECTING ROD

CRANKSHAFT

PUSHROD VALVE TRAIN

OVERHEAD CAMSHAFT VALVE TRAIN

Keep your engine and drive train working

Power for your car starts with the fuel-air mix burning in the cylinders. Intake and exhaust valves are driven by a pushrod valve train or an overhead camshaft, both shown here. Automatic or manual transmission brings power from the crankshaft via the flywheel to the drive shaft. It drives rear wheels through the differential and axle

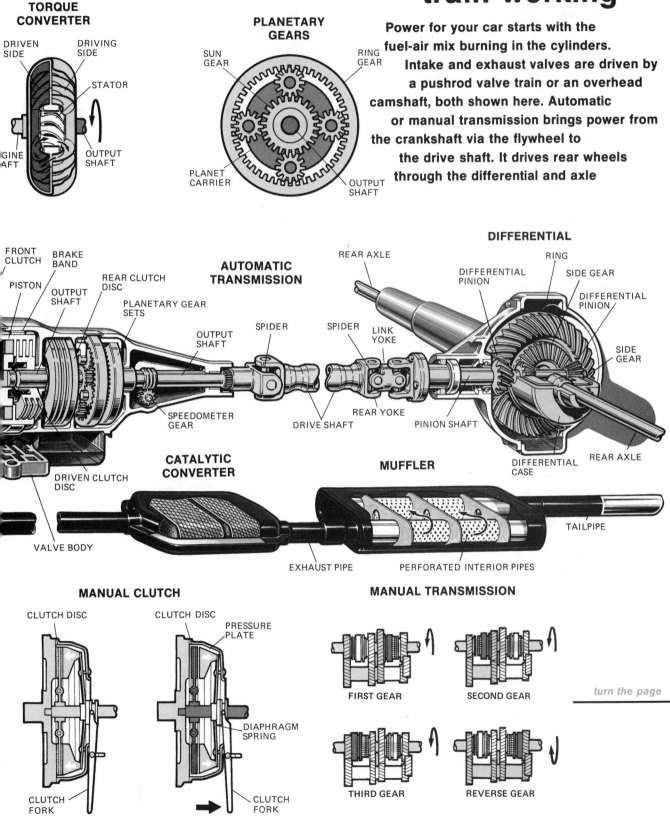

TORQUE CONVERTER

DRIVEN SIDE
DRIVING SIDE
STATOR
GINE AFT
OUTPUT SHAFT

PLANETARY GEARS

SUN GEAR
RING GEAR
PLANET CARRIER
OUTPUT SHAFT

AUTOMATIC TRANSMISSION

FRONT CLUTCH
BRAKE BAND
REAR CLUTCH DISC
PISTON
OUTPUT SHAFT
PLANETARY GEAR SETS
OUTPUT SHAFT
SPIDER
SPIDER
LINK YOKE
SPEEDOMETER GEAR
DRIVE SHAFT
REAR YOKE
DRIVEN CLUTCH DISC
VALVE BODY

REAR AXLE

DIFFERENTIAL

RING
DIFFERENTIAL PINION
SIDE GEAR
DIFFERENTIAL PINION
SIDE GEAR
PINION SHAFT
DIFFERENTIAL CASE
REAR AXLE

CATALYTIC CONVERTER

EXHAUST PIPE

MUFFLER

TAILPIPE
PERFORATED INTERIOR PIPES

MANUAL CLUTCH

CLUTCH DISC
CLUTCH DISC
PRESSURE PLATE
DIAPHRAGM SPRING
CLUTCH FORK
CLUTCH FORK

MANUAL TRANSMISSION

FIRST GEAR
SECOND GEAR
THIRD GEAR
REVERSE GEAR

turn the page

■ TWO TESTS—compression and vacuum—tell whether an engine is performing at peak condition. To do a compression test:

1. Warm the engine up to normal operating temperature and then shut it off.

2. Blow dirt from around sparkplugs with an ear syringe or by blowing through a soda straw. Remove sparkplugs, making sure you mark or remember which plug goes with which cylinder. This is important later.

3. Examine each sparkplug. Look for signs of trouble as follows:

• Oil fouling—wet, sludgy deposits indicate that oil is entering the cylinder through worn piston rings, valve guides or bearings.

• Burns and/or blisters—a ghostly white or blistered insulator nose and eroded electrodes indicate ignition timing is way out of specification, there's an obstruction in the cooling setup, or preignition is taking place. Preignition—a very serious problem—means that ignition is occurring before the sparkplug fires. Hot carbon in the cylinder is normally the cause.

• Carbon fouling—dry, black deposits indicate your engine's been operating on an overly rich fuel mixture, you've been idling for excessive periods, sparkplugs aren't the right ones, or there's a breakdown in ignition. If sparkplugs show little electrode wear and have tan or brownish deposits, they're okay to this point. If plugs aren't badly worn, they can be cleaned, regapped and returned to the cylinders from which they were taken after you complete the compression test.

4. Remove the carburetor air cleaner and set the throttle plate(s) in the wide-open position by wedging open the throttle shaft and lever assembly. You can use a block of wood or simply tie the cam open with a length of string or wire.

Make sure the choke plate is also wide open. With the engine warm, automatically controlled choke plates should be fully open. If not, there's a hangup in the choke assembly.

5. Push a compression gauge firmly into a cylinder. It has to be tight so no compression is lost. Use a remote starter to crank the engine, or ask someone to give you a hand. A remote starter allows you to crank the engine from beneath the hood. Its terminals attach to the solenoid terminal (marked S) on the starter solenoid and to the battery's positive post. The engine is then cranked by pressing the button on the tool.

6. Crank the engine through a *minimum* of four complete compression strokes to get the highest reading. Repeat the test for every cylinder, recording each reading.

You need the compression specification for your engine, which can be gotten from a dealer or by consulting a general automobile repair book, such as *Motor's Auto Repair Manual,* for foreign or domestic cars, available in most public libraries. Some owner's manuals provide the specifications, as do car service manuals.

Conclusions you can reach from this test are as follows:

• If all cylinders test within manufacturer's compression specification limits, overall engine condition is sound.

• If compression in any cylinder fails to climb during all cranking strokes, or remains the same on the first two strokes and then climbs higher on the following strokes, a sticking valve exists.

• If compression reads below manufacturer's compression specification limits, worn rings or a bad valve (burned, not seating) exists. To test for worn rings, pour a tablespoon of heavy motor oil into the cylinder, crank the engine to distribute oil and test compression again. If the reading shows a sharp rise, rings are worn, but if the reading remains the same, the valves are in trouble.

• If there is a compression loss below manufacturer's limits between adjacent cylinders, there's a good chance that the head gasket is bad, resulting in a compression leak occurring between cylinders.

• If compression reads more than 10 pounds *above* manufacturer's limits, carbon is building up in the cylinders. This results in very sluggish starting of *warm* engines, even though they start fine when cold.

what a vacuum test can tell

In some cases, an engine vacuum test can reveal some of the same malfunctions that a compression tester will turn up. However, the two instruments test different functions, and each of them can give you valuable and different information.

A vacuum reading of 17 to 21 inches of mercury at sea level that holds steady is generally regarded as a normal reading. However, this is not true for every engine, and you should seek the manufacturer's specified reading for your engine.

Keep in mind, too, that altitude affects vacuum, and that vacuum gauges are calibrated for sea level. For every 1000 feet above sea level, subtract one inch of vacuum from the readings you get.

To take a vacuum reading, reinstall sparkplugs if you have just done a compression test, and warm the engine up again if it has cooled below normal operating temperature.

Connect the vacuum gauge. Every engine has at least one vacuum port.

Start the engine, let it idle and observe the reading (making compensation for altitude, if necessary). One of the following is the result you'll get:

VACUUM TEST RESULTS

Vacuum reading	Meaning
Gauge needle floats over range of 4 to 5 inches.	Carburetor out of adjustment.
Needle holds steady, but below spec.	Ignition timing out of adjustment.
Needle drops Intermittently about 4 inches.	Valves are sticking.
Needle drops and rises alternately.	Burned valve or insufficient valve clearance—a leaky valve, that is.
Reading normal at idle; vibrates when engine is revved.	Weak valve springs.
Needle vibrates at idle, but holds steady when engine speed is increased.	Worn valve springs.
Needle vibrates at all speeds.	Leaking head gasket.
Needle drops slowly to zero as engine speed is increased.	Restriction in exhaust system.
Steady reading that is low.	Valve timing is off.
Needle holds steady, but is low.	Leaky intake manifold or carburetor gasket.

Notice that a leaking intake manifold or carburetor gasket and incorrect valve timing results in the same kind of reading. Most times, the cause is a bad gasket, but this can be easily verified.

Apply a good deal of heavy motor oil around intake manifold and carburetor joints. If a leak exists, the vacuum gauge needle will rise as the engine idles.

Even if you get a normal reading to show that engine vacuum is adequate, there might still be a loss of vacuum from a leaking hose. Hoses connect vacuum-operated components, such as the distributor vacuum advance and headlamp covers, to the source of vacuum—the engine.

Disconnect the vacuum gauge and allow the engine to idle. Trace each vacuum hose from its connection on the engine to its vacuum-operated component. Listen carefully. If a hissing sound comes from the hose, replace it.

examine the exhaust system

Examine the exhaust system, which should be done routinely every year or as soon as you suspect an exhaust system leak because of, say, roaring. Stopping such leaks may be a matter of life and death. Lethal carbon monoxide fumes escaping from a bad component can leak into the passenger compartment.

The examination should be meticulous. Here's how to do it:

1. Examine the connection formed by the exhaust manifold and exhaust pipe flange. This can be done from beneath hood. If there are whitish deposits around the joint, the gasket has probably gone bad and exhaust is escaping. Replace the gasket and make sure that bolts are tight.

2. Lift the car and carefully examine the exhaust pipe, exhaust extension, muffler, tailpipe, and all other pipes and parts, such as resonators, that are used. Run your hand over each part feeling for soft spots where rust has eaten nearly through the metal. Naturally, any part that has a hole or split should be replaced.

3. To check parts for internal failure (many times parts fail from the inside, where acid collects), tap each with a wrench or pair of pliers. If the part is sound, it will ring. If it is failing or has failed, it will give a dull thud.

4. See to it that all parts are secured by tightened clamps and hangers. A part that vibrates against the floor pan, frame, fuel tank or whatever will soon destroy itself.

5. Look beneath the exhaust manifold for the manifold heat-control valve (not all cars have one although most do). The valve should move freely when you manipulate the counterweight. If it doesn't, try to tap it free with a soft-nosed hammer.

Lubricating the manifold heat-control valve is a job to do whenever you lubricate the chassis. Use manifold heat-control-valve lubricant or graphite. If this valve sticks, it causes many different kinds of problems, including rough idle and stalling, poor gas mileage, shortened sparkplug life and burned valves.

emissions control

The type and number of antipollution devices on an engine depend on the car's year and manufacturer so check your service manual for what's on your car. The following information outlines the most widely used emission controls and how to service them:

positive crankcase vent (PCV)

The earliest of the emission controls, PCV was first put on engines in 1963. The system has been in use ever since to prevent hydrocarbon emissions from the crankcase from getting into the atmosphere. It is serviced as follows:

CHECK your PCV valve periodically.

• Start the engine and locate the PCV valve (consult your owner's manual). Pull the valve from its seat. You should hear it hissing.
• Cover the end of the valve with your finger. You should feel a strong pull (vacuum). If the valve does not make a hissing noise and does not provide vacuum pull, turn off the engine, clean out any deposits that have formed in the PCV valve hose and replace the valve with an exact duplicate.
• Examine the hose from the PCV valve to the exhaust manifold, and the one from the carburetor air cleaner to the cap covering the rocker-arm cover. See that they are straight and free of cracks. Replace a cracked hose with a new PCV hose that is oil-resistant.

PCV HOSES should be kept clean inside.

• Remove the carburetor air cleaner cover. You may find a small filter element on the other side of the spot where the PCV hose intercepts the air cleaner. Some filters are mesh and are stuffed into the hole in the side of the air cleaner. Others are cotton and are placed in a small plastic hold-

THIS PCV filter is made of replaceable mesh.

er. Replace this filter every 12,000 miles, or more often if it gets dirty.

Many foreign cars employ a gulp valve rather than a PCV unit to control crankcase emissions. To service this valve, remove the cover, which is probably held by a spring clip. Examine the diaphragm inside, and replace it if it's damaged. Clean the inside of the valve and make sure the small metering hole is not clogged. If necessary, ream it out with a piece of wire, but take care not to enlarge the hole.

thermostatically controlled air cleaner

Beginning with some 1968 models, carburetors have been outfitted with this device which helps reduce hydrocarbon and carbon monoxide levels by maintaining the air entering the carburetor at a minimum temperature (100°F). This permits carburetors to be calibrated for the leanest possible fuel mixture. Service the air cleaner every 12,000 miles as follows:
• Remove the filter element and replace it if it's damaged or clogged with dirt.
• Clean the air cleaner housing. Place the assembly back on the carburetor and tighten the fastener.
Caution: The wingnut or bolt holding the air cleaner in position should not be overly tight. Excess pressure may damage the carburetor.
• With the engine cold, look into the snorkel. The valve should be closed. Start the engine. As

THIS PCV filter is the fiber type in a holder.

it gets warm, the valve should open. If the air cleaner doesn't function this way, its diaphragm assembly or sensing thermostat has malfunctioned. Parts can be replaced.

electric-assisted automatic choke

Beginning with some 1972 models and continuing with 1973-74 models, many cars were equipped with a device that introduces electric current to open choke plates fully as soon as possible. This cuts down on the amount of exhaust emissions given off by cold-starting cars.

THE GULP valve diaphragm needs regular checking.

If your automatic choke linkage and plate pivot points are clean so the choke won't bind, the choke plate should open within 60 to 90 seconds after starting a cold engine. If it doesn't there is a problem with the electric choke switch or heating element, both of which should be tested.

exhaust gas recirculation (ERG)

This was added to many models beginning in 1973. The valve sends metered amounts of exhaust gas into the intake manifold to dilute the fuel mixture, thereby reducing the combustion chamber temperature at which nitrogen oxides are formed. Service the EGR valve every 12,000 miles as follows:
- Remove the valve from the engine and hold it in your hand. Don't clamp it into a vise where it can be damaged.

THERMOSTATICALLY controlled air cleaner parts are (1) temperature sensor and (2) damper valve.

REMOVE the EGR valve in order to service it.

- Tap the sides and end of the valve lightly with a plastic hammer to loosen deposits that have formed on the valve seat. Blow deposits out by mouth.
- With a wire brush, buff deposits that remain from the mounting surface and from around the valve.
- Depress the valve diaphragm and examine the valve outlet. If there are deposits, loosen them with a screwdriver, but carefully.

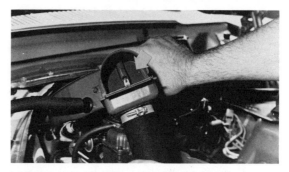

DAMPER valve (arrow) is closed on cold engine.

fuel evaporation emission control

This system has been in use since 1971. It seals off open vents in the carburetor and fuel tank, directing fuel vapors that build up into a charcoal canister instead. The canister is mounted in the engine compartment of U.S. and most foreign cars, and in the luggage compartment of other imported cars.

U.S. automobiles and many made overseas have canisters that possess filters in their bases. These filters should be replaced every 12,000 miles.

Other imports don't have filters. In these, the canister itself should be replaced every 50,000 miles.

think transmission

Given occasional service, the transmission will probably serve you for the life of your car. Without care, it will eventually fail, and you will face a stiff repair bill.

ADJUST the automatic transmission bands.

One reason for an automatic transmission malfunction, such as delayed shifting, is fluid level that's getting too low. Fluid may be lost because of a leak, so check the level frequently.

Every owner's manual outlines the procedure for checking transmission fluid, but it's usually as follows:

1. Warm the transmission up to its operating temperature by driving the car about 10 miles.

2. Park the car on a level surface and place the transmission gear selector lever in Park (P). Turn off the engine if manual so states.

3. Locate the automatic transmission fluid dipstick in the engine compartment. Wipe dirt from the dipstick tube with paper toweling or a lint-free rag. Do a thorough job. Dirt that gets on the dipstick or falls into the dipstick tube will contaminate the fluid.

4. Pull the dipstick from the tube and "read" the level. The level should fall on the "Full" mark or between the "Add" and "Full" marks.

5. Add fluid if the level is low by inserting a clean funnel into the dipstick tube and pouring fluid into the transmission through the funnel. Use the type of automatic transmission fluid specified by the manufacturer.

6. Do not overfill the transmission. Fluid level should not go above the "Full" mark on the dipstick. Excess fluid in the transmission causes aeration—that is, foaming which causes gear slipping and erratic shifting.

Once every 25,000 miles, fluid should be drained and the transmission oil pan removed. Once inside the case, the fluid filter should be replaced and the transmission bands should be adjusted to specification if the manufacturer recommends this.

The transmission pan should be cleaned before it is bolted back in place. Use a new gasket. Finally, the transmission should be filled with fresh transmission fluid.

about manual transmission

A manual transmission requires an occasional fluid level check which can be done when you lubricate the chassis. Another important service, which is often overlooked, is adjusting the clutch for free play—that is, for the amount of free movement before the clutch releases.

As a clutch is used, it loses its free play. If this is not restored, clutch parts rub against each other when they aren't supposed to, and wear results.

By restoring free play, you may get the clutch to last for the life of the car. The frequency of making adjustments depends on the car, so check your owner's manual. Some manufacturers, for example, recommend an adjustment every 6000 miles, while others suggest one every 12,000 miles. However, more frequent adjustment, or at least checking free play, can't damage anything.

The clutch adjustment is done differently from car to car. Consult your car's service manual, if you have one, or general auto-repair manuals in the library.

Whichever method your manufacturer calls for, the procedure is probably not difficult. In most cases, it's a matter of measuring the free movement by pressing the clutch pedal until resistance is met. Generally, the clutch needs adjustment if free movement is more or less than ¾ inch.

Making the adjustment is usually a matter of loosening a locknut and turning an adjustment screw on the clutch release lever.

driveshaft and differential

To determine if universal joints are wearing (U-joints allow the propeller shaft to "kink" slightly between the transmission and differential), grab the propeller shaft with both hands near each U-joint and attempt to move the shaft. There might be slight movement, but it should not be excessive.

If the prop shaft demonstrates sloppy motion, it means the U-joint is wearing. The safe thing to do is drop the prop shaft and remove the universal joint for repair or replacement. Universal joint failure can cause you to lose the propeller shaft while driving.

The only service required by the propeller shaft is an occasional cleaning when the car is on a lift. If much mud cakes on the shaft, it can throw angularity out of balance, causing propeller shaft "whip" which could produce the unexplained vibration you may be experiencing.

With a clean cloth dampened with mineral spirits, kerosene or some solvent, wipe the prop shaft down.

The differential (rear end) requires very little care. Just check its fluid level regularly.

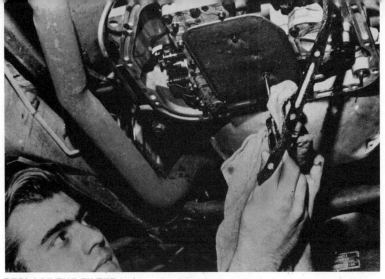

By MORT SCHULTZ

REPLACE THE FILTER before changing transmission fluid. The pan gasket must also be replaced whenever the pan is removed.

How to troubleshoot your automatic transmission

■ IF YOU THINK you have trouble with your car's automatic transmission, the first step is to be sure you genuinely have a problem. You may not. Imagination or misinterpretation of symptoms can cost you money.

Car owners have been known to pay for gearbox "repairs" because their cars didn't upshift precisely at 15 mph, 20 mph, 35 mph, or some other exact specification. What a waste that is. The peculiarities in driver behavior can vary a particular shift point by as much as 25 mph with varying engine demands transmitted through varying pressure on the accelerator.

Other variables have such strong influence that no one can tell you at what exact speed a transmission will shift. Cars with the same transmissions have different tire sizes and rear-axle ratios, requiring different shift points. A major reason for an automatic is its ability to accommodate such changes.

Nevertheless, an abnormal delay in shifting is possible—and it's significant. Under typical, reasonable city driving conditions, your transmission should upshift to direct drive within the normal city speed limit of 25 mph. If it doesn't, the box isn't acting right.

A slipping transmission is a candidate for repair. Slipping becomes apparent when engine speed runs away before the transmission upshifts.

whine can mislead

Transmission whine is one of the most misleading symptoms of all and has caused many drivers to pay for needless service. A certain amount of whine is normal.

Gears in an automatic transmission are in constant mesh. In first gear and reverse, a whine produced by gear rotation increases as car speed increases. An objectionably shrill sound spells trouble, as does a whine in high gear when gears are not rotating.

Grinding, knocking, scraping and clicking sounds coming from the gearbox, no matter under what conditions, indicate a sick transmission. Another problem is a drop of transmission fluid that appears somewhere on the case. This leak requires repair. An oily film at a bolt or gasket joint is normal seepage, so leave it alone.

A sure sign that an automatic transmission needs attention is when it's in gear and the car won't move. Not so obvious is a car that won't start with the transmission selector in Neutral or Park, or one that starts with the selector lever in any position. Both problems are caused by a neutral safety switch contact that's worked loose or by a damaged switch. This part is found on the side of most transmissions. One thing you should have to pinpoint it is the car's service manual or other manual such as *Motor's Auto Repair Manual.*

For all problems except a leak and neutral

NEUTRAL SAFETY switch contact must be tight on the switch. If that's not the problem, replace switch.

USE ONLY fluid specified by the manufacturer. Don't try to save pennies with the "cheap stuff."

DISCONNECT kickdown valve linkage at carb, then road-test car to see if valve is problem.

TRANSMISSION fluid level is first thing to check. Read dipstick with unit at operating temperature.

safety-switch trouble, inspect the fluid level, while the transmission is at operating temperature. This requires that the car be driven about five miles. If the fluid shows "overfilled" on the dipstick, drain excess. An overfilled transmission causes fluid to aerate, which lowers pressure and leads to slipping and erratic shifting.

always use right fluid

If the transmission fluid level is below the "full" mark on the dipstick, harshness, shifting delays and noise could result. Add fluid—always the type specified by the maker of your car. If transmission fluid is very low or has been lost, the car won't move with the transmission in gear.

Now, suppose fluid level is okay and your problem is harsh, slipping, delayed or erratic shifting. Some transmissions have an electric kickdown switch which should be disconnected while you run a road test. If the problem no longer exists, this switch is at fault and should be replaced.

Other transmissions have a manual kicking valve controlled by a pressure linkage on the carburetor. Take this valve out of the system by disconnecting the linkage. If the valve is causing the problem, the transmission will now perform normally during a road test. With this out of the way, you should now drain and drop the transmission oil pan. Some transmissions have drain plugs. Most don't.

To drain fluid when no plug is provided, remove all bolts except two opposing ones, which should be loosened. Now pop the pan loose with

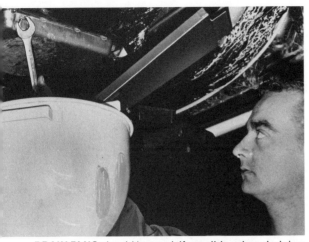

DRAIN PLUG should be used, if possible, when draining transmission fluid to keep your garage neat.

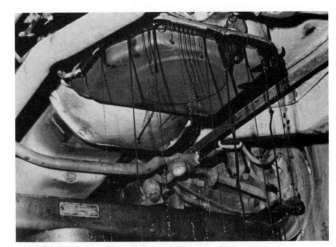

IF DRAIN PLUG isn't available, remove pan bolts, pry pan loose and stand back from the downpour.

a puttyknife or screwdriver, but get back fast so you aren't splattered by fluid.

drain torque converters

The converter should also be drained. Most cars have one drain plug, but some (Ford, for example) have two. Remove both to get all fluid out of the converter.

Examine the pan and fluid for debris warning of part failure. Also check fluid for color (it should be red—not black or orange) and odor (it should not smell like varnish). These tell you transmission parts have failed.

A major overhaul is probably needed, although you may avoid it if damage hasn't gone too far, by tuning the transmission. Tune-up in-

volves adjusting the transmission bands and linkage, cleaning parts, replacing the transmission oil filter, and installing fresh fluid of manufacturer's specification. You'll often need a torque wrench calibrated in inch-pounds for the band adjustment unless specifications are in metric units—newton-meters. Conversion tables inside the back cover of this book tell what metric specs mean in customary units, but using the right wrench makes the job easier. If your pan inspection found no internal problem, just adjust front and rear bands.

Most transmissions (Chrysler products are exceptions) have a vacuum control unit. It would pay to spend a few cents to replace this part.

FAULTY VACUUM control (modulator) causes many transmission problems. Replacing it may solve yours.

CRACKED converter drive plate was discovered to cause the clicking in this transmission.

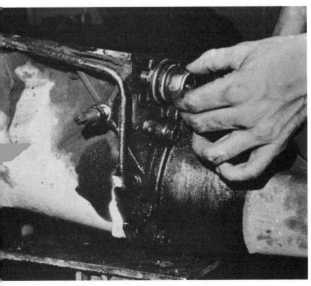

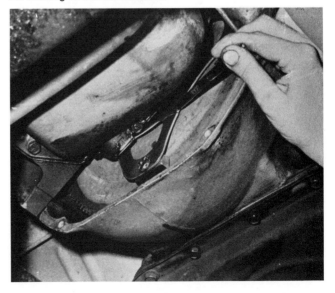

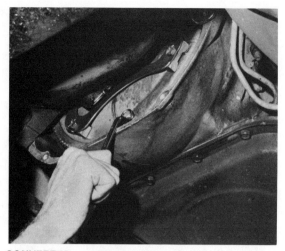

CONVERTER, as well as gearbox, should be drained. Sometimes there are two drain plugs.

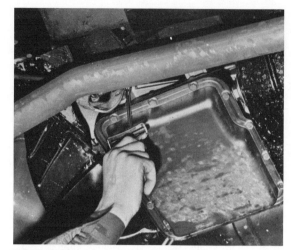

MOST FRONT bands can be adjusted without removing pan. Torque to manufacturer's specifications.

meaningful noises

What about noise? A grinding gear noise necessitates tear-down of the transmission. If there's a knock, click or scrape, inspect the torque converter. Chances are it's loose or has a cracked drive plate.

The noise easiest to correct is a whine or buzz. Try to determine if it is coming from the gearbox or converter by putting the car in gear while on a rack or jacks and listening at each part.

If the noise comes from the converter, that part will probably have to be replaced. If it's from the gearbox, drop the pan and inspect for debris. If no part failure is indicated, the noise is probably a faulty vacuum control unit.

You can repair many fluid leaks yourself. Replacing the rear oil seal is also within your province, although the prop shaft has to be dropped and you'll need a rear oil-seal removal tool (about $5).

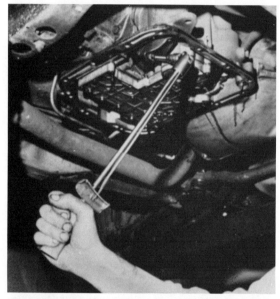

ADJUSTING REAR bands is not as easy. Pan must be removed to make them accessible for adjustment.

BAD SPEEDOMETER adapter O-ring may cause a leak. Remove speedometer gear housing from the gearbox.

REMOVE DAMAGED speedometer adapter O-ring by prying it loose, then slip a new one into position.

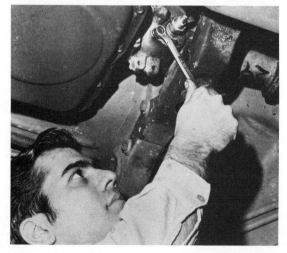

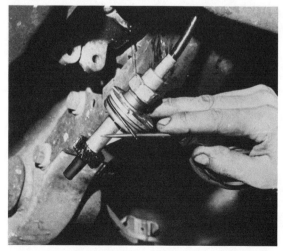

TWO OR MORE magnetic spring-type paper clips and a steel plate can be as useful as an extra pair of hands in the shop. The magnets adhere firmly to the steel plate, yet can be shifted around to position the attached clips for holding wires to be soldered, small parts for gluing or tiny items to be painted.

AN EMPTY plastic spray bottle used for deodorant provides a handy way to carry a small amount of water in a toolbox. Water is often needed to thin brazing flux, moisten an abrasive stone for sharpening a tool or for other on-job uses. Bottle shown has a screw cap covering a spout that was cut off a bit to get a less-scattered squirt.

IF YOU HAVE an electric drill of the type having a screw-in auxiliary handle, a short pipe nipple and a flange will let you use it as a bench polishing head. The thread of the nipple matches that on the handle, and when the flange is screwed to your benchtop and the nipple turned into the drill, you have a handy drill stand.

A TUNGSTEN-CARBIDE blade, primarily made for use in a sabre saw, can be extra handy when fitted with a detachable handle and used as a small handsaw. Made by Remington Arms Co., Inc., Bridgeport, CT 06602, these carbide-coated blades cut like a diamond and will saw through such hard-to-cut materials as glass, ceramics, transite, and even hardened steel.

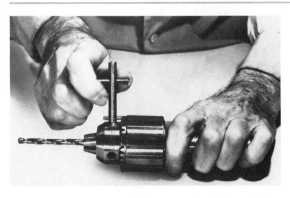

WHEN A GEARED drill-chuck key is lost, an emergency one can be made from a rod that fits the keyholes snugly, and a couple of ⅛-inch diameter nails. A short piece of nail is driven tightly into a cross hole so the tips will engage the teeth on the chuck shell. A longer piece at the opposite end acts as a handle.

All about transplanting

■ THERE ARE SEVERAL KINDS of transplanting, but certain guidelines apply to them all. For instance, *correct planting time is extremely important, even critical.* If you do not know the correct planting time in your area for a certain plant, by all means check your catalogs or call a reputable local nursery. *Transplant only at the optimum time.* If possible, choose a cool and cloudy or rainy day without wind.

Select the sturdiest and best-shaped specimens for transplanting. Dig holes for them that are straight-sided and are deep and wide enough to accommodate the roots without crowding. Expose the roots to the air no longer than is absolutely necessary because in some cases just a few minutes of exposure is too much. Protect the roots, if the soil falls off, by putting them into water or a moistened plastic bag. Trim off broken or bruised roots with a sharp knife or shears.

For best results, prepare a good soil mixture to surround the transplant. Dig in humus like peat moss, rotted manure or compost to lighten the soil and make it hold more water. The humus will encourage the young plant—whether a tomato vine or a tree—to root quickly and well. One caution—if you use fertilizer, place it in the dirt well beneath roots or stem, so it does not touch them.

Most plants should be set the same depth as they were growing originally. Firm the soil gently around the roots but don't pack it in. Make a surface basin, and water it thoroughly to settle the soil. Around a tree this basin should be extended each year as the roots spread.

If you have an especially large, delicate transplant, you may be able to ease the shock of transfer by a two-stage process. A few days before the actual transplanting, prune the roots by driving a spade down in a circle around the plant. This will give the plant some time to recover from the initial shock.

balled, burlapped and potted plants

Many trees and shrubs, including evergreens, are sold balled and burlapped. The nursery encases the entire root system in burlap and ties it with twine. In handling such plants: 1. Do not bump or jar the root ball, which can cause the soil to separate from the roots. For the same reason: 2. Do not use the trunk as a handle, even though it invites you to do so. If the weight is not

IF YOU'RE PLANNING to transplant seedlings from a flat, water the flat the day before you start. When you are ready to transplant, jar the flat by striking one end sharply against the ground.

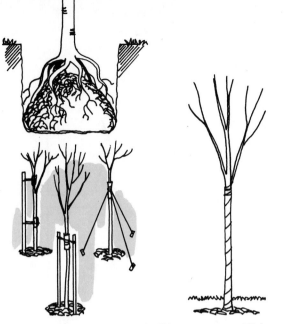

too great, cradle the root ball in your arms. Using a sling of stout cloth, two people can carry a heavier plant. If necessary, a third can support the trunk.

Dig the planting hole *about twice the diameter of the root ball,* and deep enough so there will be 8 or 10 in. of loosened soil under the ball. That loose soil is very important. Set the plant so the top of the ball is just a bit higher—say, half an inch—than the surrounding surface. This will allow for settling. Now split the burlap and fold it back from the top but leave it on the rest of the ball. It will not hurt the plant, and will gradually rot away. Fill the hole with enriched topsoil, firming it with a tamper made from a 2x4, and water thoroughly. Make sure that the plant stands straight and its best side faces in the direction you want.

If your tree or shrub comes in a large pot, allow the soil to dry out somewhat before planting. Then turn the pot on its side and grasp the trunk. Pull gently as you tap around the rim of the pot. The whole soil mass will slip out and the plant then can be handled in much the same way as a balled and burlapped one.

bare roots and "canned" plants

During winter and early spring you can buy bareroot dormant trees and shrubs that are less expensive than plants in containers sold months later. If the ground is still frozen when you buy bare-root plants, heel them in until you can plant them.

In setting a bare-root plant, form a mound in the hole, using the native soil from the hole mixed with an equal amount of organic material such as peat moss. Spread the bare roots over this mound. Fill the hole, and water as with other plants.

Plants are sold in cans in some areas. After preparing the planting hole, use tin shears to cut off the can (many nurseries will slit the can for you). Make two cuts directly opposite each other. While supporting the trunk, slip the can off the soil mass. Loosen the roots a bit, and set the plant. Be sure you use gloves in handling the can, as the cut edges are very sharp.

after trees and shrubs arrive

Sometimes an emergency arises. You may not be able to set out your plants as soon as you get them. In that case, heel them in. In particular, this applies to bare-root plants.

Newly transplanted trees may need helpful support. *Before transplanting the tree,* drive a single stake 6 to 8 ft. long and 1½ to 2 in. in diameter into the transplanting hole. Position the stake on the same side of the tree as the prevailing winds. For even more support two stakes, or a combination of stakes and guy wires, may be used. Use turnbuckles to keep any wires taut. And never loop wire directly around the trunk; use cloth ties or rubber against the bark. Sometimes the trunk of a tree is wrapped with tarred paper. This conserves moisture and prevents sunscald.

bulbs and perennials

When you transplant perennials or bulbs, resist the temptation to do it just after the plants have bloomed, while foliage is still green. That is the time the bulbs are being nourished by the leaves and developed for next year. Instead, you can fold the foliage and tie it neatly with a rubber band, then plant a shallow annual to cover the leaves when they turn brown, after which bulbs can be dug and stored.

In general, it is best to plant summer and fall-blooming perennials in the spring and to plant kinds that bloom in very early spring and summer in the autumn. But transplant irises in June or July, right after they bloom.

PLAN

SHELVES

2 x 3
FRAMING

3/4" EXTERIOR
PLYWOOD

SIDE ELEVATION

ROOF OVERHANG on a rear porch makes the latter an ideal spot for a trash-can hide-away. Doors to the trash-can space are of perforated hardboard, provide ventilation. Space above can be used for seasonal storage after installation of several adjustable shelves.

Four ways to hide trash cans

Trash cans are a necessary evil. Unfortunately, they can be a real eyesore. The secret is to conceal them but keep them handy. These four designs do just that

■ WHAT CAN BE DONE to hide that backyard eyesore—the cluster of needed, but unaesthetic, trash cans—from view? We asked Gerald Geerlings, A.I.A. to tackle the problem. It's interesting to note that all four of his practical solutions have two good design ideas in common:

SIDE ELEVATION

OPEN

2 x 4
DECK

4 x 4
POST

2 x 3 CLEAT

PLAN

BOARD-AND-BATTEN
CONSTRUCTION
(4 SIDES)

DOOR JOINT

ROOFLESS PORCH can also be used for small structure, but top of enclosure should be pitched to provide positive water runoff. Though board and batten construction is shown here, exterior of bin can be sheathed with materials that complement the house.

SEE ALSO
Fences . . . Garden shelters . . . Gazebos . . . Storage buildings . . . Trash compactors

PLAN

REAR DOOR

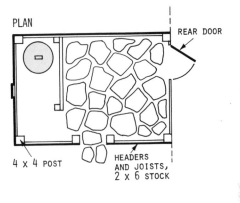

4 x 4 POST

HEADERS
AND JOISTS,
2 x 6 STOCK

AIRINESS of gazebo-like structure adds charm to a ranch or Cape Cod-style home. The enclosure can also serve as a king-sized playpen for toddlers if two gates are added and turkey wire is stapled to outside of fence rails.

• *Location:* Each is convenient to the service entrance, keeping trash-hauling steps at a minimum.

• *Design flexibility:* Each allows for a custom exterior that suits the house design. Though the four types shown are attached to the house, they can be built as free-standing units if property lines and location make this solution more desirable.

Bearing corner posts are of cedar, treated with wood preservative, plywood is exterior grade and if you add wood members such as battens, redwood is recommended. Use galvanized nails or brass screws.

IF GARBAGE ROUTE in your locale includes a back-yard pickup, this built-in should keep collector happy. To ease hinge strain, drop door used by the collector can be equipped with two sturdy chains.

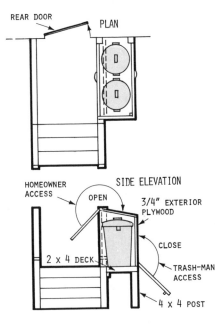

REAR DOOR

PLAN

HOMEOWNER
ACCESS

SIDE ELEVATION

OPEN

3/4" EXTERIOR
PLYWOOD

CLOSE

2 x 4 DECK

TRASH-MAN
ACCESS

4 x 4 POST

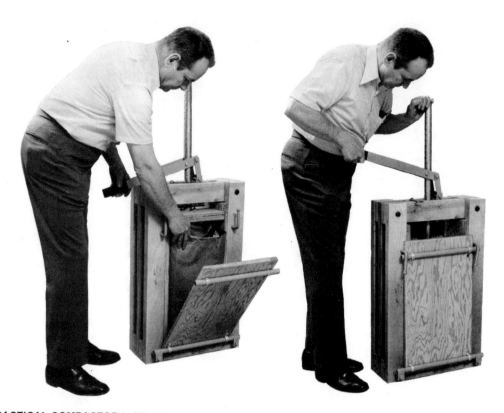

PRACTICAL COMPACTOR is filled by tilting open the removable door and placing trash in the bag above. The author leaves his masher beside the garbage cans for use primarily on bottles and paper.

DOOR is locked before the pressure foot is pushed down. Silicone spray or wax is recommended on the bag-space surfaces to reduce friction and to give waterproofing in case of trash leakage.

Homebuilt masher puts the squeeze on trash

By R. S. HEDIN

WHEN I LEARNED that commercial trash compactors cost something like $200, I decided to make my own and pocket the savings. It's not as fancy as the manufactured models, but it does the job. In fact, my out-of-pocket expenses for building it were about $15.

The masher is designed to be kept near the garbage cans, and its operating cost is low because ordinary supermarket bags are used, not special ones. The masher even crushes cans and light bottles if they're laid on their sides.

The force multiplication is about seven times from the handle to the pressure foot, so a 200-pound man can exert quite a bit of force on the trash inside.

The frame is easy to assemble if the corresponding 2x4 parts are cut accurately to length, then drilled with a fixture in a drill press to make all the hole locations exactly the same. Stack the pieces on ½-in. bolts, gluing each joint. After stacking, square up the frame and tighten the bolts, then you can glue and nail the plywood in place.

Use ample grease on the pivot bolts and make certain that the pawl pivots freely when you're assembling the linkage. And finally, apply a silicone spray or a paste wax on all surfaces of the bag space to reduce friction.

To use the squasher, simply put in the trash bag and lock the door. Pull the gate hook and

SEE ALSO

Garbage disposers ... Kitchens ... Trash cans

TYPICAL LOAD of trash after squeezing by the author. The door and paint were left off this prototype masher for the photo. Builders are advised to complete mashers by painting with quality exterior paint.

HERE IS A CLOSE-UP view of the pressure mechanism assembly. Note that an ordinary gatehook is used to hold the pressure foot up.

AS SHOWN in this rear-view photo of the masher the back is attached using lagscrews and bolts about 14 in. long. The masher shown utilizes typical supermarket bags that every housewife gets her groceries in. The manufactured compactors require costly commercial bags. You will save money initially—and every time you mash!

push the pressure foot down. As you push the handle it causes the pawl to engage one of the notches in the pipe. You raise the handle to release the pressure and raise the pawl in position so you can catch a higher pipe-notch. Pump the handle several times to compress the trash and hold down on the lifting handle when raising the pressure handle because there will usually be some spring-back.

When the trash is compacted, release the pressure, lift the pawl rod to a horizontal position and raise the pressure foot. Engage the gate hook to hold the foot up, open the door and remove the compacted trash.

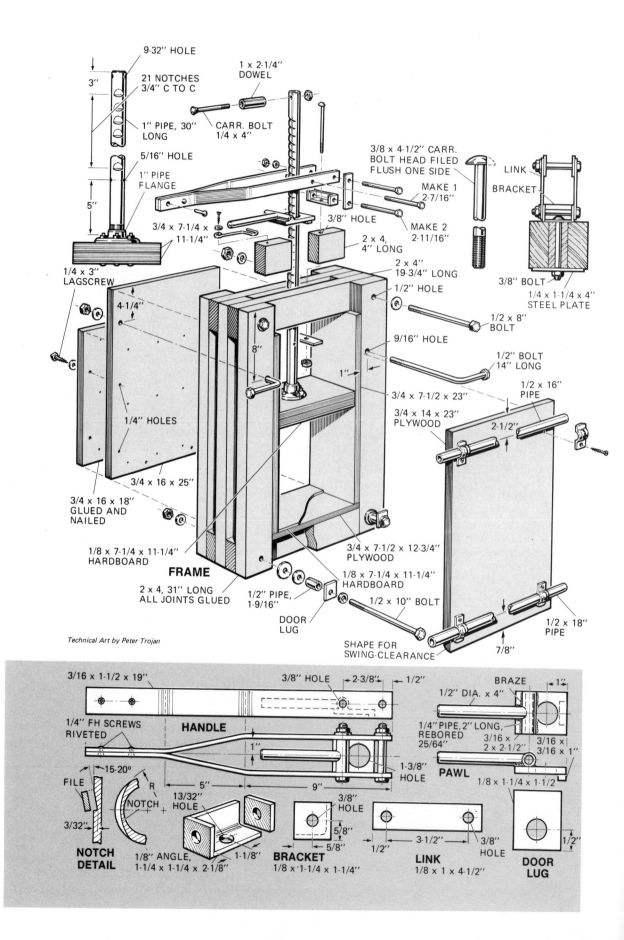

9-32" HOLE

3"

21 NOTCHES 3/4" C TO C

1 x 2-1/4" DOWEL

CARR. BOLT 1/4 x 4"

1" PIPE, 30" LONG

5/16" HOLE

3/8 x 4-1/2" CARR. BOLT HEAD FILED FLUSH ONE SIDE

LINK

BRACKET

MAKE 1 2-7/16"

1" PIPE FLANGE

3/8" HOLE

MAKE 2 2-11/16"

3/8" BOLT

1/4 x 1-1/4 x 4" STEEL PLATE

3/4 x 7-1/4 x 11-1/4"

1/4 x 3" LAGSCREW

4-1/4"

2 x 4, 4" LONG

2 x 4, 19-3/4" LONG

1/2" HOLE

1/2 x 8" BOLT

9/16" HOLE

8"

1"

1/2" BOLT 14" LONG

3/4 x 7-1/2 x 23"

1/2 x 16" PIPE

3/4 x 14 x 23" PLYWOOD

2-1/2"

1/4" HOLES

1/4" HOLES

3/4 x 16 x 25"

3/4 x 16 x 18" GLUED AND NAILED

1/8 x 7-1/4 x 11-1/4" HARDBOARD

FRAME

2 x 4, 31" LONG ALL JOINTS GLUED

1/2" PIPE, 1-9/16"

DOOR LUG

1/8 x 7-1/4 x 11-1/4" HARDBOARD

3/4 x 7-1/2 x 12-3/4" PLYWOOD

1/2 x 10" BOLT

SHAPE FOR SWING-CLEARANCE

7/8"

1/2 x 18" PIPE

Technical Art by Peter Trojan

3/16 x 1-1/2 x 19"

3/8" HOLE

2-3/8"

1/2"

BRAZE

1"

1/4" FH SCREWS RIVETED

HANDLE

1/2" DIA. x 4"

1/4" PIPE, 2" LONG, REBORED 25/64"

3/16 x 2 x 2-1/2"

3/16 x 3/16 x 1"

1"

1-3/8" HOLE

PAWL

1/8 x 1-1/4 x 1-1/2

FILE

15-20°

R

NOTCH

5"

13/32" HOLE

9"

3/8" HOLE

3/32"

NOTCH DETAIL

1/8" ANGLE, 1-1/4 x 1-1/4 x 2-1/8"

1-1/8"

BRACKET 1/8 x 1-1/4 x 1-1/4"

5/8"

5/8"

1/2"

3-1/2"

3/8" HOLE

LINK 1/8 x 1 x 4-1/2"

1/2"

DOOR LUG

Year-round heat

I'm considering the installation of a year-round heating system in my vacation home. The home will be opened mainly on weekends, but I have the problem of year-round maintenance of sufficient heat in the place to prevent deterioration of the structure and freezing in the colder months. What heating system can you recommend?—David Seinfeld, Brooklyn, N.Y.

If the cost of electricity were no object, electric radiant heat would be most desirable. This would eliminate the problems of antifreeze in a hot-water system, deterioration owing to lack of heat and possible concern about continued operation of the system in your absence, and would provide a reliable minimum temperature throughout the cold months.

My second choice would be gas-fired warm-air heating, which could be planned for central air-conditioning as well, to be installed at the same time or later. Hydronic (steam or hot-water) heat would be cheapest, *if* piping could be run in easily.

Shoddy tile base

Ceramic tile around my bathtub (with shower) has loosened and some of it has fallen off. I've replaced some of the tile. It doesn't adhere although I use the cement recommended. My home is only two years old. What's wrong?—A.J., Calif.

I'd assume right away that the backing, that is, the wall on which the tile is installed, is at fault. Water from the shower may have leaked through the tile joints to the wall and destroyed the adhesion. I think it likely that to cure this trouble permanently you will have to remove the tile, as well as the backing, and reinstall the tile on a cement grouting over wire lath. This is the generally accepted procedure when installing ceramic tile in a shower stall.

If you don't feel up to doing this job yourself then have the work done by a qualified contractor.

Making throw rugs nonslip

I have several rugs that slip on my hardwood floors. Is there a way to slip-proof these rugs—before somebody breaks bones in my home?—Mrs. J.B. Shell, Fresno, Calif.

There is a liquid-rubber backing that can be applied to nearly all types of fabric rugs. It comes in a container that also acts as a spreader. Or, you might try double-faced tape designed for this use. Most hardware and department stores stock both items.

Boxing-in a basement beam

I'd like to know how to box-in a 4x8-in. steel beam in my basement ceiling. Lally columns were easy to cover, but how can I make that beam attractive?—Bill Chase, Baltimore.

The simplest way is to use pieces of ¼-in. paneling on the beam sides and set them into a length of grooved ¾-in. stock placed along the bottom of the beam. If you have a steel I-beam you can run 1x2 furring strips next to each side of the beam's top plate and nail them to joists above. This provides a nailing area for upper edges of the panels.

Lagscrew those steps

My basement stair treads are loose and even large nails no longer hold them, although the stringers seem to be strong, showing no sign of rotting. How can I anchor the treads so they no longer tilt and squeak?—Roger Smyth, Lansing, Mich.

Lagscrews will usually hold where nails won't. Drill and counterbore for ¼ or 5/16-in. lagscrews at the center of each tread, making sure that the pilot holes are undersize so that the screw threads will take snugly. Use a suitable washer on each screw. Draw the screws down tight but not too tight, or you may strip the thread they cut in the wood.

Brass changes color

The brass weights and pendulum in my grandfather clock are changing color. It's not a very old clock—what can I do to restore the original bright brass?—B. Hanscom, Atlanta.

There is such a thing as "old brass" but it's more likely a special lacquer coating on the brass is changing color—rather than the metal itself. The lacquer tends to darken slowly with age—I wouldn't remove it as it protects the metal. If the metal is turning color, use a commercial cleaner intended for brass.

Wallpaper on door panels

I'm planning to wallpaper two rooms and I want to put the same paper on the door panels. The doors are enameled and my question is, if I apply the paper with a flour paste, will it stick?—Mrs. Emily Richards, Nashville, Tenn.

I know of no reason why it shouldn't if the surface is clean. Wash with a mild detergent to make sure you remove any grime and especially finger marks. Then, to make doubly sure, go over the panels lightly with medium steel wool to cut the gloss and give a better "tooth" for the adhesive.

by W. Clyde Lammey

Build a folding snack server

By WAYNE C. LECKEY

This folding cocktail snack server can be right at the center of the action at your parties. You can make it of fine hardwood to match the rest of your furniture. After the party is over, it can be folded flat and placed out of the way in a closet

■ WHEN HOME PARTIES reach the point of help yourself, this handsome hors d'oeuvre server will soon become the center of the party. Loaded with tempting cheese dips, chips and the makings of a drink or two, this self-service server will receive a standing ovation in more ways than one.

You'll find it equally as useful at bridge, or wherever snacks are served. Best of all, the server folds flat for storing. Start with the legs. These are twin assemblies which are cut in pairs, following the pattern. All four legs are bored for ¾-in.-dowel rungs, but keep in mind that the blind holes must be bored in facing surfaces. One pair of legs is drilled for four roundhead brass screws which serve as pivot-pins for the trays, and here you'll wisely drill the holes through both legs at the same time to insure identical spacing. If you own a router, run a bead cut along the curved edges of the legs; it will relieve their plainness and give that store-bought look.

One pair of legs is joined at the top with a crossrail which is shaped like the legs and then glued and screwed to the pair of legs previously drilled for the pivot screws. Two flathead screws are used at each end of the crossrail to fasten it.

Each tray consists of a hardwood-faced plywood center which is faced around the edge with a ¼ x ¾-in. molding, neatly mitered at the corners, then glued and nailed. Stop pins, made of nails with the heads cut off, are driven into the

BETWEEN PARTIES, if you don't want it standing around, you can fold the server flat and stow it away. Trays lap and nest between the hinged legs.

WHEN OPEN the sturdy server gives two generous-size surfaces for holding snacks and libations. Closed (photo at the right), the space-saving table folds flat for convenient out-of-sight storage in the closet until your next party.

SEE ALSO
Lazy Susans ... Mobile furniture ... Party tables ... Servers ... Serving carts

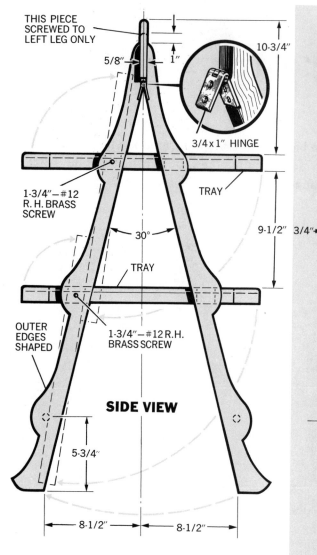

THIS PIECE
SCREWED TO
LEFT LEG ONLY

10-3/4"

5/8"   1"

3/4 x 1" HINGE

1-3/4"—#12
R. H. BRASS
SCREW

TRAY

30°

9-1/2"

TRAY

OUTER
EDGES
SHAPED

1-3/4"—#12 R.H.
BRASS SCREW

SIDE VIEW

5-3/4"

8-1/2"   8-1/2"

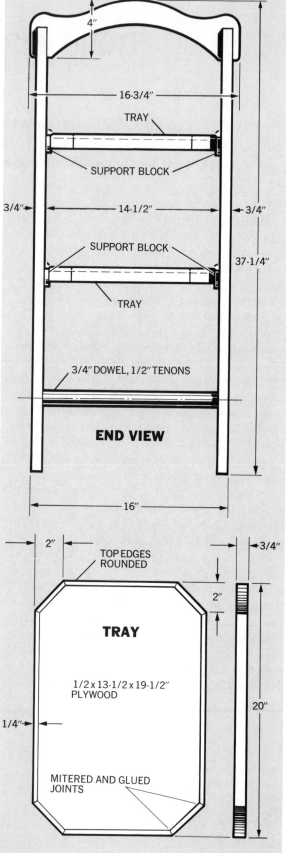

4"

16-3/4"

TRAY

SUPPORT BLOCK

3/4"   14-1/2"   3/4"

SUPPORT BLOCK

37-1/4"

TRAY

3/4" DOWEL, 1/2" TENONS

END VIEW

16"

2"   3/4"

TOP EDGES
ROUNDED

2"

TRAY

1/2 x 13-1/2 x 19-1/2"
PLYWOOD

1/4"

20"

MITERED AND GLUED
JOINTS

trays to rest in support blocks glued to the second pair of legs. The pins must not project so far that they rub and mar the legs. Wooden washers keep the trays from rubbing as they pivot for folding.

Pick small brass hinges to hinge the legs at the top. The hinge pins must be first driven out (if you can't get loose-pin hinges) so that the hinge leaves can be screwed in place. The pins are then replaced and your stand is completed.

Finishing the stand depends on the kind of wood you used. If it's walnut, you'll need to fill the open grain of the wood with a paste filler, then stain as desired. Two coats of rubbed-effect varnish will make a mighty handsome piece.

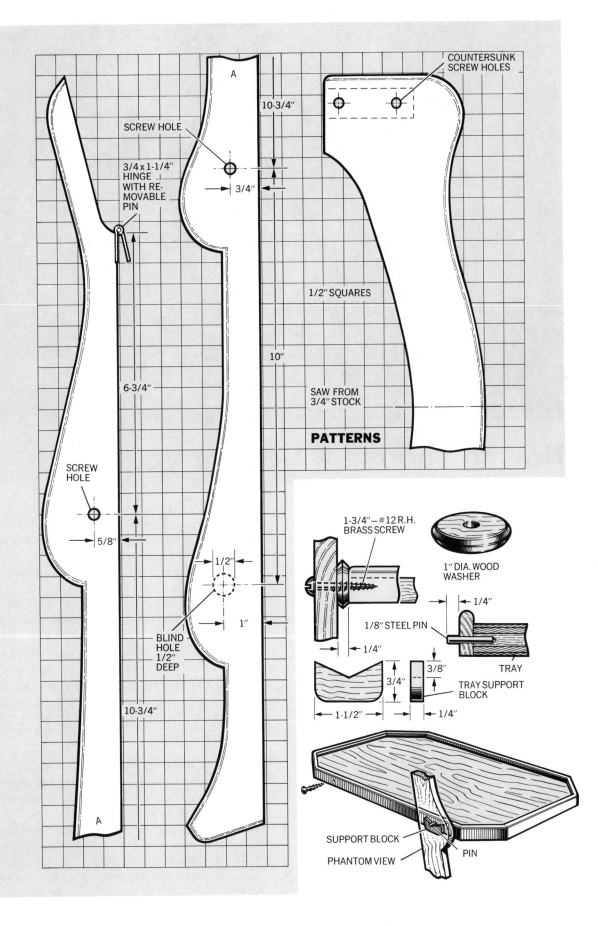

A

SCREW HOLE

3/4 x 1-1/4" HINGE WITH RE-MOVABLE PIN

COUNTERSUNK SCREW HOLES

10-3/4"

3/4"

1/2" SQUARES

10"

6-3/4"

SAW FROM 3/4" STOCK

PATTERNS

SCREW HOLE

5/8"

1/2"

1"

BLIND HOLE 1/2" DEEP

10-3/4"

A

1-3/4" – #12 R.H. BRASS SCREW

1" DIA. WOOD WASHER

1/8" STEEL PIN

1/4"

1/4"

1/4"

TRAY

3/8"

3/4"

TRAY SUPPORT BLOCK

1-1/2"

1/4"

SUPPORT BLOCK

PHANTOM VIEW

PIN

How to choose a tree for your yard

Trees serve many different purposes. What do you want yours to do for you?

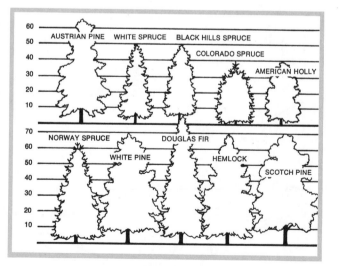

A TREE can be the most important part of your landscaping plan. And, because there are so many kinds of trees, it can be the hardest part of the plan to decide upon.

Perhaps the best way to choose a tree is to start with the qualities you're seeking, the "job" you want it to do for you and your family. Trees are for cooling shade in the summer, warming windbreak in the winter, fruit, blossoms, showy berries and colorful leaves. They are for climbing, building treehouses in, swinging from.

Basic practicalities must be kept in mind. In a shade tree, for example, you want a species that grows well where you live, that leafs out early and holds leaves until late in the fall; that is deep-rooted so you can garden or grow grass beneath it; and that is resistant to pests and disease. Shade trees are undergoing major changes today, brought about by improved propagation techniques, widespread research to find varieties that are disease-resistant and pollution-tolerant.

Local climate is the first consideration in selecting a tree that will perform well over a long period of time. Trees native to the area are usually the very safest bet, if you don't mind limiting your selection.

Certain types of trees do better in an acid soil, others in alkaline ground (although minerals can be added to the soil to change its "sweetness"). Some trees thrive in dry soil, others in wet. For specific recommendations about the most appropriate types for your area, check with your local nursery, arboretum, or the county office of your state Agricultural Extension Service.

Favorite shade tree recommendations by region include: *High Plains* (as in Colorado): thornless honey locust, green ash, Norway maple, hackberry, littleleaf linden. *Midwest* (as in Minnesota): sugar maple, Norway maple, green ash, Crimean linden, white oak. *Southeast* (as in Georgia): evergreen live oak or willow oak, American holly, magnolia grandiflora, dogwood, loquat. *North Central/East* (as in Ohio): Norway maple, sugar maple, red maple, littleleaf linden, pin oak. *Desert* (as in New Mexico): Arizona ash, pecan, thornless honey locust, fruitless mulberry, Aleppo pine. *Southern California* (as in Los Angeles): fruitless mulberry, fern pine, magnolia grandiflora, Koelreuteria integrifoliola, Brazilian pepper.

Flowering trees stay small, give a burst of bloom in season and all are useful for light shade. They fit well into a small lot, especially at corners, make an excellent privacy screen if planted closely along the edge of the yard, and look well placed three or more in a clump to achieve a full, natural effect. Favorites include redbud, crab apple, English hawthorn, European mountain ash, flowering cherry, peach and plum, dogwood, franklinia, fringe tree, golden chain.

Evergreens provide shade all year and are outstanding as a winter windbreak. Kinds that mature at 30 feet or larger include American arborvitae and holly, Austrian pine, Black Hills spruce, Cedar of Lebanon, Colorado spruce, Douglas fir, Eastern hemlock, Norway pine.

Almost any variety of tree has some disadvantage that must be weighed against its good points. Thus, it's not a good idea to choose elms, willows, poplars or maples for planting near drainage pipes, because the roots of these trees can clog sewers. Species with shallow roots rob lawns of moisture and if planted near a sidewalk can break the pavement.

Some trees are extremely susceptible to insects or disease. A notable example is the graceful American elm, favorite street tree of U.S. cities until it was decimated by Dutch Elm disease.

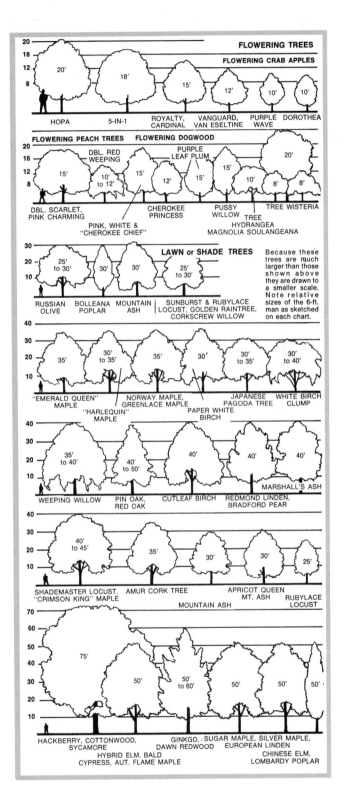

TREES ARE THE MOST important plantings you will make in your landscape. You plan for your own pleasure and that of future generations. Because of the long-range effects of planting a tree, consider its overall shape and expected size at maturity before you plant. For guidance, consult the chart above prepared in cooperation with the Henry Field Seed and Nursery Co., Inc., Shenandoah, IA.

How to fell and limb a tree

There are right and wrong methods for felling and limbing a large tree. Stick to these suggestions and you will find that the job will go easier with a lot less chance of injury

■ BASICALLY, there are three reasons why a homeowner has to take down a tree on his property: 1. Room is needed for an addition; 2. The tree has died and poses a safety threat with the first heavy windstorm that comes along, or 3. A dense cluster of trees requires some prudent thinning.

There are, of course, correct methods for felling, bucking and limbing trees that will make the job easier and—more important—safer. For example, when felling trees, one of the first rules to observe is to always *make gravity work for you.*

However, this often is not possible in crowded suburban areas. The tree is, just as likely, leaning toward your or a neighbor's house or garage. Here it is essential to cut the tree down in stages, using ropes to make certain that the tree limbs and trunk pieces will fall exactly where you want them to.

Felling a tree with a handsaw or ax is now a thing of the past. If you don't own a chain saw, it is well worth the few dollars it will cost to rent one.

Planning pays off. Before starting, take the time to study the wind's direction and velocity. These factors will have a direct bearing on how the tree will fall. *Don't ever attempt to bring down a tree in a heavy or gusty wind.*

Be sure you have a clear escape route. It should be at an angle of 45° in the opposite direction from the line of fall. Play it safe and clear away all potential obstacles along your escape route.

Felling of large-diameter trees and trees in crowded suburban neighborhoods should never be attempted by an amateur. Unless you have full confidence that you can drop the tree where you want it, in the long run you'll save money and aggravation by calling in a professional.

SEE ALSO
**Chain saws ... Fireplaces ... Firewood ...
Firewood sheds ... Landscaping ... Log projects**

STUDY TREE TO SEE IF BRANCHES ARE HEAVIER ON ONE SIDE

← TREE SHOULD BE FELLED IN THIS DIRECTION.

Study the tree first

The initial step is to closely examine the tree to determine which way it will fall. Although almost every tree leans in some direction, just how the tree will actually fall depends upon how you make the felling cuts. Even in relatively open country, the direction of the fall is important. There may be other trees in the area that you do not want damaged.

When working in close quarters, you are well advised to use a hefty guy rope tied near the top of the tree and a pulley. Have a helper put a strain on the rope to guide the falling tree. The pulley keeps him out of the path of fall.

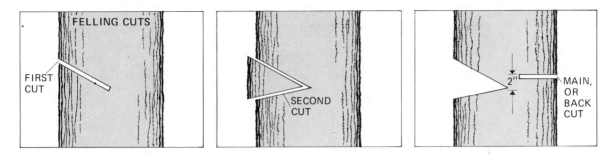

Basic sawing techniques—notching and felling

Done properly, it takes three cuts to fell a tree: two passes to make the undercut (notch) and a back cut on the opposite side of the trunk. If you are a beginner, mark all three cuts waist high on the tree trunk with chalk. The notch should be cut in the sequence shown above to a depth of approximately one-third tree diameter, and perpendicular to the line of fall. After making the first two cuts, remove the wedge from the trunk.

Make the back cut at least 2 in. higher than the notch so as to leave a "hinge" of uncut wood to guide the tree over. *Do not cut through the notch.* Besides guiding the tree, the hinge will also prevent the tree from twisting as it falls. As the tree starts to fall, pull your saw free. Immediately turn off power and retreat quickly along your pre-planned escape route. From here on, gravity takes over.

When to use a felling wedge

If you suspect the tree may not fall in the desired direction, or may tilt back causing the saw to bind, do not complete the back cut. Withdraw the saw and use wood, plastic or magnesium wedges to open the cut and tilt the tree in the desired direction of fall. *Caution: When using wedges, make certain the chain saw does not come into contact with wedge or the saw will kick back.* Felling wedges are available at most chain-saw dealers or you can cut your own of hardwood.

With the tree felled, you can now trim off the waist-high stump close to the ground, repeating the three-cut method mentioned above.

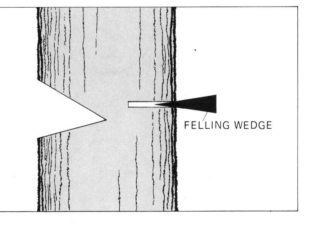

continued ⟶

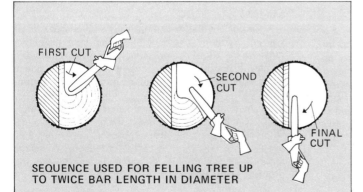

Sawing sequence for large-diameter trunks

As a rule of thumb, large-diameter trees (up to twice the chain-saw-bar length in diameter) should be handled by a professional; cutting one down is not a job for a fledgling woodcutter. However, if you are confident of your tree-felling ability, and the tree is standing out in open terrain, you should always use felling wedges in the manner described above.

To fell a large tree, use a series of cuts as shown at left. Notice that the cuts are made so that the third and final cut leaves the hinge wood parallel to the notch cut. This is a must, so make the cuts with maximum care.

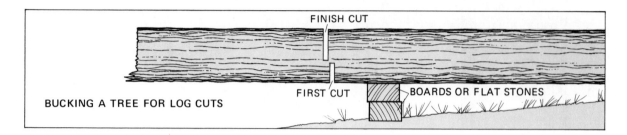

FINISH CUT

FIRST CUT

BOARDS OR FLAT STONES

BUCKING A TREE FOR LOG CUTS

Relieving stress is necessary to cut through logs

Once the tree is down, keep in mind that the wood is heavy and that it will bend and pinch the saw if improperly supported. (The trunk will weaken at the point where you make the cut unless the tree is lying on perfectly flat ground or supported as shown.) If you make the cut with the tree on the ground, don't let the saw's chain dig into the earth; it is harmful for the saw, and you stand a good chance of being struck by flying debris. To cut the trunk, use the bucking and two-cut sequence shown. The first cut should be no deeper than one-third the trunk diameter.

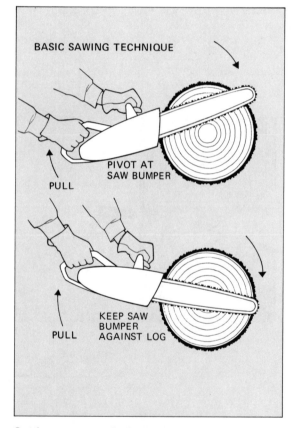

BASIC SAWING TECHNIQUE

PIVOT AT SAW BUMPER

PULL

KEEP SAW BUMPER AGAINST LOG

PULL

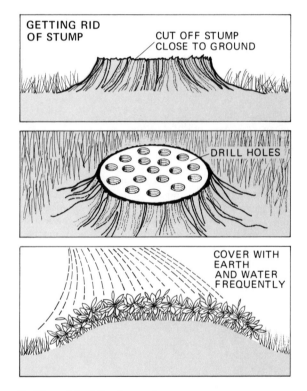

GETTING RID OF STUMP

CUT OFF STUMP CLOSE TO GROUND

DRILL HOLES

COVER WITH EARTH AND WATER FREQUENTLY

Cutting up a small-diameter trunk

Most homeowners cut up a felled tree trunk for fireplace logs—usually about 24 in. long. When the trunk is of a diameter smaller than the saw's bar length, the cut can be made in one pass if the tree is supported properly as described above. If necessary, to avoid the cut closing on the bar, insert a wedge into the cut to hold it open and away from the bar. Start the cut with the saw's bumper snugged against the tree trunk and with the blade held at an angle. Holding the saw firmly, fully open the throttle and slowly lower the traveling chain into the wood. Keep the throttle full-open throughout the cut.

Getting rid of the tree stump

The most popular method of getting rid of a tree stump is by burning. Present environmental conditions now make this not only undesirable but, in most areas, illegal. The alternatives?

1. Dig out by hand, cutting away sections of root as you go. If you must remove the stump immediately (to make way for a footing, for example), you are well advised to call in a professional nurseryman with his power equipment which will chip out a stump in a half hour or less.

2. The cheapest way to eliminate a stump is to simply bury it. Cut the stump off close to the ground and cover it with soil. To speed the rotting process, bore holes 6 in. deep before burying. For aesthetic reasons, cover the mound with ground-cover plantings. To speed the rotting process, water frequently.

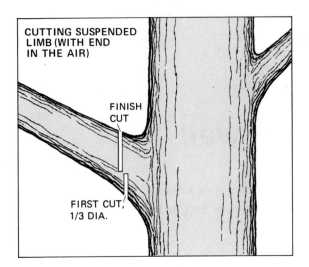

CUTTING SUSPENDED LIMB (WITH END IN THE AIR)

FINISH CUT

FIRST CUT, 1/3 DIA.

Limbing a tree

There are two things to guard against when limbing a tree: First, the possibility that the cut branch will whip back in the direction of the woodcutter, and second, the impulse to work from an improperly positioned, thus unsafe, ladder.

To prevent the first, use the cutting sequence shown. To saw off a large limb supported only by the trunk, first cut one-third of the way through the limb on its underside. Make second cut through the limb from the top. Make certain you lash the ladder securely to the tree. Run a rope around the trunk a couple of times, then tie it securely to the top rung. Plant the ladder so that its feet are level and are placed a distance from the base of the tree that is equal to one-quarter of the vertical height.

LOGS CUT AND SPLIT, THEN STACKED TO PROVIDE AIR CIRCULATION

Stacking fireplace logs

For use as firewood, the logs should be stacked and allowed to dry. There is a difference of opinion on whether to split logs before or after they are dry. Splitting goes quickest if you use a steel splitting wedge and a wooden maul rather than an ax. And it's a lot safer.

Twelve or fourteen logs may be stored without danger of toppling over. One cord of wood equals 128 cu. ft. Assuming you've cut your logs into 24-in. lengths, it would take a pile 16 ft. long and 4 ft. high to equal this volume.

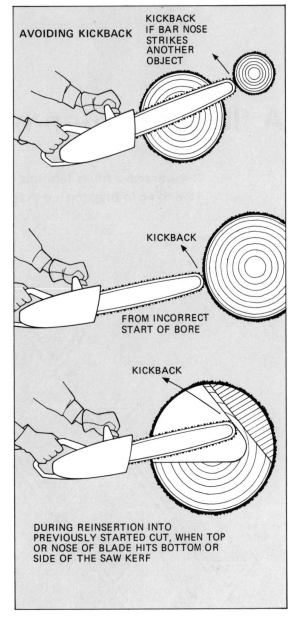

AVOIDING KICKBACK

KICKBACK IF BAR NOSE STRIKES ANOTHER OBJECT

KICKBACK

FROM INCORRECT START OF BORE

KICKBACK

DURING REINSERTION INTO PREVIOUSLY STARTED CUT, WHEN TOP OR NOSE OF BLADE HITS BOTTOM OR SIDE OF THE SAW KERF

Avoiding kickback

When cutting with the nose of the bar, take extra care to protect against chance of saw kickback. It will occur when any of the three conditions illustrated above exists.

Safety rules you should always observe:

1. Think the job out beforehand and stick to your plan.
2. Plan an escape route at 45° angle opposite the direction of tree fall.
3. Wear a hard hat if there is any chance of timber or branches falling from above.
4. Don't wear loose-fitting clothing. It could become caught in the chain saw or falling limbs. Always wear work gloves.
5. If your job collects a crowd, stop. Keep bystanders, especially children, clear of your cutting site and area of tree fall.
6. Work only with a sharp saw chain.

A flower garden on the wall

**This attractive trellis lets you move a bit of nature indoors. It's just
the thing to brighten up that blank wall in your den or living room**

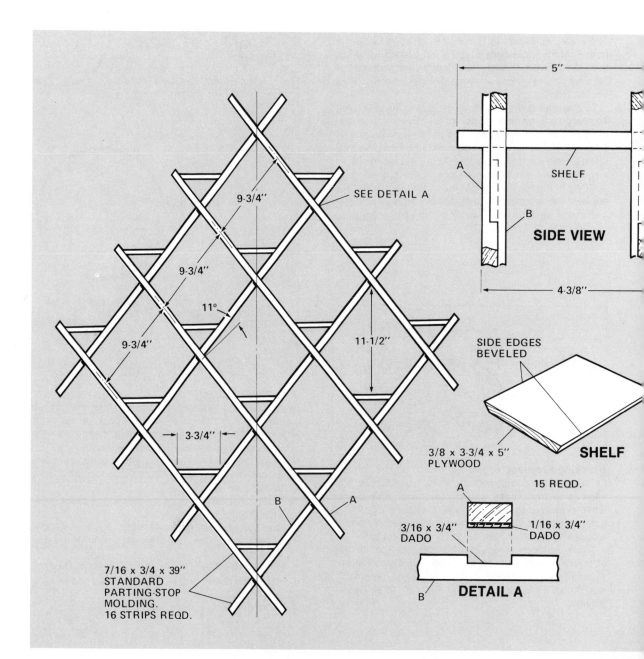

SEE DETAIL A

9-3/4"

9-3/4"

11°

9-3/4"

11-1/2"

3-3/4"

B   A

7/16 x 3/4 x 39"
STANDARD
PARTING-STOP
MOLDING.
16 STRIPS REQD.

5"

A

B

SHELF

SIDE VIEW

4-3/8"

SIDE EDGES
BEVELED

3/8 x 3-3/4 x 5"
PLYWOOD

SHELF

15 REQD.

A

3/16 x 3/4"
DADO

1/16 x 3/4"
DADO

B   **DETAIL A**

■ THIS COLORFUL PLANT TRELLIS is a decoration that literally "grows" on the wall. Fifteen potted plants give it an ever-changing look as new foliage and blossoms appear.

The trellis consists of two identical frames of crisscrossed strips spaced apart by 15 shelves. The strips are lumberyard moldings which measure approximately ½ x ¾ in. You'll need 16 strips (39 in. long)—8 dadoed ³⁄₁₆ in. deep and 8 dadoed ¹⁄₁₆ in. deep to automatically register one strip over the other. The dadoes are cut with a table or radial saw, and with a stop attached to the fence to space the cuts uniformly 9¾ in. on centers. The blade, or the miter gauge, as the case may be, is set 11° left of 90°; the same setting is used in dadoing all 16 pieces. The ends of the shelves are beveled to suit and then the shelves are glued even with the front and back strips.

Finish the completed trellis with white paint. Shop around for some colorful pots and add the plants of your choice.

THE WHITE-PAINTED trellis with its varicolored collection of pots contrasts beautifully when hung on a dark paneled wall. A couple of screws through holes in the back strips are used to hang the entire unit. The plastic pots can be found in a variety store; shop around until you locate some that you decide are both attractive and inexpensive.

SEE ALSO
Dry sinks . . . Gardening . . . House plants . . .
Planters . . . Plexiglass projects . . .
Radial-arm saws . . . Table saws

Neat photo edges every time

By R. S. HEDIN

■ PHOTO PRINTS are sometimes hard to trim evenly on a paper cutter because their edges are usually curled. Unless you hold the paper firmly, it's likely to slip slightly as the cutter blade comes down, resulting in a crooked or ragged cut. This spring-loaded hold-down arm does the job for you. As you lower the blade, the arm automatically clamps the paper snugly against the cutting board, flattening the edge and preventing it from shifting.

The arm can be fitted to any paper cutter—simply adjust its length to suit the size board you have. The rear end must be shaped to fit over the cutter blade's pivot. The dimensions shown here will work with most cutters, but you can check the fit first with a cardboard cutout.

As the cutter blade is raised, it engages a dowel run crosswise through the top of the hold-down. This lifts the arm clear of the board so paper can be inserted under it. The other end of the dowel acts as an anchor point for a short, stiff spring. Attach the spring with a small ring bent from coathanger wire. The lower end of the spring is held by a screw eye in the ruled guide strip. Pad the bottom of the arm with cork, felt or rubber to give it a good grip.

SEE ALSO
**Cutting boards ... Dryers, photo ...
Mountings, photo ... Photography ... Photo hints ...
Prints, photo**

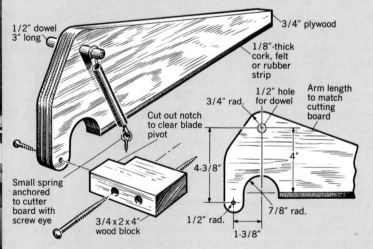

1/2" dowel 3" long

3/4" plywood

1/8"-thick cork, felt or rubber strip

Cut out notch to clear blade pivot

3/4" rad.

1/2" hole for dowel

Arm length to match cutting board

4"

4-3/8"

Small spring anchored to cutter board with screw eye

3/4 x 2 x 4" wood block

1/2" rad.

7/8" rad.

1-3/8"

Camelot

A little box can be a work of art

**Here's a clever idea that should stretch your imagination.
Using a throwaway lotion box you convert it into a handsome chest.
Choose an appropriate theme and begin looking for decorations**

IT ALL STARTED with a gift from his wife. That's when Al Mesnooh, New York artist and freelance art consultant, began "tinkering around" making these handsome one-of-a-kind trinket chests.

The gift was a bottle of English Leather cologne by Mem which came in such a nicely made wooden box that Al just couldn't throw it away.

Since that first bottle, Al has used a lot of

By WAYNE C. LECKEY

SEE ALSO
Boxes, trinket ... Gifts, Christmas ... Jewelry boxes

Byzantine

Gothic

NICELY MADE of redwood, throwaway after-shave lotion box becomes "work of art" trinket chest when decorated and fitted with brass hardware.

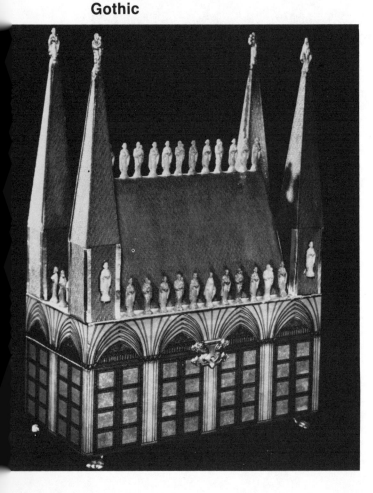

cologne for he has created a lot of chests from the empty boxes. His works of art have been displayed at countless banks, museums and art fairs in and around New York City. Many have brought a handsome price.

Appropriately named Camelot, Byzantine and Gothic, the three chests shown on these pages are good examples of how his interest in ancient history and architecture have been put to use.

Asked where he found the tiny plastic figures, he answered: "Here and there, in hobby stores, gift shops and souvenir counters. Finding enough of them is my biggest problem."

An artist, Al decorates most of his boxes with his own exclusive designs, but, as he explained, "You don't have to be an artist to produce a handsome chest. In the case of my Camelot chest I made use of the embossed metallic designs from the carton of a bottle of Chivas Regal Scotch whisky, antiqued them gold and applied them to the sides, ends and top. Magazines are a good source of appropriate pictures; so are cards and gift-wrapping paper. That's the fun part of it all, starting out with a theme and tracking down suitable figures and illustrations. Of course, when you can make your own designs, the fun is ever greater."

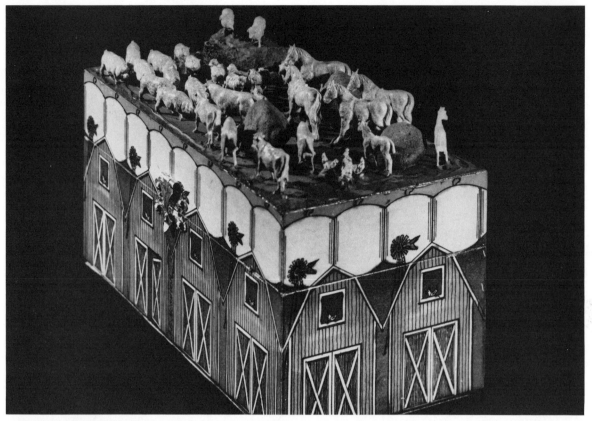

A COUNTRY THEME is achieved in the chest above by adding tiny farm animals to cover the chest. Barn illustrations then are used to cover the sides.

Actually no specific box is required to start with. Anyone who is handy can make a suitable box from thin wood. Where the corners of the chest are left exposed, the "dovetailed" joints of the cologne box do add to the appearance of the completed chest as you see in Camelot. In cases where the box is to be completely covered, how the box is put together and what wood is used makes little difference as you see in the other examples.

The top of the cologne-bottle box actually becomes the bottom of the chest and the bottom, the lid; the cardboard liner is discarded. The lid is held in position by two tiny brass hinges. The latter, plus the feet and lid clasp, can be purchased from most well-stocked hardware stores.

COMPLETE WITH PYRAMIDS resting in desert sand, the exotic chest below is decorated with appropriate pictures to give it an authentic Egyptian motif.

CALLED BEN HUR, this handsome chest is decorated with stately columns. A chariot race of tiny figures, picked up at hobby stores, completes the theme.

Look what you can make from metal tubing

By WALTER E. BURTON

**Tubing of brass, copper, steel
or aluminum can be made into all kinds of unusual
and useful objects. It is easy to work
with, requiring few sophisticated
or expensive tools to produce handsome products**

SOME METAL TUBING can be bent satisfactorily simply by wrapping it around grooved pulley wheel (sheave). Here, ⅜-in. aluminum tubing is bent this way.

■ MANY USEFUL OBJECTS can be made from aluminum, copper, brass or steel tubing. Metal tubing is cut with a hacksaw, tubing cutter or lathe. Cut ends are file-finished, or smoothed in a lathe. For smooth surfaces, abrasive cloth or a flap-type sanding wheel is used and a final luster is given with metal polish. Tubing can be joined by soldering, brazing, welding—or even using epoxy or plugs (either metal or wood) and

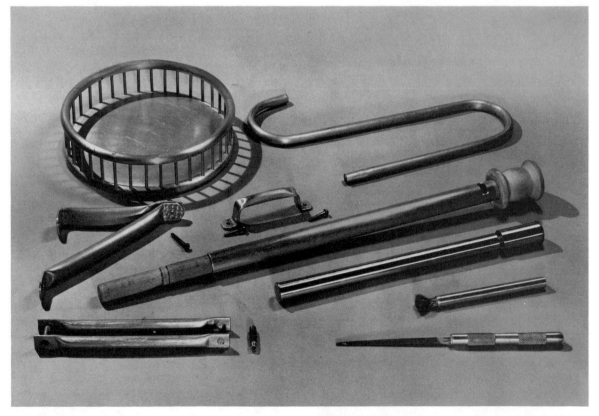

VARIOUS ITEMS that can be made from metal tubing include 1) ring basket or tray, 2) siphon, 3) shelf bracket, 4) drawer or door pull, 5) slide whistle, 6) metal tubing with ends flattened, connected by peened spacers, 7) adjustable shelf post/bookend, 8) spacer, 9) brush handle and 10) file handle.

SPACER with the diameter of the ends reduced connects the flattened ends of the larger tubing. Here, the spacer ends are peened to hold ends together.

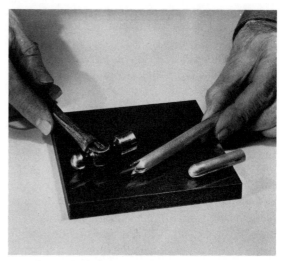

ALUMINUM TUBING can be closed and rounded by first cutting it as shown. Then, use a hammer to lightly tap the cut ends until it is round.

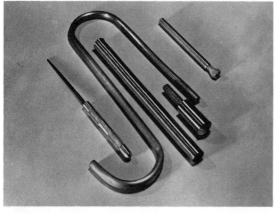

TOOL HANDLES and siphon made from ⅜-in. aluminum tube; post bookend from ¾ and ⅝-in. copper tubes.

ADJUSTABLE BOOKSHELF POST serves as a bookend and as an added support for the upper shelf.

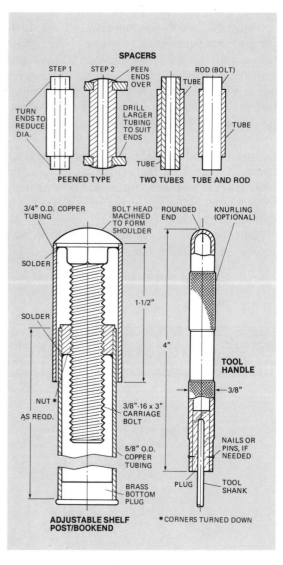

screws, pins or nails. Bending can be done with coil-spring sleeves or the method shown in the photo.

Details on six metal tubing projects follow. All sizes of tubing given refer to outside dimensions.

Spacers. Short lengths of tubing are often used as spacers between two plates, strips or other elements of a mechanism. One type of spacer is made from a single tube, with the ends turned or filed down to form shoulders and peened over after installation. A tube, rod or bolt within a tube might also be used.

Tool handles. Improvised tool handles can be made easily from tubing. A common way to anchor the tool shank is to drive a wood dowel into the tube and drill a hole in the dowel for the tool. The relatively new "plastic-metal" preparations or an epoxy filler could also be used. Outer end of the handle can be left open, plugged or closed by using the method shown or by spinning or bending the metal. Light knurling makes a handle less slippery.

Adjustable shelf post/bookend. This dual-purpose item is made from ⅝ and ¾-in. copper tubing with a ⅜-16 x 3-in. carriage bolt and nut providing the adjustable movement. Nut corners are turned down for about ⁵⁄₆ of their length, forming a shoulder to rest on end of ⅝-in. tubing (see drawing). The bolt head is machined to form a shallow shoulder to rest on the end of ¾-in. tubing. Nut and bolt head are soldered to their respective tubes by fluxing the joints, placing bits of solder inside the tubes and heating over stove burner. Plug at bottom of post prevents denting of the shelf.

Shelf bracket. By flattening ends of two lengths of aluminum tubing and drilling screw

SHELF BRACKET is made from ½-in. aluminum tubing; whistle from ¾-in. aluminum tubing, dowel and spool.

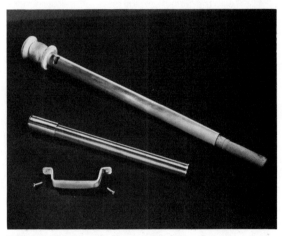

FROM TOP: assembled slide whistle, adjustable bookshelf post, drawer pull from ⅜-in. aluminum tubing.

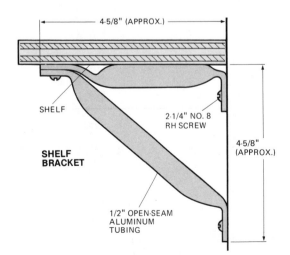

4-5/8" (APPROX.)

SHELF

2-1/4" NO. 8 RH SCREW

4-5/8" (APPROX.)

SHELF BRACKET

1/2" OPEN-SEAM ALUMINUM TUBING

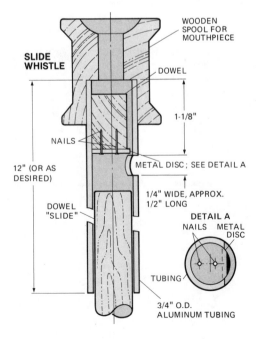

SLIDE WHISTLE

WOODEN SPOOL FOR MOUTHPIECE

DOWEL

1-1/8"

NAILS

METAL DISC; SEE DETAIL A

12" (OR AS DESIRED)

1/4" WIDE, APPROX. 1/2" LONG

DOWEL "SLIDE"

DETAIL A
NAILS   METAL DISC

TUBING

3/4" O.D. ALUMINUM TUBING

NAILS IN clamped wood hold metal ring in place for drilling holes in center of rim to receive "side rods."

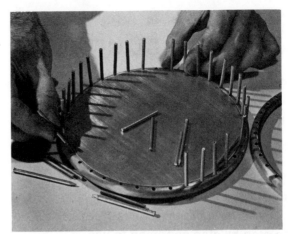

"SIDE RODS" (nails with heads cut off) are inserted in bottom ring holes; sheet aluminum bottom fits inside.

BASKET made from ⅜-in. seamless aluminum tubing and aluminum nails makes attractive server.

holes in them, a handy shelf bracket can be made.

Slide whistle. A slot in the tube is made by drilling two ¼-in. holes tangent to one another and filing out intervening metal. The plug is a short piece of dowel; a metal disc with a flat area on its circumference is nailed to one end of the plug and positioned at slot edge. The slide is a free-moving length of dowel, the mouthpiece, a wood spool.

Ring basket. Two lengths of metal tubing are bent to form two circles with 7-in. outside diameters. Ends of each circle are joined by inserting a maple plug and nailing through tubing into plug. The circles are joined with 36 "side rods" made by cutting heads from ⅛-in.-dia. aluminum nails. A total of 33 "rods" engage holes drilled through one side of each ring; the other three are longer and extend through rings with their ends peened. The bottom piece is sheet aluminum cut from siding scrap and glued in place with epoxy cement.

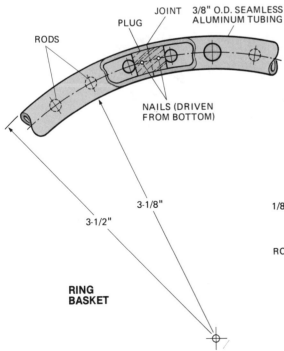

RODS

PLUG

JOINT　3/8" O.D. SEAMLESS ALUMINUM TUBING

NAILS (DRIVEN FROM BOTTOM)

3-1/8"

3-1/2"

RING BASKET

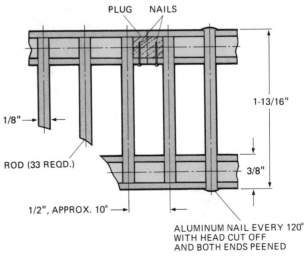

PLUG　NAILS

1-13/16"

1/8"

ROD (33 REQD.)

3/8"

1/2", APPROX. 10°

ALUMINUM NAIL EVERY 120° WITH HEAD CUT OFF AND BOTH ENDS PEENED

A basic course in engine tune-up

By MORT SCHULTZ

A complete tune-up goes well beyond the slap-dash treatment you may get down the street. It's more thorough— and far more important. Here's the step-by-step approach to use

■ TUNE-UP KEEPS AN engine running smoothly and economically. It helps curb pollution and uncovers hidden problems. And it's called for at least every 12,000 miles or 12 months, whichever comes first. The sequence of services we suggest here will help you be sure you're touching all the bases.

In the procedure we suggest, some tools are named that you may consider exotic or expensive. But, with the modern automobile, they're necessary. And when you spread their cost across all the jobs you'll be able to do for yourself, their real cost is comparatively low. Besides, the right tools and instruments make the work simple.

Some jobs, however, will require costly professional tools. And they may well require the touch of a professional mechanic. We include them, nevertheless. Even procedures that you decide you can't handle should be understood. When you turn some part of the job over to a professional, you may get better work if you know what his job will entail.

We have two purposes, then: To help you handle all the maintenance and service that's reasonable for a do-it-yourselfer. And to make you knowledgeable enough that you can see when a mechanic's work is done properly—or improperly.

compression test

The best tune-up won't be able to compensate for the inefficient performance that comes from low or uneven compression. If the engine idles roughly because of a sticky valve, that idle can't be smoothed out by other tune-up procedures. So, if you have any doubt, you should rule out these problems with a compression test on each cylinder.

This calls for a compression gauge. Like the other tools and supplies we mention here, one is available from your auto parts and accessories dealer. You'll press the end of the gauge stem into each spark-plug port while the piston travels up and down a few times. The gauge reading will indicate the pressure built up inside the combustion chamber.

The first step in a compression test is to warm up the engine so the choke plate is wide open. Then disconnect all the ignition leads from spark plugs. Don't pull the leads themselves, however; pull and twist the *boot* around the contact at the end of each plug. Ignition leads aren't designed for great physical strength; their role is to conduct high voltage. Pulling directly on a lead can damage its insulation or separate the lead from its terminal. You may well disrupt the current flow or cause more misfiring—perhaps the very illness you're hoping to cure.

Be sure plug leads are marked so you can restore them to the proper plugs, also numbered, or you'll mess up the firing sequence. (Masking tape works well. Traditionally, cylinders are numbered from front to rear. Number plugs and leads the same way. When you take plug leads from the distributor cap, use the same numbering system on distributor cap towers—with an L or R to distinguish left-bank connections from the right.)

Blow debris from the well around each plug port—a rubber ear syringe or an ordinary soda straw works nicely. Then remove the plugs. If yours have metal gaskets, save them. You'll

need them for any plugs you return to service.

For the actual test, you'll have to be sure the choke and throttle plates don't close. Open the throttle with the throttle lever. Unless you have a co-worker inside the car who will hold the accelerator pedal to the floor, reach for a screwdriver. Extend it carefully down the carburetor throat past the choke plate to hold the throttle wide open.

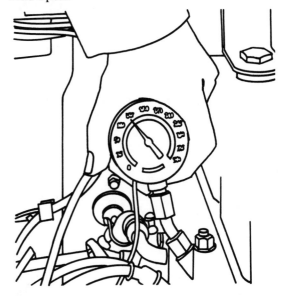

the test itself

For the test, hold the end of the gauge firmly in a plug port while someone uses the starter motor to crank the engine a few revolutions. Note the highest reading you get for that cylinder and move on to the next for the same procedure.

You'll quickly have all the data collected. The next question: How does one interpret it?

You needn't be particularly surprised if compression readings vary somewhat from cylinder to cylinder. It would be much more surprising if every cylinder, from end to end, maintained new-car compression for several years.

The *amount* of variation is what's significant. The lowest compression should be no less than 80 percent of the highest. Cylinders with too little compression alert you to problems beyond the scope of a tune-up—but they're problems that you'll need to know about as soon as possible.

A cylinder that can't build up enough compression may have a valve sticking so it doesn't close as fast as it should. Or a valve that's burned, so it can't seal tightly. Or piston rings that are seriously worn. The condition of the end

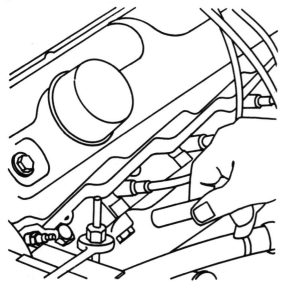

of the spark plug and any engine tendency to burn oil will go a long way toward confirming that last failing.

Compression specifications for your car are in the car's service manual. You'll also find them in general automotive references such as *Motor's Auto Repair Manual*, usually available in public libraries. As you become adept, you may want to get a copy for yourself. Or you may be able to get specs from the service department of a dealer that sells your make of car. Perhaps even by telephone.

To avoid wear on the points, it's a good idea to disconnect the coil-to-distributor primary wire from the coil before you crank the engine with the starter motor. This is the thin wire from the side of the distributor to the coil.

sparkplug service

New sparkplugs are recommended every 12,000 miles, but you may be able to get lots more wear out of them. If they aren't damaged or badly worn, they're well worth checking and servicing.

Clean old plugs by scraping deposits from the lower insulators with a hacksaw blade that you've ground to a point at one end. Use an ignition file to smooth and brighten the electrodes. Reset the plugs' gap with a sparkplug feeler gauge, the kind with round wire feelers of different diameters. Before you buy a gauge, check the gap size specified for your car; few gauges will have enough elements to check *every* possible plug gap exactly.

Your owner's manual will specify the right plug gap. So will the emission-control label mounted on or near the radiator.

Your plug gauge should include a bending tool to bend the outer or ground electrode. Don't use pliers and don't try to bend the center electrode. Either approach can easily ruin the plug.

Remember that you'll have to gap new plugs properly before installing them. They aren't necessarily gapped for your car when new.

Carefully clean the threads in the spark plug port. The best tool is a small wire brush that has been coated with grease. That will help it pick up any deposits. A little grease getting into the combustion chamber isn't serious. It will burn away quickly.

Name-brand plugs—and most others—come with metal gaskets. Unless the seats for your plugs are tapered, you'll need to use the gaskets with new plugs. If you re-use old plugs, be sure you've saved their gaskets to reinstall with the plugs.

Set the plugs into their ports by hand, taking care not to cross-thread them. When they're hand-tight, seat them firmly but not too tight—about ¼ turn past hand-tight for gasket plugs, $^1/_{16}$ turn for tapered-seat plugs. The ideal is to set them with a torque wrench, tightening them to manufacturer's specs—normally 15 to 21 lb.-ft. (20 to 28.5 Nm). Check the shop manual or a dealer for the exact specs.

Wipe the ignition leads clean with a dry rag and check them and the boots. Replace any that are cracked or brittle. Push the wire terminals firmly on the plugs when you finish.

battery service

Use a hydrometer to test battery specific gravity; it tells the proportion of sulfuric acid in the electrolyte. The procedure is simple: Draw some electrolyte from one cell into a clean hydrometer tube. Record the reading, return the electrolyte to its cell, and draw another sample from the next one.

Before taking your reading, let the electrolyte set for a minute while the instrument stabilizes. Be sure the float is riding free of the tube's sides, then hold the hydrometer at eye-level to take your reading.

Many low-cost hydrometers are available. The best have a built-in temperature compensator, a useful characteristic since temperature affects specific gravity to some degree.

Specific gravity of a fully charged battery is between 1.260 and 1.280. If the overall reading isn't above 1.230, charge the battery—as slowly as possible. If that doesn't bring the reading up, your battery is about shot.

A cell or cells with specific gravity readings as much as .050 below the others is weak. It may continue to serve you for months, but frequent checking is called for lest you get stuck with a dead battery.

clean the battery

Keeping the battery clean is hardly complicated. And it will pay off in promoting longer battery life and in preventing discharging.

To clean it, remove it from the car. First take off the ground cable (usually the negative one) then the "hot" one. A battery terminal puller

does the best job of removing the cables and it avoids the danger you might damage posts with a screwdriver or pliers.

Take the battery out, tighten the vent caps, and cover the vents with masking tape so the cleaning solution (a base) doesn't contaminate—and begin to neutralize—the acid. Scrub the case with an ammonia-water or baking-soda-water solution, then rinse it with plain water. Keep repeating the process until the cleaning agent no longer fizzles.

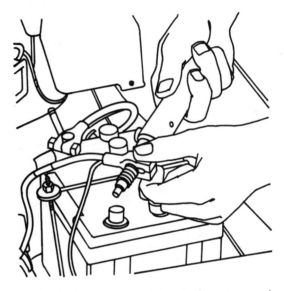

Wash the battery pan with solution, too, and check the battery cables. If they're damaged, replace them. Clean any corrosion from the cable terminals as well as the battery posts with the wire-brush elements of a battery cleaning tool. Only then should you replace the battery.

Reconnect the "hot" cable first, then the ground. Draw the terminal clamps up tight on the posts. A light coat of petroleum jelly over the entire connection will help to retard corrosion.

ignition service

Start your ignition servicing at the distributor. Remove sparkplug wires from distributor-cap towers and mark the towers for identification, just as you did for the compression test. Each wire must go back into its own tower.

Now remove the distributor cap, wipe it clean, and inspect it closely inside and out. You're looking for hairline cracks, carbon tracks, and burned or corroded terminals. Such damage usually means terminals haven't been making good contact. Current has been arcing across an imperfect connection. If the cap is damaged,

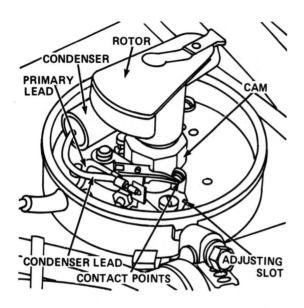

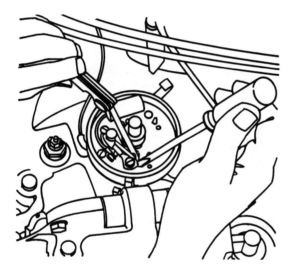

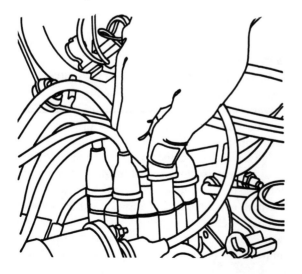

replace it. If not, clean particles of debris from within the towers.

Pull off the rotor and inspect it for cracks or a corroded or broken metal contact. If it's damaged, get a new one.

Then carefully spread apart the distributor contact points and study them. Points with a general gray color, points that are only slightly roughened or pitted, can be kept in use. Certainly those that are badly pitted or burned must be replaced. But it is at least as important to find the reason for their condition and repair it.

Pitted or burned points usually indicate one of about six problems. Most serious are a poorly adjusted or inoperative voltage regulator or ballast resistor, or a defective or incorrect condenser, or high condenser-circuit resistance. Less serious are oil or vapor in the distributor because of a clogged engine breather, excessive distributor-cam lubricant picked up by the points, a weakened contact-point spring, or points improperly gapped.

servicing points

If points are in good shape, clean off scale by passing a clean, fine-cut point file between them a couple of times. Don't use emery cloth or sandpaper; loose grit will foul things.

Set the breaker-arm rubbing block on the high

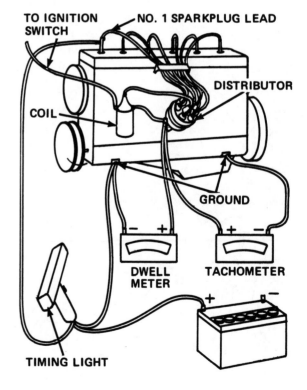

point of a cam lobe and adjust the point gap with a flat feeler gauge. Find proper gap setting on the vehicle-emission-control label or in the owner's manual or shop manual.

If your distributor has a wick-type cam lubricator, replace it. If there's no built-in cam lubricator, apply cam lube yourself. A single drop, about the size of a match head, goes on one cam lobe only.

Reinstall the rotor and distributor cap and seat each plug wire firmly into its tower by pushing down on the boot while squeezing it to release any trapped air.

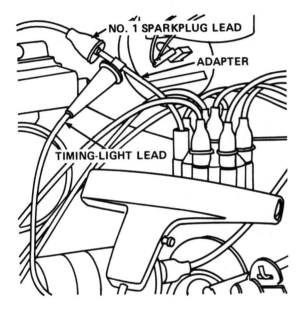

Clean out the high-tension-lead tower of the ignition coil and make sure the high-tension lead is seated firmly in the tower. Also tighten the ignition primary wire connections on the coil.

If you have a dwellmeter, set the contact-point dwell angle to specifications. Without a dwellmeter, you can make an approximate dwell adjustment by ear if the distributor cap has an access cover. Let the engine idle. Raise the access cover and turn the point adjusting screw until the engine barely starts to misfire. Then back the screw up half a turn. When you finish, be sure the access cover is tightly closed so dirt doesn't get into the distributor.

ignition timing

Timing the ignition comes next. You'll need a stroboscopic timing light and a tachometer. Like other tune-up specs, the proper timing specifications are on the emission control label and in the standard service books.

Warm up the engine. Hook up the tachometer, leaving it where you can see it as you work on the engine. Hook the timing light into the No. 1 sparkplug circuit—but *not* by puncturing the plug lead insulation for a good contact. If you use one of the new induction lights, you'll need only to place an induction coil segment around the plug wire. Otherwise contact will be by way of an adapter that goes between the plug and its cable. Some go at the distributor end of the plug cable.

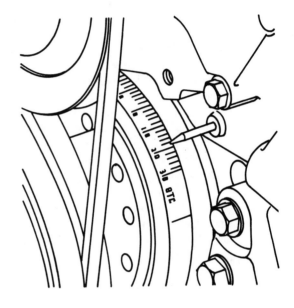

Disconnect the hose from the vacuum-advance control unit on the distributor and plug the end of the hose with a pencil. Any vacuum leak would throw the timing out of whack. Once the engine is warmed and idling at the specified speed, aim the timing light at the timing mark and pointer. Sight straight down along the beam and don't tilt the light or you can throw the reading off.

You can save yourself lots of frustration by checking a manual ahead of time for the location of your car's timing marks. Locate them, and even daub a bit of white paint on them. Everything will be easier.

The engine is properly timed when the light's flashes seem to freeze the mark in the right relationship to the pointer. You shouldn't see the timing marks appearing to shift.

If timing has drifted away from specifications, loosen the bolt that holds the distributor housing. Rotate the distributor until the timing marks line up properly and hold steady. If moving the distributor in one direction doesn't bring the timing marks closer to position, move it the other way. Then tighten the distributor housing.

Don't neglect to recheck the timing after you've tightened the distributor. It's an irritating fact of life that, in many cases, the mechanic finds the timing has, unaccountably, shifted slightly—after he thought he was all through. The right response: Loosen the distributor housing again and readjust the timing.

vacuum advance timing

Now test the performance of the vacuum advance unit by shifting the timing light from the No. 1 cylinder to the alternate-firing one. On a V8, that will be the fifth in the firing order; on a Six, it will be the third. Check your service data for the firing order to identify the cylinder—and ignition circuit—you're looking for.

Then check the timing again. There's likely to be some difference between timing at No. 1 and timing when hooked to its alternate. But that difference shouldn't exceed 3°. If it does, the distributor is worn and needs repair.

Now hold the vacuum hose near its connection on the vacuum-advance unit. Keep the light aimed at the timing marks. While a co-worker behind the wheel gradually increases engine speed, push the hose onto its connection, then pull it off. The timing mark should continue seeming to shift quickly back and forth. If it doesn't or if movement is sluggish, the vacuum advance diaphragm has ruptured. The unit will have to be replaced.

fuel system service

If the fuel system sends a badly proportioned air-fuel mix to the combustion chambers, your car will be hard to start. It will miss and stall. And it will use more gas than necessary. Service of the fuel system is basic to a healthy car.

Begin by checking the carburetor air filter. Follow the owner's manual recommendations about replacing its element.

On the chance that the fuel filter has gathered foreign matter that's impeding fuel flow, manufacturers generally recommend a new fuel filter at tune-up time. You'll have either an integral filter where the fuel line enters the carburetor fuel bowl or an external one in the line from the fuel pump to the carb.

Remove the external filter by slipping clamps off the line. To get at the spring-loaded integral filter, remove the fuel line at the carb. But be careful not to lose the spring; you'll need to re-use it.

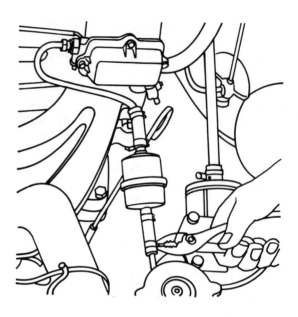

After servicing those filters, it's time to check the choke. Press the accelerator to the floor once; the choke plate should close across the carburetor throat. Then start the engine. The plate should open gradually and be wide open by the time the engine reaches running temperature.

Dirt around parts of the choke linkage or the butterfly plate's pivots can prevent smooth operation. If your choke doesn't operate well, clean the linkage and pivots with choke cleaner. Don't use any lubricant; it will just collect more dirt—and cause the choke to stick.

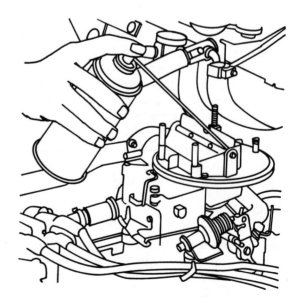

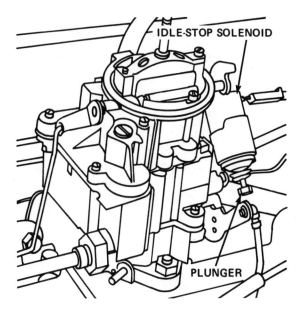

Now recheck the choke's closing and opening. If cleaning didn't help, the thermostatic spring, or choke piston, or electric choke-assist element has weakened and should be replaced.

idle-speed controls

Today's carburetors are generally equipped with an idle-stop solenoid that prevents engine run-on by letting the throttle close completely as soon as you shut off the engine. That tendency of an engine to keep chugging on is also called "dieseling."

To see whether you have trouble here, check whether the solenoid's plunger rests against the throttle-plate lever as the engine idles. Then see whether, as the engine is shut off, that plunger retracts to let the throttle valve close. If not, the smart step is to replace the solenoid.

On such a carburetor, you set the idle speed by turning the plunger until a tachometer reaches the specified idle speed. Older-style carburetors rely on an idle-speed adjusting screw to correct the speed.

In any case, the engine should be warm to set the idle speed. The hand brake must be set. A manual transmission must be in *Neutral*; separate idle-speed specs are established for automatic-transmission cars according to whether the gear box is in *Neutral* or *Drive*. Take your choice.

Federal emission standards require factory-set idle speeds, with little chance for you to modify it, on post-1968 cars. Efforts to defeat these restrictions are against the law.

emission-control gear

Engines may have three separate systems to combat pollution. Since 1963, all models have been equipped with emission control systems meant to ensure more complete burning of the fuel. A recent addition to this system has been exhaust-gas recirculation, incorporated in 1973 to help cut oxides of nitrogen. (The chemical symbol for this group of pollutants is NO_x; hence they're commonly referred to as "*nox*.")

An evaporative-emission-control system, virtually trouble-free, was introduced in 1970 to help trap fuel vapors from such sources as the fuel tank before they get into the air.

• *Crankcase-emission* controls are the place to start servicing. Pull out the PCV (positive crankcase ventilation) valve. On a V8 engine, it's probably in the push-rod cover. On a Six, it's in the rocker-arm cover.

Automatic replacement time for the PCV valve doesn't come until 24,000 miles have passed. Its performance should be checked at every tune-up, however. Just cover the valve with your thumb as the engine idles. If you don't feel a strong pull, replace the valve and check the rest of the system.

Inspect PCV hoses for deterioration. Since 1966 models, there's been a hose from the carburetor air cleaner to the rocker-arm cover. Check it, too.

Many crankcase emission control systems also have a cotton or mesh filter in the air cleaner. Some are filter-and-holder assemblies; others are filters only. If loose dust falls out on tapping or shaking the element, replace it.

• *Exhaust emission controls* include temperature sensors, damper valves and hoses. A large-diameter hose goes to the air-cleaner snorkel. A smaller one leads from the air cleaner's temperature sensor to a source of manifold vacuum.

With the engine cold, look into the snorkel's throat as someone starts the engine. The damper should close fully across the snorkel. As the engine warms, the damper should open gradually until it's fully open when the engine is at normal running temperature.

If it fails, either the temperature sensor or the valve control is faulty. But before repairing these, check the manifold heat-control valve; it has a direct effect on damper-valve operation.

• *Evaporative-emission controls* need nothing beyond replacement of the filter found in the base of a carbon canister. Most cars, especially U.S. production, now have such canisters.

cooling-system service

Engines today are designed for their greatest efficiency within a particular—sometimes narrow—temperature range. They should reach that temperature as soon as possible, but shouldn't exceed it from then on. It's the job of the cooling system to hold the engine at that temperature. And that's an important job.

Keeping the engine in tune should include, at least during every other annual tune-up, basic cooling system maintenance work. That involves only four general steps: checking for leaks, draining the system, flushing it, and refilling it.

• *Check for leaks* when the engine is off. Look for any dampness or deposits at each end of upper and lower radiator hoses, heater hoses, or other coolant connections. Significant deposits will be either rust-colored or a rather dirty white. This is the time to check the radiator cap, thermostat, drive belt surface and tension, and water pump, as well.

• *Drain the system* with the engine at running temperature and the heater turned *On*. For a complete drain job, remove engine plugs, too. They are in the lower block, but may not be easy to locate. Sixes normally have one and V8s, two.

• *Flush the system* after closing the drain valve and reinstalling the drain plugs—securely. Fill the system with water plus a commercial fast-flush cooling-system solution. Methods vary

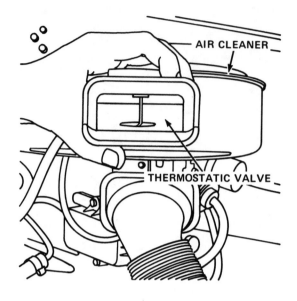

somewhat with such solutions; follow the directions on the can. You'll keep scale from accumulating.

• *Refill* your system with a coolant mix. A standard-brand ethylene glycol antifreeze should be mixed with water in proportions to meet the lowest temperature you expect. The directions on the container will show how to get the right mix. Even if your system is perfectly tight and operating flawlessly, you should replace this antifreeze every other winter. Check

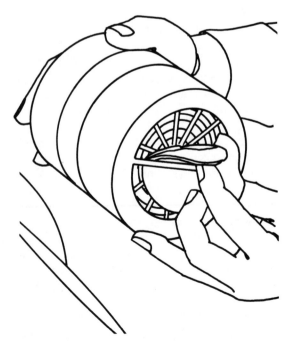

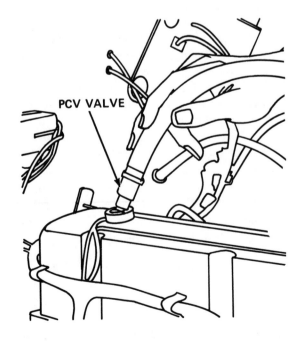

its potency every winter using a hydrometer.

You should also check the temperature warning light among the "idiot lights" likely to be in your instrument panel. When you turn on the car's switch, it should go *On*, too. As soon as the engine starts, the light should go *Out*. If it doesn't, the fuse or bulb have given up or the circuit has otherwise failed. It deserves a prompt fix.

other tune-up services

• That *manifold heat-control valve,* in the exhaust manifold, helps warm up a cold engine by closing off the manifold and trapping hot exhaust gases. It's thermostatically controlled to open as the engine warms. That releases these hot gases to prevent overheated and blistered spark plugs.

Not every engine has such a valve. But if there is one in your exhaust manifold, its counterweight will be under the manifold. You can check by feeling under there for the counterweight.

If that counterweight can't be moved easily by hand, the valve isn't working. Lubricate its pivot well with graphite or a special lubricant and, if necessary, rap the counterweight with a mallet. If that doesn't free the valve, replace it. Lubricate it when you grease the car.

• *Drive belts* should be inspected for wear, damage, and glaze. Replace any bad ones. Check belts for tension, too. The most accurate way is with a drive-belt tension gauge.

If a gauge isn't available, press the belt with your thumb midway between pulleys. If the belt gives no more than ½ in. under heavy pressure, you're OK. If you want to be thorough, check service literature for correct tension and use a gauge. Tension specifications vary.

To tighten drive belts, push against the center of the alternator or air-conditioner compressor, depending on the belt, and tighten the bracket nuts. Be sure both pulleys continue to run in the same plane.

• *Charging system* problems can be many, but often the trouble is nothing more than a loose belt. So, when your idiot light stays lighted or your ammeter shows a slow charging rate, check belts first. Also check for clean and tight battery connections. If your battery needs water more often than usual, the charging rate is probably too fast.

When overcharging is the problem, check the alternator or generator and the voltage regulator.

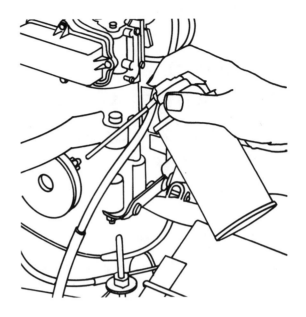

• *Air leaks* at the base of the carburetor or between the intake manifold and head can cause the loss of vacuum that will defeat other tune-up work. Spread heavy oil around these areas and start the engine. If there are leaks, you'll be able to see the oil being sucked into the engine. Tighten all the bolts and try again. If leaks persist, you'll need to replace whichever gasket is appropriate.

• *Road testing* is the moment of truth—the time when you find out how well you actually did. But just taking the car "out for a run" is no real test. To avoid missing anything, you should follow a planned, programmed test schedule. Here's one that makes sense:

Accelerate slowly from a dead stop—several times. Then drive several blocks at constant low speeds. Next, head for the open road. Entering the highway, accelerate briskly from a dead stop—and repeat that several times if you can find safe locations. Accelerate sharply and drop back abruptly from various speeds. Then try accelerating slowly from different road speeds. Finally, try a few miles at a good, constant highway speed.

The odds are strong that your car will perform flawlessly if you've done the tune-up properly. If it doesn't, the engine problems are more than can be cured by a simple tune-up.

Even so, you will have eliminated a host of other malfunctions, many potentially serious. And those are the camouflage that so often confuses even a professional's diagnosis. You're well rid of them.

Tune-up instruments for the Saturday Mechanic

■ THE FIRST INVESTMENT toward good car care should be in instruments that let you tune up your car at home. The test equipment needed to keep your car in tune yourself also makes it possible for you to troubleshoot and diagnose problems that would otherwise cost you money to have someone else solve.

We're not talking about the basic things that all car owners should have just to keep their cars running—distributor point files and feeler gauges, sparkplug gapping tools, battery hydrometers and chargers—but the instruments that can tell you *how* your car is running; or *why* it's not running, or not running right; or just *where* the problem lies.

The instruments that tell you what your senses can't tell you about your engine can be as simple and inexpensive as a compression tester or as sophisticated and costly as a diagnostic oscilloscope. In between are the instruments essential for accurately setting ignition timing, cam angle or dwell and generator or alternator output voltage; and those for checking primary and secondary sides of the ignition system, engine vacuum and fuel-pump pressure and even exhaust emissions.

These are the instruments that will free you from scheduling service appointments, suffering aggravation and incurring expenses that could have been avoided.

Engine analyzer

If you don't own any other test instruments, the analyzer is the best all-around unit to consider. It combines in one package the functions of the dwell meter, tachometer, ignition tester and voltmeter. A good engine or automotive analyzer, as it's variously called, represents an investment of anywhere from $40 to over $100—depending on its features. Engine analyzers and most of the other instruments, too, are available in kit form so you can build them yourself.

Included with any good analyzer will be a

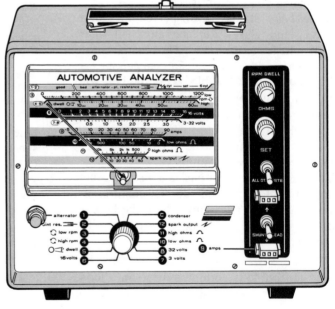

complete operation manual that details the tests the instrument will perform and the connections to be made under the hood. Don't buy any instrument that doesn't include instructions on how to use it!

For portability, analyzers contain built-in power supplies—usually several C or D cells which are installed in a battery tube. A good habit to get into is removing the batteries after you use the analyzer and before you put it on the shelf for what may be several months; you'll avoid a mess and possible damage to the instrument if the batteries leak inside the case.

A typical automotive analyzer, such as that shown on the opposite page, has a large, easy-to-read meter face with scales that correspond to the positions of a main function switch. The meter should utilize a D'Arsonval movement, which is the most accurate and sensitive type. The circuits in the analyzer are designed to measure specific functions. You just turn the function switch and take a reading from the appropriate scale on the meter face.

Here is a list of some of the work you can do with the analyzer. Refer to the switch positions in the drawing:

• **Alternator diodes.** The diodes in your alternator, which convert the alternating current (a.c.) that has been produced by the alternator into direct current (d.c.), can be checked as good or bad.

• **Distributor point resistance.** Excessive resistance across closed points indicates that you have burned or misaligned points, poor grounding of condenser or distributor, or other wiring problems.

• **Low rpm check.** Measurement of engine revolutions per minute in increments of 10 allows you to make an accurate idle adjustment.

• **High rpm check.** A zero to 6000-rpm scale allows testing and adjustments of timing advance, charging system and carburetor.

• **Dwell measurement.** Dwell is the amount of time that ignition points remain closed, as measured by degrees of rotation of the distributor cam. This angle, which is about 60° for a four-cylinder engine, a little less than 40° for a Six and about 30° for an Eight, affects the spark timing and must be adjusted accurately. Adjustment is made by setting the point gap.

• **16-volt scale.** Measurement of voltage with a full-scale deflection of 16 volts allows accurate setting and diagnosis of 6 and 12-volt systems. Very accurate adjustment of voltage regulators is possible.

• **3-volt scale.** A full-scale deflection of three volts allows incremental measurements of .1 volt for tracing voltage losses.

• **32-volt scale.** This can be used for measurements on 24-volt charging systems.

• **Ammeter.** The zero to 90-ampere current measurement scale is used for checking current regulator settings, alternator output and the current draw of components in the electrical system.

• **Low ohms.** Resistance measurements are made in checking for continuity; no resistance indicates possible shorts, infinite resistance an open circuit. It checks coil primary windings and ballast resistors, for example.

• **High ohms.** High resistance measurements are necessary for checking such things as condenser leakage, ignition cables and coil secondaries.

• **Spark output.** Check of ignition coil output is read on a relative scale on a zero to 50 scale. If equal readings for all sparkplugs are not obtained, your problem exists with the coil, ballast resistor, cables or plugs.

• **Condenser.** A substitute condenser is placed in the ignition circuit to check whether the installed condenser is open or shorted.

Dwell/tachometer

When you do a basic engine tune-up, you set dwell and engine revolutions per minute. If you're just getting started in do-it-yourself work on your car, and think that simple tune-ups are all you'll be doing, the combination dwell meter/tachometer is the best instrument to start with. Later, you may find you want to do more yourself, but for a gradual approach to acquiring test equipment, a dwell/tach is the best start. Many models are priced less than $50.

If you start to build your car-maintenance arsenal with such a meter, don't be surprised to find some are sold as "dwell/tachometers" while others are called "tach-dwell meters." They're the same instrument, but the industry hasn't agreed on a name for them.

As mentioned, dwell is the amount of time your distributor points remain closed, and if you've ever set points using a feeler gauge, you might wonder why a meter is needed to check the dwell. Even careful setting of the points won't always result in an accurate dwell angle. Variations within established tolerances and wear and age take their toll in the precision fit of most moving parts. New points might vary slightly in fit from those you've just replaced; wear on the breaker cam or distributor shaft

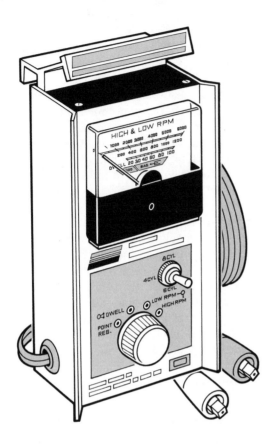

bearing might create a "wobble" to throw off your feeler gauge setting; also, there could be some malfunction in the ignition circuitry that you'd miss by setting and adjusting mechanically. It's always better to make settings and tests while the engine is running, and the dwell meter is the tool that makes this possible.

Specifications for your engine will indicate what the dwell angle should be, and your goal is to meet those specs. When your dwell meter is combined with a tach, you have the primary tool for a wide range of tests, since so many use engine speed as a basic factor. Only with a tachometer can you measure engine speed with precision you can count on.

Combining the dwell meter and tachometer is common since, in an electronic sense, the two instruments measure different aspects of the same curve. The dwell meter tracks the period during which the points are closed and current flows to the coil. And the tach reports the frequency with which a plug fires. That frequency, of course, is a function of how often points open, collapsing the coil's primary field and inducing the vastly higher ignition voltage in the secondary windings.

adjusting the dwell

To begin with, be certain you have switched your dwell/tachometer to **dwell.** If some adjustment is needed, you'll work on the gap between the breaker points. Move them only slightly closer together to increase the dwell, farther apart to decrease it.

Some distributors have a small door in the side that lets you adjust this gap with an Allen wrench while the engine is running. More often, however, you'll have to shut off the engine and remove the distributor cap and rotor in order to change the point gap. It's a cut-and-try operation; quite possibly it'll take a couple of tries before you get it right.

Timing light

A moment's thought will explain what happens: Since dwell is a measure of the time the points are closed, a larger gap will mean they're closed more briefly and a smaller gap means they close faster and stay closed longer.

The timing light is simply a strobe light connected to a running engine in such a way that its flashing will make the timing marks appear to stand still.

In operation, the timing light is aimed toward timing marks located on the engine's lower front fan pulley. If the engine has accumulated a film of dirt and oil, it may be necessary to wipe off the pulley and timing index plate before starting the engine. Many mechanics use yellow chalk or crayon to make the timing marks even more visible.

With the engine running, the timing marks appear to stand still. You can see if the index mark coincides with the correct degree of advance mark as recommended in the owner's manual (or on the under-hood decal on newer cars). If

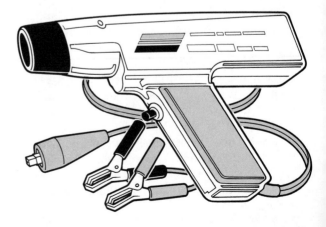

there's a difference, loosen the distributor hold-down nut and turn the distributor body to align the marks.

New engines should be set exactly to spec. It's the surest way to meet exhaust emission requirements and get the best performance from the engine. There's usually a 2° to 3° tolerance in the timing requirements. The greater the advance, generally, the more engine pep you'll get, but don't go beyond the limits, or you'll get "ping." This can sometimes be eliminated by using a higher-octane gasoline, but it can produce problems with the emission control systems installed on newer engines.

Generator-alternator-regulator tester

There's not much you can do to maintain or troubleshoot your car's charging system without a voltmeter/ammeter to measure its output. The voltmeter and ammeter functions of this instrument (also found in the all-in-one auto analyzer) make it possible to check that the alternator or generator is producing current and voltage to spec, and that the regulator is controlling this output to keep your battery fully charged but not overcharged.

Basic voltmeters and ammeters are inexpensive, but the features of an automotive generator-alternator-regulator tester add to versatility—perhaps more than they add to cost. The

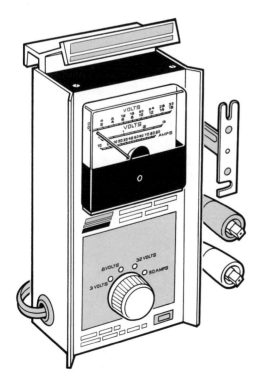

most sophisticated will measure and check diodes, resistance, battery capacity, voltage losses, fuses and shorts. They also include (since current must be measured in series with a circuit) a battery-post adapter or ammeter shunt that allows the ammeter to be placed in the circuit quickly and conveniently.

Output at the terminals of both alternators and generator is d.c. (the diodes in an alternator have already converted the alternating current to direct). This output is being generated as long as the engine is running. The advantage of the alternator, of course, is that the same output is generated at much lower rpm.

It's the job of the regulator to control the charging rate to the battery. The regulator incorporates three "switches" to do this: the cutout relay, voltage regulator and current regulator.

The cutout relay opens the circuit to keep the battery from discharging when the engine is stopped or the generator is rotating slowly and generating a voltage less than that of the battery (with an alternator, the cutout relay is not needed since the diodes perform this "switching" function).

The current regulator automatically protects the generator from overloading when the current requirements of the electrical system are high and the battery is low. It limits output to a safe value.

The voltage regulator protects the battery from overcharge and the electrical system from excessively high voltage. It does this by automatically cutting resistance in and out of the circuit as necessary.

Adjustment of the all-important regulator is easy with the instrument designed to do the job.

Ignition tester

The two automotive systems requiring diagnosis when your car turns over but refuses to start are fuel and ignition. You can almost check that fuel is reaching your engine cylinders by just using your sense of smell, or better, looking into the carburetor throat while you actuate throttle linkage. If you're getting fuel, you've quickly isolated the problem to the ignition system. But troubleshooting ignition system components, more often than not, requires a measuring instrument to find out why ignition voltage isn't being produced or, if it is, what's happening to it and why it's not firing your plugs.

The ignition tester will check both the primary

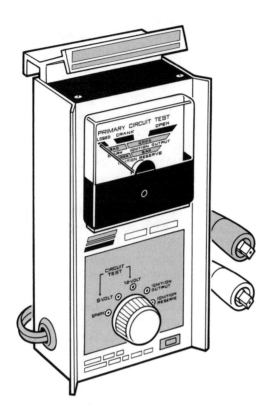

sparkplug hole after all plugs are removed or screwed into place if the gauge is the more desirable screw-in type. Crank the engine for at least four compression strokes and note the reading obtained for each cylinder.

With a sound engine, the normal readings should build up evenly to the compression specs for your car, and the variation between cylinders should not vary much more than 10 pounds.

When the piston rings are worn, you'll get a low reading on the first stroke and pressure will build up on successive strokes but not to spec.

A valve problem is indicated whenever you get a low compression on the first stroke and compression doesn't build up much on successive strokes.

If you repeat the procedure after squirting about a tablespoon of SAE 30 oil into each cylinder and get an increase in readings, you can be sure the problem is worn or poorly seated piston rings; no increase in readings confirms bad valves. Other diagnoses are also possible: Low readings in two adjacent cylinders, for example, point to a leaking head gasket.

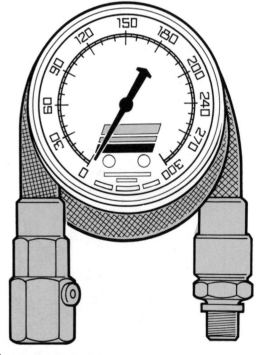

side of your ignition circuit and the secondary side—the high-voltage spark-output side.

With the better testers, you can diagnose the problem even when you're unable to start the car. Points, distributor cap, ignition switch, ballast resistor, condensor, coil output and polarity, plug wires and resistance can all be tested.

Most instruments come with foreign and domestic sparkplug adapters and some include insulated pliers also.

Compression tester

A reading of the pressure built up in each cylinder by the piston on its compression strokes reveals the condition of rings and valves. New-car owners usually don't need a compression gauge as a diagnostic tool until they have many thousands of miles on their car. Since it provides a quick check of the condition and operation of piston rings and valves, it's a good instrument to use in checking older cars and good to have along if you're looking at used cars.

You simply record readings for each cylinder and analyze the results. The gauge is held in the

Vacuum gauge

Recent years have been big ones for the old vacuum gauge. They're being mounted on the dashboard in many new cars and being called names like mileage minders and fuel savers. All they do in that capacity is help you pay attention to how hard you're stomping on the gas pedal. Connected to your engine's intake manifold, the

gauge measures the difference between the pressure inside the manifold and the atmospheric pressure outside, or more practically speaking, how hard the pistons are drawing in air for combustion.

Throttle position and engine speed affect the vacuum reading which at idle is normally between 15 and 22 (inches of mercury). Open your throttle too wide and too suddenly and the reading drops off into the wasteful fuel consumption range marked on the face of the gauge.

It's as an engine diagnosis tool, though, where the simple, inexpensive vacuum gauge pays for itself many times over. (Good gauges also will have capability to measure pressure so you can check operation and condition of your fuel pump.)

By observing the action of the pointer needle on the vacuum gauge you can diagnose dozens of possible engine malfunctions. For example, a pointer that wanders erratically is a sure sign of a problem that's not affecting all cylinders equally. If a pointer steadies at higher rpm (about 2000), suspect ignition and timing and the centrifugal advance in your distributor. On the other hand, if the erratic sweeps become shorter and more rapid, check for sticky valves, broken or weak valve springs and intake system leaks.

A steady but low reading on the gauge means a loss of power that has affected all cylinders alike. Test for late timing and intake-system leaks—possibly a warped intake manifold or a leak past the carburetor flange gasket, or a vacuum leak in vacuum-operated accessories.

The vacuum gauge will also check malfunctions in other systems, the PCV system for example. It can be used in setting carburetor idle mixture (on older models, where that's legal) and in checking for restrictions in the exhaust system.

Exhaust gas analyzer

Exhaust emissions are now being measured as part of some states' annual inspections. If they're not within specs for your car, you fail. You've got a certain amount of time to tune up or hand over your registration. As with safety inspections, if you can check out your car at home and repair it beforehand, you'll be sure to pass and save yourself a lot of trouble.

Exhaust gas analyzers or combustion analyzers for home use are rather costly, but still may be worth the investment—especially as more states require emissions inspections.

The instrument measures the completeness of combustion in your engine by analyzing the contents of the exhaust gases. The sensing unit, shown opposite, has a pickup hose that is inserted in the exhaust pipe. Some sensors can be attached to the rear bumper so you can take readings as you drive. The readout on the meter indicates air-fuel ratio from rich to lean, and percent of dangerous carbon monoxide in the exhaust.

Since the instrument measures combustion efficiency, it is a valuable for checking your carburetor and getting as many miles per gallon that you can from your car. An engine running at

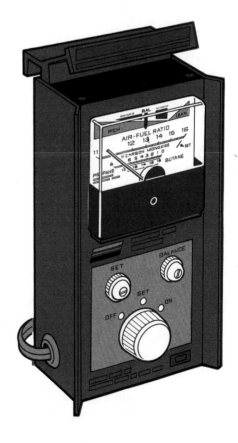

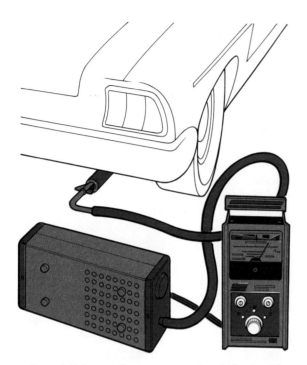

circuit voltage to the vertical deflection terminals. The horizontal sweep is linear and represents relative time during the ignition cycle. Also on the horizontal is a scale marked off in degrees for reading dwell angle.

To analyze the primary side of your system, you pick up the voltage across the distributor points and you read the 40-volt vertical scale. The picture you get starts with the spikes showing the spark as the points open and ends with a steady horizontal line showing zero voltage when the points are closed. You can read the length of the line on the dwell scale. Also visible are the coil and condenser oscillations.

To analyze the secondary, high-voltage side, you pick up the voltage at ignition coil secondary output to the center of the distributor cap, and you read the 40-kilovolt vertical scale. The secondary picture or trace also is comprised of a spark zone showing when the points open, a coil and condenser zone and a dwell zone when the points close again. The pattern you get is easily compared to a standard trace. Variations are diagrammed in operating manuals so you can diagnose malfunctions.

Not only does the scope pinpoint malfunctions in any ignition component and wiring, but it lets you "see" harder to diagnose problems like ex-

about 2000 rpm, for example, should be burning a mixture of air-to-fuel of about 14 to 14.5 to 1. If you read anything richer, check the carburetor float level, metering rod, jets and look for air restrictions. Similarly, if the reading indicates too lean a mixture, check carburetor components again and look for air leaks.

In addition to enabling you to pass emissions inspections and diagnosing your carburetor, the exhaust gas analyzer can be used by the more enthusiastic to study carb performance with the engine under load. During a road test, the metering system can be thoroughly analyzed. A similar test at a shop that also sells you a fully rebuilt carb will cost as much as the instrument. Take your pick.

Diagnostic oscilloscope

The cathode ray oscilloscope, long used by the professionals for analyzing voltage waveforms and magnitudes in the primary and secondary circuits of your car's ignition system, is becoming increasingly available to the amateur mechanic at prices he can afford. Some basic units have been available for less than $200. For the advanced electronics hobbyist, some are sold in kit form.

Once you've used the "scope" it's hard to go back to what you'll consider primitive meters. The waveforms or patterns you read on the scope are produced by applying your ignition-

cessive cam wobble. The diagnostic oscilloscope also checks your alternator, letting you analyze the pattern of its voltage ripple.

Sometime you may want to spend $3 or $4 for a remote starter switch. It lets you start your car from under the hood. What luxury!

A table for twin beds

By ROBERT L. HOPPOUGH

■ TALL ENOUGH to let one bed slide under it when not in use, this clever corner table provides a handy night table for two beds and saves space in a shared room.

Built something like a card table, except that the legs don't fold, the table has aprons only on three sides. It's made from stock lumber, 2x2s for the legs, 1x6s for the aprons, 1x2s for the cleats, plywood for the top, and ready-made molding for the edges. Metal corner braces anchor the legs. Wood screw plugs and plastic laminate hide screwheads. The molding around the top is mitered.

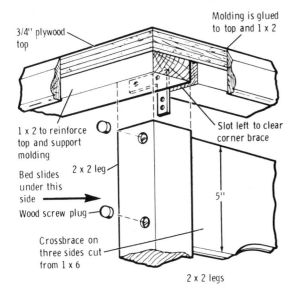

3/4'' plywood top

Molding is glued to top and 1 x 2

1 x 2 to reinforce top and support molding

Slot left to clear corner brace

2 x 2 leg

Bed slides under this side

5''

Wood screw plug

Crossbrace on three sides cut from 1 x 6

2 x 2 legs

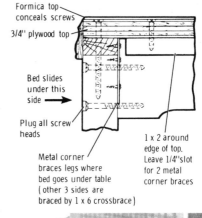

Formica top conceals screws

3/4'' plywood top

Bed slides under this side →

Plug all screw heads

Metal corner braces legs where bed goes under table (other 3 sides are braced by 1 x 6 crossbrace)

1 x 2 around edge of top. Leave 1/4''slot for 2 metal corner braces

How to sharpen twist drills

By FRED W. SCHULETER

MASTER MACHINIST, FORMERLY OF STEVENS INSTITUTE OF TECHNOLOGY

Different materials need different drill points. Here's how to give your drills the right ones

■ IT TAKES A PRO just a few deft strokes on a grinding wheel to sharpen a twist drill, but his know-how just didn't happen. He, too, was once told the importance of maintaining equal lips.

This is the cardinal rule to follow when grinding a twist drill, since it's the perfectness of the lips that determines the roundness of the hole.

Upon examining a new drill you will note the angle is rather blunt. This is fine for drilling hard materials like alloy steels, but it doesn't work as well when drilling soft materials like aluminum, brass and plastics. The standard blunt end just doesn't work for all materials. Here is where it's worthwhile to know how to alter the original shape to produce clean, burrless holes in any material.

While lip clearance is not critical, and the angle can be anywhere from 5° to 15°, the degree of angle *must* be the same on each side. If you have normal vision, it's fairly easy to see when the lips are even, but it's still good practice to check them with a drill scale. If you find one side has been ground lower than the other, take a little off the high side.

It takes practice and a certain deftness to do this freehand. First you hold the drill with both hands, as in the photo on the next page, and gently touch the lip of the drill to the flat of the wheel. At the same time you give the drill an upward sweep with a rotating motion as shown in the drawing. Do this several times to each side while holding the drill at a 15 to 30° angle. Dip

SEE ALSO

**Drill presses . . . Drills, portable . . .
Grinding wheels . . . Sharpening, tool**

FIVE VARYING DRILL SHAPES, left to right, are the normal, wingtip, masonry, recessed, and flat. Each is ground to suit the material.

THE DRAWING and photo illustrate the proper way to hold and grind a shape best for steel.

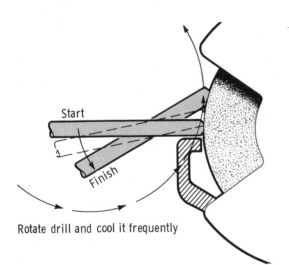

Start

Finish

Rotate drill and cool it frequently

the tip in water or oil occasionally so it doesn't overheat and turn blue. You'll wind up with an extremely sharp cutting edge which will go through the toughest of materials, including stainless steel.

To drill soft materials you need a bit which has the same lip clearance as for steel but a recess ground on the face of the lip. The recess prevents sudden catching of the drill in the work—which often results in breakage—and produces a clean, burrless hole upon breakthrough. To grind the recess, you hold the drill vertically at a 45° angle with the point down as shown in the upper left-hand photo on the next page. Then, with just slight pressure against the edge of the wheel, let the contour of the lip be your guide in a forward motion. As before, it is important to grind both sides so that they will be equally recessed.

A most versatile shape is the wingtip which produces a perfect burrless hole in the thinnest metals. The point acts much like the screw point on an auger bit in locating itself on a centerpunch mark. To grind a wingtip on a bit, place the lip at the right-hand edge of the wheel. Hold it at an opposite 5° angle and follow the same upward motion as used before.

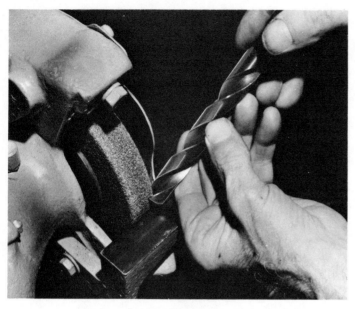

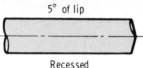

5° of lip

Recessed

TO GRIND A RECESSED LIP, hold a twist drill at the corner of the wheel with the point downward, and at a 45° angle. Touch the wheel lightly and swing the drill up.

Another shape often required is the 60° angle used for drilling masonry, plaster and tile. It's wise to use an old drill on these materials since there's a chance that you may break it, particularly when you're using the bit in a portable electric drill. To grind such a point, you simply hold the drill as before, but at a 60° angle.

By grinding both sides of the drill completely square you can make a bit which will produce a flat-bottom hole. Lip clearance is needed here, but only slightly.

The proper speed is important when drilling and should be determined by the material and the size of the twist drill. A general rule to follow is use a slow speed for hard stock and a fast speed for soft stock. The larger the drill, the slower the speed. The smaller the drill, the higher the speed. In all cases, use normal pressure. Don't force the drill, let it do the work.

When drilling a deep hole, it is good practice to withdraw the drill occasionally to free it of chips. This is particularly important when drilling aluminum and plastic. Also, when you near breakthrough in drilling, ease up on pressure and let the bit slowly sink through. You'll wind up with a neat, clean-cut hole.

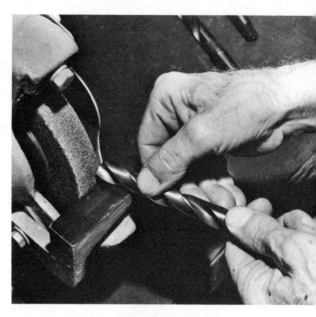

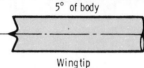

5° of body

Wingtip

TO GRIND A WINGTIP, place the lip against the right-hand corner of the wheel, hold at a 5° angle, and swing drill up. Do it on each side to form a point.

WHEN GRINDING a normal or masonry shape, always rotate the twist drill so it won't overheat and turn blue. Dip the end in water occasionally.

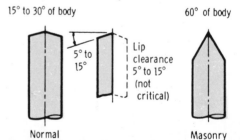

15° to 30° of body

5° to 15°

Lip clearance 5° to 15° (not critical)

Normal

60° of body

Masonry

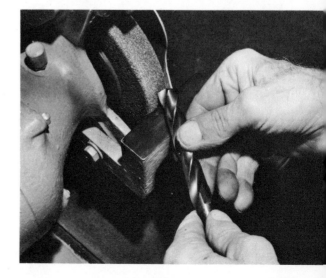

MOST HOME HANDYMEN have a favorite way to hold a paint can when working on an extension ladder. But I've yet to see a simpler setup than the "hook" I use. I tighten a C-clamp anywhere on the ladder and hang the pail on the threaded portion.—*Jackson Hand, Westport, CT.*

TO UNFREEZE a vise handle quickly use your lathe. Clamp one end of the handle in the chuck with the ball end inside to clear jaws and, with screw resting on a protective cloth, slide a file along the handle as it turns. Reverse the handle to file the other half.—*B.W. Ervin, Kent, OH.*

WHEN SOLDERED to a suitable wall bracket, a funnel makes a novel dispenser for a ball of twine that unwinds from the center. The twine is pulled through the spout. If you sharpen one bracket arm, you will also have a handy built-in twine cutter.—*Walter E. Burton, Akron, OH.*

WHEN THE METAL STRAINER BASKET for my swimming pool rusted out, I made a serviceable and noncorrodible one from a heavy plastic pail. I picked one that would fit the skimmer hole, cut it down to match the old basket, drilled countless $1/16$-in. holes in the bottom and sides and finally attached a handle with pop rivets.—*John R. Orend, Orlando, FL.*

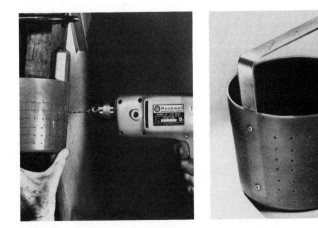

The fascinating world of underwater photography

By DICK JACOBY

A fast-growing sport almost as popular
as skin and scuba diving, marine photography
is easier than ever with scads of new equipment

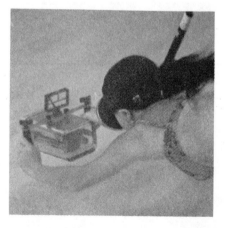

■ I HELD THE CAMERA against my mask, staring at a million silver anchovies that schooled in front of the viewfinder. The sight was amazing, but even more amazing was that I could photograph it.

Back on the boat, off Andros Island in the Bahamas, I carefully unsnapped the latches that held my camera in its plastic housing. The camera was dry, protected from the seawater by a tough Lexan housing sealed with O-rings. A week later my pictures were processed, and they, too, came out well. The ocean's irridescent blue actually helped my picture taking because it contrasted with the silver of the anchovies.

Underwater photography is popular because it's challenging, and because the results sometimes are fantastic.

Only skin and scuba divers know the incredible range of brilliant colors in the creatures that dwell in the coral reefs—and in the reefs themselves. And only a photograph can bring a record of this fantastic world to the surface.

To take photographs underwater it isn't necessary to be 1) a professional photographer, 2) a super swimmer, 3) a super scuba diver, or 4) rich.

The key to shooting good pictures underwater is to get as close to your subject as you can. Five feet usually is considered the outside limit, because at greater distances sea water dulls your pictures. In fact, water is 800 times denser than air and contains tiny bits of matter that scatter light. Even in the Caribbean, trying to photo-graph something 20 feet away is a little like putting the bottom of a coke bottle in front of your lens.

Getting close to fish underwater isn't difficult, though, because, like most living creatures, they are curious. Move up on them very slowly, pulling yourself along the bottom with your fingers. Should you suddenly descend from above they are sure to swim away, just as you would run if a giant bird flew toward you out of the sky.

Once you reach the place where you saw them, the fish probably will have moved a few feet further away. Don't worry, though; they'll return to within that five-foot shooting distance once they feel that you are safe. You may have to wait a few minutes, but the results will be worth it.

The time to snap a fish's picture is the moment it swims towards the center of the viewfinder. At the same time, the fish should be located just above the coral so that blue water backgrounds him. The resulting portrait will show the fish in clear water, accented by a bit of landscape beneath. You've got to stay low to shoot pictures like this, but the results are really worth it.

"People pictures" are even easier, because your subjects understand what you want to do. Be sure to discuss your plan with them before entering the water, though, so that they don't look at the camera when you shoot. Dress your subject (model) in a simple oval mask—any color but black—and check for flying straps that make divers look like uncoordinated octopuses.

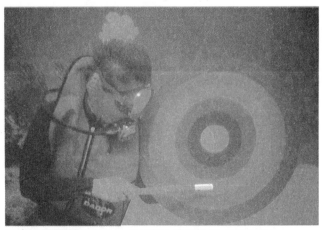

OCEAN WATER acts as a giant filter that strains out every color except its own, usually blue-green. The brilliant color bull's-eye at left is shown above at a depth of 60 feet in the available light. Only blues and greens retain their hues.

At the close shooting distances required underwater, plan to photograph just your model's head and upper body. Indeed, there is no prettier picture than a bikini-clad model wearing no scuba equipment at all; snap it just at the moment she dives toward the camera.

In most South Atlantic and Caribbean waters, plenty of sunshine is available to light your pictures just below the surface. And if you're new to underwater photography, it's probably a good idea to wait awhile before getting involved with flash attachments. Because water filters out warm colors such as red and orange first, confine your shots to within the first 10 or 15 feet of depth. Exposure is best there, too.

Use negative film with the resonably priced pocket or Instamatic type cameras. Kodacolor 400 works fine because it responds satisfactorily to low light levels underwater. When used at shallow depth, the film also tends to make people and fish appear slightly redder in the blue water.

With 35-mm and larger format cameras, it's OK to use slide film, such as Eastman Kodachrome or Ektachrome. The more sensitive

(faster) films (Ektachrome 200 and Ektachrome 400, for example) are the easiest to use. When you shoot with slide film you must adjust the controls on your camera when exposure conditions change. Example: shooting that bikini-clad girl on a sunny day just below the surface, try Ektachrome 200 film with exposure set at f/8 to f/11 at 1/125 of a second. Increase your exposure to f/5.6 to f/8 when you descend to fifteen feet.

Screw a red filter in front of your lens to make the skin tones of your model appear more natural. A CC30R filter works great, but make sure you stay close to the surface where the water hasn't filtered out too much red and orange. You'll need to change your settings a little, too: use the same f-stops, and set your shutter speed to 1/60 second for the model swimming toward your camera.

Scuba gear lets you turn the underwater world into a photographer's studio. Adjust your buoyancy so that you are a little bit negative on the bottom, but take care not to stir up the silt. Then enjoy the passing parade of fish until you get the pictures you want.

But scuba equipment isn't absolutely necessary for underwater photography if you have a mask, snorkle and fins—and the ability to hold your breath for several seconds. Sink five or ten

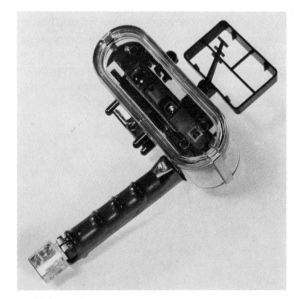

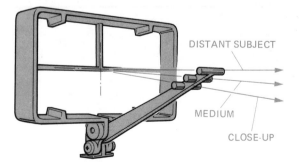

DISTANT SUBJECT

MEDIUM

CLOSE-UP

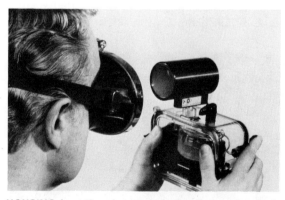

HOUSING for 110-series pocket cameras can be used with or without flash. Ikelite, at left, puts its flash on the bottom of the handle. Pointing a camera is difficult under water, and external sportsfinders help considerably. You operate the open sportsfinder at left by aligning the crossbar with various "rungs" on the ladder sight, depending upon the distance to the subject. "Optical" sportsfinders, such as the one above by Seacor, frame the picture area with a series of removable masks; the mask used depends upon the lens.

feet below the surface, grab your picture, and ascend.

Most amateur underwater photographers start with an inexpensive camera that fits into a pressure-proof housing at relatively little expense. The 110 camera series manufactured by Kodak, Canon and Minolta slip easily into molded Lexan housings from Ikelite Underwater Systems. Price: under $50 for the housing.

Ikelite also builds housings priced between $40 and $70 to fit 126 series Instamatic cameras. Indeed, whatever camera you own, there's probably a housing to fit. There's even one for Polaroid's instant SX-70 camera.

Many pocket and Instamatic cameras don't focus closer than three or four feet. The least expensive camera, Kodak's Trimlite 18, doesn't focus closer than five feet, so the camera's inside

FOR SLR SHOOTERS, highly sophisticated housings are available. The two shown top center are Ikelite's Lexan housing and Farallon/Oceanic's aluminum model. Ikelite's adapts to several makes of camera, and Farallon/Oceanic's is compatible with top-of-the- line models by Nikon and Canon. Bottom right, Sea Research & Development custom-builds housings to fit user's needs. Lower right, Ikelite even builds a housing for Polaroid's SX-70. As this was written, the cost was about $100.

focusing limit corresponds to the outside limit for underwater pictures. However, the camera still makes underwater photography for an investment of less than $75 for camera and housing combined. (All prices in this article, of course, are subject to change.)

As your experience grows you'll want to move up to more expensive equipment. Several housings are on the market for 35-mm and larger cameras, ranging from clear plastic housings under $200 to aluminum ones for $600 and up. Nikon and Canon systems used with either Ikelite or Farallon/Oceanic housings allow exact through-the-lens viewing so you can see exactly what your picture will look like.

Most viewfinders, though, are separate attachments perched on top of the housing. Viewing through them is a simple matter, but you don't see exactly what you get on film, particularly at distances less than three feet.

There's one special camera on the market that is used with a viewfinder but requires no housing. The Nikonos looks like a regular 35-mm camera with controls for focus, shutter speed and aperture, and it's a tough, all-weather camera topside. The big difference is that it's waterproof, pressure-tested to a depth of 165 feet (50 meters).

Like its topside cousins, the Nikonos accepts different lenses for different purposes, making it extremely versatile. Because of its popularity,

specialty manufacturers market all sorts of accessories—trays, handles, meters, brackets, trigger releases, optical wideners, closeup equipment, and flash connectors. Price of the Nikonos III (the third model in the Nikonos series) and 35 mm lens is in the $400 range. Accessories can up your total outlay several hundred dollars more.

Flash cubes work well with pocket and Instamatic cameras, but sooner or later you're going to want electronic flash. Here the price runs from slightly over $100 to ten times that much.

It's great to bring electronic sunshine beneath the surface because it puts all those warm colors back in your subject. However, you don't need flash if you do your picture taking just inside your water wonderland, still near the sun.

Whether you borrow, rent or buy your first underwater photo equipment, be sure to read the instructions carefully. The most common error made is not reading and following instructions.

For catalogs, prices and additional information on underwater photo equipment, write the following manufacturers: Aquacraft, 3280 Kurtz St., San Diego, CA 92110; Dacor Corp., 161 Northfield Rd., Northfield, IL 60093; Farallon/Oceanic, 1333 Old County Rd., Belmont, CA 94002; Glenn Beall Industries, 887 South Route 21, Gurney, IL 60031; Green Things, 5111 Santa Fe, Suite K, San Diego, CA 92109; Hydrophoto,

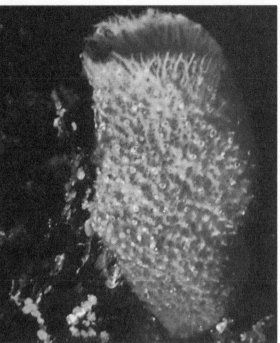

3909 13th Ave., Seattle, WA 98108; Ikelite Underwater Systems, 3303 North Illinois St., Indianapolis, IN 46208; Ehrenreich Photo-Optical Industries, Inc., 623 Stewart Ave., Garden City, NY 11530; Sekonic, Copal Corporation of America, 5825 Queens Blvd., Woodside, NY 11377; Seacor, Inc., 10575A Roselle St., San Diego, CA 92121; Sea Research & Development, Inc., P.O. Box 589, Bartow, FL 33803; SubSea Products, Inc., 210 Brant Rd., Lake Park, FL; Sunpack, Div., Berkey Marketing, 25-20 Brooklyn Queens Expy. West, Woodside, NY 11377; Toshiba Photo Products Co., Ltd., Elmo Mfg. Corp., 32-10 57th St., Woodside, NY 11377.

Check your local dive shop if you are interested in renting before you buy. One underwater photography rental store that ships anywhere in the U.S. is Helix, Ltd., 325 W. Huron, Chicago, IL 60610. Write for their rental catalog.

SLEW OF ACCESSORIES is available for Nikonos. Those at left include light meter, meter mount, handle assembly and trigger, viewfinder, strobe arm and strobe. You can also put topside strobes in pressure housings as shown at right. Don't be confused. The units are posed upside-down on table because they all have cords coming from base.

Upholstery worn? Springs
sagging? Stuffing sticking out?
Then reupholstery is for you.
Not only can you restore a fine
look to your chairs and sofas, but
you save a bundle of money

By LEN HILTS

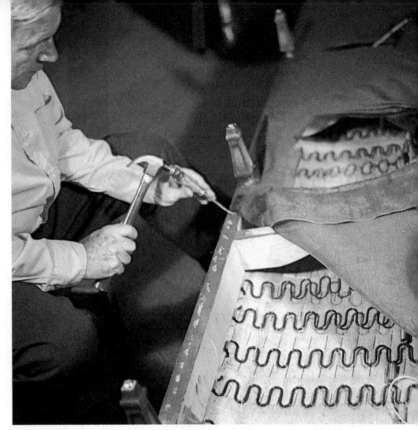

THE FIRST STEP in any reupholstery job is to take off the old fabric. Here a tack lifter and hammer are used to remove the tacks holding the dust cover on a sofa. Using the hammer with the lifter speeds the work.

A basic course in upholstery

■ YOU CAN SAVE $200 or more by reupholstering your own sofa. And you can save up to $100 by reupholstering an old chair. Substantial savings like this are good reasons why you should find out how to do your own upholstery work. It is one kind of do-it-yourself activity that truly pays for itself.

To begin with, most reupholstery work is simple and straightforward, so it is easy to learn. You don't need many tools, and the ones you do need are not expensive. And tools and materials are readily available all over the country in upholstery and fabric shops.

The best way to learn to reupholster is to find an old chair or two and practice on them. Look for chairs that are simple in design—ones without special pleating, unusual shapes or obviously complicated covering jobs. Later, you'll be able to do work like this, but for now, practice on jobs that aren't complex. Buy some inexpensive cover fabric and rework these chairs from the frame out. By the time you have finished them, you'll have gained both experience and confidence. Then you'll be ready to work with fabrics which cost $20 a yard and more, and be able to do a creditable job on your good furniture. You'll work your way out of your mistakes—and you'll end up with a couple of useful chairs.

The tools needed are few and inexpensive. You can buy a kit for around $10 at most fabric and upholstery stores. It contains a magnetic tack hammer, a tack lifter, a webbing stretcher and several large sewing needles. Add to this a couple of screwdrivers and a pair of pliers and you have everything you need.

Recently, a lot of upholstery work has been done with staples instead of tacks. Staples offend the traditionalists, who feel that they cheapen the work, but I have found that staples are effective in 90 percent of the work—and in some cases are better than tacks. For example, staples are less likely to split the wood, especially when you drive them near the edge of a seat rail.

SEE ALSO
Armchairs . . . Caning . . . Chairs . . . Sofas

The trick in using staples is to use staples that are long enough. Also, use a gun which has enough power to drive the staples completely into the wood. The ideal tool, when you use staples, is an electric staple gun. These are available for about $30 and are a good investment if you intend to do much upholstery work. Buy a gun which can drive staples of different lengths (most will) because you need to be able to choose the size of the staple. When putting on a cambric dust cover, for example, you need a very short staple. But when you must tack through several layers of fabric, you need a staple with legs ½ in. long or more.

You also can staple with a hand gun. The gun should be able to drive staples of different lengths, too, and should be powerful enough to drive them all the way into the wood. Most furniture frames are made of hardwood, which resists staples, and a gun which isn't powerful enough will not drive long staples all the way.

The electric gun is particularly good when you upholster a couch, where you must drive hundreds of staples. With a hand gun, your hand will be aching by the time you finish. With an electric gun, you can do the work quickly and without fatigue.

Upholstering materials—tools, fabric, and padding are easy to find. Most professional upholstery shops will sell you what you need, and

CORNERS ON UPHOLSTERY work should be firm and square. As you apply the final fabric, use wads of cotton or polyester to shape them.

fabric shops today carry a full line of upholstery goods.

In many cases, you'll find you can reuse the padding from the piece you are redoing. You can also reuse the springs. You'll need new webbing, perhaps some new padding and, of course, new fabric for the final cover.

TO FIT THE FABRIC around leg and arm posts, you must make cuts. Here the fabric is cut to fit around the back posts of a sofa.

A LONG, SMOOTH STICK serves as a stuffer to help push the fabric through the slot between the sofa back and seat. Fabric is tacked at the back.

A TACKING STRIP with the tacks already embedded in it is handy for making closures. You can buy these strips by the foot at fabric stores.

THE TACKING STRIP is placed in the folded end of the material, with the tacks pointing down toward the frame. Push the tacks through the material.

USING PLIERS to pull the fabric tight, you then drive the tacks into the frame. The tacks are invisible and the result is a neat blind tacking job.

Keep in mind that your first chair is your best textbook in upholstering. Strip the old upholstery from it slowly and with care. Study the chair as you work, noting how the fabric was applied, how the corners were made, where the upholsterer used a needle and thread and where he used tacks. Don't just rip the old cover off, even if it is badly worn, but remove it carefully, a

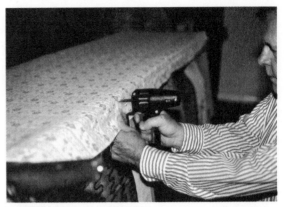

ELECTRIC STAPLE DRIVER is a very handy tool for upholstery work. Look for one which will drive staples of different lengths.

piece at a time. Save each piece of fabric and padding, because these can serve as patterns when you cut and shape the new materials.

Pay special attention to the way the fabric is folded, pleated or tucked at the corners, since corners usually prove to be the biggest mystery for the beginner. If necessary, make notes and sketches in a book for later reference. Watch to see how the material was cut to fit around posts, keeping in mind that when you apply the new cover, you'll want to cut the fabric the same way.

One final equipment note: It is very helpful to have a sewing machine available when you upholster. Almost every upholstering job requires welting or cording, which you must make from the fabric you intend to use as a final cover. Hand sewing of welting can be a long and tedious job. You'll also want a sewing machine for joining pieces of the cover and for sewing stretch tabs of old fabric to your new cover material. This latter gimmick cuts down on the amount of expensive fabric you need, since in using it, you use an old fabric as a pull tab and use the good fabric only in the places where it shows.

Here is some information on the upholstery materials you will need:

Tacks. Upholstery tacks are the standard tacks with which you already are familiar. They come in sizes identified by numbers. No. 1 (1 oz.) tacks are small, used to tack the dust cover on the bottom of furniture. Nos. 3 and 4 are all-purpose tacks, used for tacking on muslin covers, final fabric, and burlap. Most of your work is done with these sizes. No. 6 tacks are larger, used for tacking through folded material and very heavy materials. Nos. 12 and 14 tacks are jumbo-size, for tacking down jute webbing, anchoring seat twine, etc. If you intend to use tacks in your work, buy boxes of these sizes, with emphasis on Nos. 3 and 4.

Webbing. Furniture webbing is made of jute and is used to support the coil springs. It usually is available in a 3½-in. width. You'll use 10 to 12 yds. on a typical chair, and 30 yards or so to do a sofa.

Rubber webbing is used in some chairs (Danish types, for example), but since it deteriorates rapidly, you should think about replacing it with jute webbing. Your final decision may be influenced by the design of the furniture. Chairs with rubber webbing frequently are designed without springs, and depend on the spring of the rubber for comfort.

Springs. There are two basic types of springs used in furniture, the coil and the zig-zag. Unless the springs in your furniture have somehow been broken, there is no need to replace them. Coil springs need to be retied, and zig-zags may need to be reanchored in the chair frame. If you should have to replace a spring, take the broken spring to an upholstery shop. The proprietor can give a replacement of the correct size and tension.

When zig-zag springs come loose from the frame, they must be repositioned by stretching them across the seat opening and renailing them to the frame.

Thread and twine. Use a heavy flax or linen thread for all upholstery work. The thread called *carpet thread* is fine for this work. Use it in conjunction with large sailor's needles, both straight and curved. Twine is used for tying the springs, and the best twine, which has the necessary strength and is slow to deteriorate, is 6-ply hemp, which can be purchased in large balls. Ordinary cotton twine and most packaging twines either break too easily or deteriorate too quickly.

Burlap. Burlap is used to cover the springs after they have been tied, and to cover layers of padding. As a rule, the 12-oz. material is best for most upholstery work.

Stuffing. Three basic types of stuffing or padding are used in upholstery work: fiber, felt and foam.

The fiber stuffings included curled animal hair (the finest); Spanish moss (next best); and excelsior (poorest and cheapest). Usually you can buy sheets of rubberized hair at fabric shops, and may find that this is best to use.

Felt stuffings include cotton, kapok and those consisting of polyester fibers, all of which come

THE FIRST STEP in installing new webbing is to lay the webbing on the bottom of the frame and anchor it with four tacks.

NEXT, FOLD the end of the webbing back across the first tacks and drive three more. Magnetic tack hammer makes driving tacks easy.

USING A webbing stretcher, pull the webbing tight across the frame. As you hold it, drive four tacks, then cut webbing 1½ in. from frame.

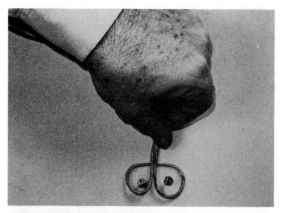

WHEN TYING SPRINGS, the tying twine is anchored to the sides of the chair or sofa rails by means of two No. 12 tacks. After looping, drive tacks in.

SPRINGS ARE TIED from front to back, then from side to side. Knot is made at each point where the twine crosses a coil. Use strong 6-ply hemp twine.

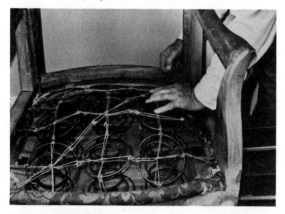

SEAT IS SHAPED as you tie the springs. Here, diagonal ties complete the shaping. Springs near the seat rail are compressed to round the seat.

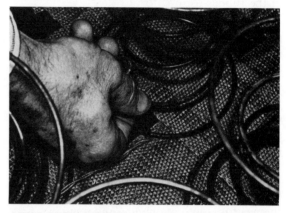

AFTER REPLACEMENT, sew springs to the webbing. Each spring is "tacked" to the webbing in four places. Thread is heavyweight carpet type.

in pads. Kapok is the least desirable because it tends to separate into lumps. Cotton is the old standby. But at present, the most available padding is polyester, which is softer and lighter than cotton. It doesn't pack down and it doesn't deteriorate. It is easy to use.

In recent years, a lot of furniture has been padded with foam. The older work was done with foam rubber, but today, much better polyurethane foams have taken over. You can buy this in sheets of different thicknesses, and in preformed cushions and pillows. You can cut this foam easily, and can make pads of different shapes by cementing the pieces together. If you are replacing an old foam padding, simply make new padding pieces the size and shape of the old ones. If you have decided to replace cotton or other padding with foam, use a sharp knife or scissors to shape the foam pieces to fit the chair.

Edge rolls. An edge roll is a type of padding used around the edge of seats and chair backs to both pad and shape the outer contours of the furniture. You can buy them ready-made, or

make them yourself by wrapping burlap around rolls of hair, cotton, or polyester. The final edge roll looks like a long sausage from ½ to 1½ in. in diameter, with a tab along one side to be used for tacking it in position. You can save any edge rolls you find on furniture as you string it, and reuse them during reupholstery.

Tacking Strips. A tacking strip is a long strip of cardboard ½ in. wide. You can buy it by the yard or in rolls. It is used in blind tacking, as shown in the photographs. You can also buy tacking strips with large tacks already inserted in the cardboard. These are used in making final closures—as when you tack down the cover fabric on the back of a sofa.

Cambric. Thin black cambric is tacked to the bottom of every upholstered piece to serve as a dust cover.

Welting. Welting is used in most chairs and sofas at those points where fabric pieces meet, to provide a finished look. Welting is made from the fabric you are using as a final cover. You do this by cutting strips of the fabric 2 in. wide and then sewing these strips around welting cord.

Measure the running feet of welting you need for your work, then cut enough strips of fabric 2 in. wide to make this much. You may need 15 to 20 feet for a chair, and three times that amount for a sofa. Begin by sewing all the 2-in strips of fabric you have cut end to end, making one long strip 2 in. wide. Trim any excess fabric from each sewn seam to prevent bulges in the welting. Now wrap the 2-in. strip around the welting cord (which can be purchased at fabric shops) and use the sewing machine to stitch through both layers of fabric right next to the wrapped cord. The finished piece of welting has the fabric wrapped tightly around the welting cord, and two flaps about ¾ in. long for tacking.

Stripping the old upholstery. The best tools for this job are a light hammer and a tack lifter. The easiest way to remove a tack is to place the blades of the tack lifter next to the tack head, and then gently tap the handle of the lifter with the hammer, guiding the blades under the tack head as you tap. The head will lift after several taps.

The first fabric to strip off is the cambric dust cover on the bottom. Turn the chair or sofa over, supporting it on a sawhorse while you work. Lift out the tacks holding the dust cover in place. While the piece is upside down, you can also remove the tacks which secure the final fabric of the seat and back which are tacked to the bottom side of the bottom rails.

Now turn the piece right side up and take off the outside back cover. If this piece has been sewn to the side fabric pieces, cut the thread to remove it—and at the same time, make a note to yourself to sew the new cover on in the same manner.

Now take off the outside arm covers. Observe carefully how these pieces have been attached to the front of the arm, and how the fabric has been cut to fit around the leg and back posts. You may find that the top of the outside arm fabric has been blind tacked, using a tacking strip. Make a note of this.

Now remove the inside back cover, starting by pulling the fabric up through the bottom frame since you have already removed the tacks holding this piece to the bottom rail. Be sure to save each of the old cover pieces to serve as a later reference. Also, as you take off each cover piece lift out the padding under it. Some of this padding may be tacked or sewn in place. Remove the tacks or cut the thread, and save the padding. You may be able to use it again, or at least use it as a pattern for forming new pads.

The next step is to remove the inside arm covers. These also were tacked to the bottom rail. Begin by pulling them up through the frame, then removing the tacks which hold them to the back and front posts of the frame. Once again, observe carefully how these pieces were fitted to the piece. In particular, see how the front of the arm was formed, and how the fabric was fitted around the front and back posts.

Finally, remove the fabric and padding covering the seat. Look to see if the fabric of the seat has been made in two pieces. Frequently, the good final fabric is used to make the forward part of the seat piece (the first 6 to 8 inches), and a heavy muslin or other fabric is sewn to it and used to cover that part of the seat which is under the cushion.

With the cover fabric and padding removed, you now see the burlap covering the springs. You'll also see any roll edges which have been used. Remove the roll edges carefully, since you can reuse them. Take off the burlap, exposing the springs. If the chair hasn't been upholstered in a long time, it is likely that the twine tying the springs has rotted and broken. Cut away all of the old twine.

The springs have been sewn to the webbing in the bottom of the piece. Cut the thread which holds the springs in place, and lift them out. Finally, remove all of the old webbing by turning the piece over again and removing the tacks which hold it in place.

The piece has now been stripped to the bare frame. Before beginning the reupholstery job, examine the frame for damage. Fill any cracks with glue, and clamp them tightly while the glue dries. Replace any wood which cannot be repaired. If you want to refinish visible wood parts, do it now.

Reupholstering. If the piece has coil springs, the first step is to install new webbing across the bottom of the seat. If the piece has zig-zag springs, these will not have been removed during the stripping. Just check to see that all are solidly anchored in the frame. If any have come loose, you'll have to restretch them across the bottom, then renail them to the bottom rail.

Zig-zag springs are stiff and hard to stretch back into place after they have come loose. One way to do it is to set up a leverage situation. Make a loop about 4 in. in dia. of three or four lengths of heavy twine. Place this loop around the second zag from the loose end of the spring. Now insert a lever (use a long-handled hammer, a pry bar, etc.) through the loop. Pull the handle

WELTING is used on most furniture. Make your own by folding a 2-in. strip of fabric around cording, then sewing close to the base of the cording.

AFTER COMPLETING the work on the seat, install any webbing needed to support the arms or back. This webbing should not be stretched in place.

toward the outside of the frame until you can rest it against the outside of the frame. This will stretch the spring almost into position. Now slowly pull the top of the lever, with the bottom of it against the side of the bottom rail. This will pull the end of the spring into position over the rail. While you hold the lever firmly, have someone drive 1-in. nails or heavy staples through the holes in the spring clip into the chair rail.

To install webbing. To install webbing across the bottom of the piece, use a roll of 3½-in. jute webbing and No. 12 tacks. Plan to place strips of webbing just as they were in the original job— usually about 1 in. or less apart, with webbing strips run from front to back and from side to side, interwoven.

Place the first strip with about 1½ in. of the webbing extending beyond the outside of the rail. Drive four tacks to hold the strip in place (see photos), then fold over the extended end of the webbing and drive three more tacks. Now stretch the webbing across the seat opening. You won't be able to stretch it tight enough with your hands, so use a webbing stretcher to pull it as tight as you can. Hold the webbing tight with the stretcher while you drive four tacks to hold it. Now cut the webbing about 1½ in. outside of the rail and fold the cut end back across the rail. Drive three more tacks to complete the job. Install all the front-to-back strips of webbing first, then do the side-to-side strips. Interweave the side-to-side strips as you put them in place.

Installing the springs. Turn the chair right-side up and position the springs on the webbing inside of the seat. They should be spaced evenly and symmetrically. Use carpet thread and a large needle to sew the springs to the webbing. Begin by sewing the spring at one corner of the seat, using a long, continuous length of thread. Sew

each spring to the webbing in four places, so that the thread makes a square pattern, then move on to the next spring. When you finish sewing, all springs will be firmly fixed to the webbing.

Next, the springs must be tied, using a 6-ply hemp twine. The twine is anchored to the chair rail by two No. 12 tacks driven at each end of a line of springs. The twine is tied to each spring as it passes over the coil, and as you tie each line of springs, you shape the seat, giving it a smooth, rounded contour. To do this, you compress the springs near the seat rails, and allow the springs to stand a little higher. Run the twine from front to back, then from side to side, tying it tightly to both sides of each spring.

Arm and back supports. In some cases the chair or sofa may have jute webbing as a support for the padding in the back or arms. Install this now by tacking the webbing strips in place. As a rule, this webbing is not stretched.

Burlap cover. Cover the newly tied springs with a layer of burlap, tacking it in place on the side rails. If edge rolls have been used to pad out or square up the front rail of the seat, install these now. Tack them in place, then sew them to the burlap cover.

Installation of padding. Next the padding of the seat is installed. This may be two layers—one of hair and one of cotton, separated by a layer of burlap. Or it may be just one full layer of cotton. Or it may be a shaped pad of polyurethane foam. Whatever the padding is, it should be positioned carefully because the final shape of the seat depends on how the padding is placed.

It is a good idea to anchor the padding in some way. You can tack or staple it to the side rails if it reaches that far, or you can stitch through it into the burlap beneath it in several places. These anchors prevent the possible slipping of the pad-

USE THE OLD FABRIC pieces as patterns to guide you in cutting the new fabric. Cut the new pieces slightly larger, then trim as needed.

HAND SEWING to join sections of the final cover is easy and makes for a smooth, good-looking job. Sew wherever tacking isn't practical.

ding under the final cover.

The muslin cover. The best furniture has a cover of muslin over the padding, with the final cover fabric applied over the muslin. Because it is very costly (in terms of labor), not much furniture is made this way any more. Instead, the final cover is applied right over the padding. But I recommend that you do it because it makes the application of the final cover much easier and provides some additional protection for the padding.

The arms and back. Now move to the arms. Check the notes you made during the stripping of the piece to see how the padding was positioned and how the fabric was cut and tacked. At this time, simply rebuild each arm as it was before, using muslin as a cover, applying the final cover after the muslin.

When covering the arms, do the insides (that part facing into the seat), and then the outsides. The fabric goes down between the seat and the lower wood part of the arm, and is tacked to the bottom of the bottom rail. The outside arm piece most often is blind-tacked at the top, then stretched down the side and tacked to the bottom side of the bottom rail.

There are two tricky spots to watch for as you cover the arms. The first is cutting the fabric to fit around the arm and back posts. Check the old fabric to see how these cuts were made, and make the new cuts carefully. If you cut too much, you may spoil the fabric and be forced to make a new piece for the arm.

The second tricky place is the front of the arm. There are at least a dozen ways in which the front of the arm may be finished. The best way, until you have become proficient at upholstering, is to remake the arm exactly as it was before. Once

again refer to your notes, and observe how the old fabric was cut and tucked or folded the first time. Sometimes the front is only tacked; other times, it may be sewn as well as tacked.

The inside and outside backs. After the arms are finished, proceed to the inside back. Put the padding in place, and anchor it by stitching. Cover it with muslin, and then with the final fabric. The inside back usually is tacked about two inches below the top of the outside of the back rail. It is then stretched over the top of the chair and down the front. At the bottom it is pushed through between the seat cover and the bottom back brace and pulled tight. The bottom edge is tacked to the bottom of the bottom rail.

The outside back now is blind-tacked at the top, pulled down tight across the back, and then tacked to the bottom of the bottom rail. As a rule, the sides of the outside back cover are sewn to the fabric of the sides with tight stitches.

Welting. No mention was made of welting until now because some chairs don't use it. However, if you use it, welting is tacked in place. It may be used, for example, to outline the back. If so, it is tacked in place after the arms and the inside back cover have been installed.

The dust cover. Once the final fabric is on, turn the piece over and tack black cambric to the bottom as a dust cover.

Protecting the fabric. After the upholstering has been finished, purchase a can or two of one of the fabric protector sprays, such as *Scotchgard*, and spray the completed work according to the directions on the can. This will help to protect the fabric from dirt and grease, make it easier to clean, and keep it new looking for a longer period.

Presto! A new piece of furniture!

How to 'respring' an upholstered chair

By LEN HILTS

Don't despair when the bottom falls out of your favorite upholstered chair. You can put it back in good order with an hour's work and a $10 bill

■ WHEN THE BOTTOM drops out of an upholstered chair or sofa, don't panic. The hanging springs and torn webbing may look like a bomb went off inside the upholstery, and the sagging seat may make the job look hopeless, but things aren't really as bad as they appear.

Unless the upholstery fabric itself is badly worn, you aren't faced with a huge bill for a complete reupholstering job. In fact, with a few materials and less than an hour's work, you can restore the piece to better than its original condition. Furthermore, you won't have to touch the upholstery fabric as you work, since all repairs can be made through the bottom.

Start by turning the chair or sofa upside down. Use a hammer and tack lifter to remove the torn dust cover and all of the old webbing. You may be tempted to leave any strands of webbing which aren't broken—but don't do it. Webbing usually breaks because it has rotted with age. If

---

SEE ALSO

UNCLE CHARLIE sat down too hard, but don't blame him. The webbing was old and ready to go. You can see that someone once retied these springs with rope.

AS THE TYING progresses, the springs stand up straight and no longer lean. When finished, each spring should have eight knots on its topmost coil.

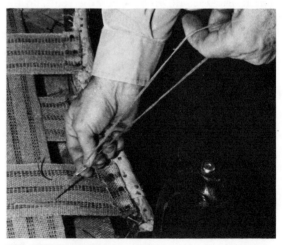

THE CURVED NEEDLE makes it easy to sew down through the webbing, around the top wire of the spring, and then back up through the webbing in one stitch.

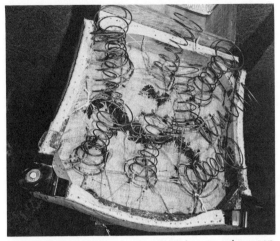

THE OLD WEBBING has been stripped away and you can see that the twine holding the springs is loose or missing. The springs are now loose and leaning.

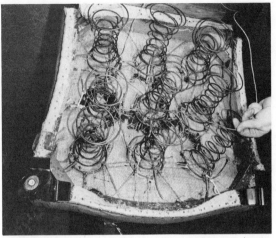

REACHING UP through the springs, use heavy twine to retie them. The ties connect the top wire of each coil to the neighboring coils.

THE WEBBING is tacked to the back rail, then stretched taut across the row of springs. Use the webbing stretcher to pull strand as tight as possible.

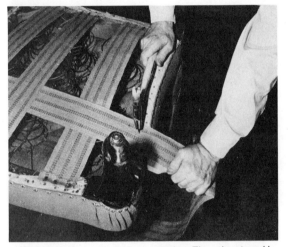

FOUR TACKS are driven into webbing. Then the strand is cut about 1½-in. outside of the tacks and the end is folded inward and secured with three tacks.

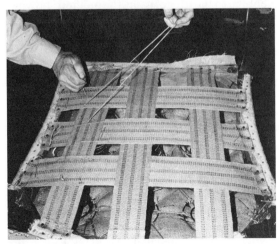

SEW THROUGH the webbing four times over each spring, making a square pattern, with the spring sewn to the webbing at each corner of the square.

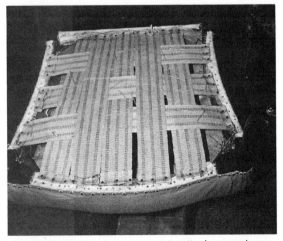

AFTER SEWING, you may want to attach several more strands of webbing to provide additional support for the seat. Here two more strands were tacked in place.

THE JOB is completed by tacking or stapling a dust cover of black cambric to the bottom. Note how flat the bottom is because the webbing was stretched tight.

'respring' a chair, continued

some of it broke, you can be sure that the rest will go soon, too. Plan to put in all new webbing.

Webbing is made of jute, is 4 in. wide, and you can buy it by the yard at most fabric stores. Count the number of strands used across the chair bottom, and then compute how much you will need, adding a yard or two to allow for stretching. Ten yards is more than enough for most chairs, but you may need 20 yards for a sofa.

In addition to the webbing, you should also buy a webbing stretcher, a magnetic tack hammer, a box of webbing tacks (No. 12s), some heavy thread (the kind used for sewing carpeting), and a large, curved sailmaker's needle. You'll find all of these items available in the upholstery section of large fabric stores. The total cost, including the tools, won't be more than $10 or $15. If you already have the tools, you can manage for $5 or less.

Once the old webbing is off, probe into the seat and check the twine which was used to tie the springs. You'll have to reach up through the springs to get at it, and if any is broken or loose, cut it away and replace it. At the start, each of the springs may be leaning in a different direction. By the time you have finished repairing the ties, each spring should be standing up on its own.

This retying is one of the secrets of this type of repair. If you simply replace the webbing without retying the springs, the seat will be lumpy and uncomfortable.

With the springs tied, apply new strands of webbing. Put one across each row of springs from front to back, then do the same from side to side. To apply each strand, tack one end of the webbing to the frame, using the method shown in the pictures—four tacks, evenly spaced, then fold the end of the webbing over and drive three tacks.

Use your webbing stretcher to pull the strand tight across the row of springs. And I mean *tight*. You are compressing the springs up against the seat, so you'll have to pull the webbing tighter than you would if you were just starting the upholstery job and the springs were not in place. You want to end up with the webbing stretched flat across the bottom of the chair.

You may have to reach under and adjust the springs as you stretch, making sure each spring is upright and in contact with the webbing. Once the webbing is tight, tack the loose end to the frame and go to the next strand.

When you have all the strands of webbing in place both ways across the springs, get out the curved needle and the carpet thread. The curved needle makes it easy to sew through the webbing, around the top wire of each spring. You want to sew each spring to the webbing in four places.

The easiest way is to make a square pattern with the thread over each spring, sewing down through the webbing around the top spring wire at each corner of the square—then moving on to the next spring to begin another square. This sewing is important because it anchors the springs and assures you that they won't shift out of position as the chair is used. If the springs remain unanchored and do shift, the seat will sag or collapse.

You will note that in this method of repair you have not replaced the webbing strand for strand, but have simply installed strands over each row of springs. This is necessary so that the springs are compressed properly. However, you may end up with fewer strands of webbing than were originally used. You may want to install several additional strands after you have finished the sewing of the springs.

Whether you do or not depends on the size of the piece and the strain which will be put on the webbing. In the chair pictured, I added two more strands of webbing because I felt the chair seat needed additional support. As a general rule, there should be no more than 1 in. between strands of webbing to give adequate support.

Finally, tack a dust cover of black cambric in place, and your upholstered piece is as good as new—with only a small outlay of time and money. You'll find it convenient to staple the dust cover in place if you have a stapling gun. The work is quicker and, since the dust cover receives no stress, strength isn't necessary.

Hints for easier work. The inside of an upholstered seat can be pretty dusty and dirty. After taking off the old webbing, use one of the tube attachments on your vacuum cleaner to reach in and get rid of the dirt before proceeding.

When you buy jute webbing, get the amount you need in a continuous piece, buying a yard or two more than you know you'll need. Don't cut strips from the webbing roll. Instead, tack the loose end, then stretch the webbing across the seat, and tack it down. Then cut the webbing about 1½-in. beyond the row of tacks you drove. Using this method, you are always sure of having enough webbing available to apply the stretcher.

When retying the springs, keep in mind that they were originally tied eight ways. That is, the twine ran from the front to the back, from side to side, and in both diagonal directions, and was tied to each wire it passed over, making a total of eight ties to each spring.

In retying, you won't be able to run a continuous length of twine in each direction. But you can tie each spring to its neighbor individually and end up with the same eight-way type of tie. Heavy twine ideal for use in spring tying can be purchased in balls at the same time you buy your webbing.

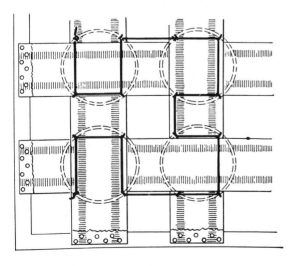

THE PATTERN to follow when sewing the springs to the webbing is shown here. By making a square over each spring, the coil can be stitched four times.

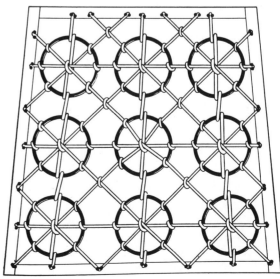

THE PATTERN followed in originally tying the springs produces eight ties on each spring. In repairing the seat, use the same number of ties.

Want to upgrade your photo equipment at a savings? Then consider buying a good used camera. Make these checks in the store or at home and assure yourself of a good buy

By LEN HILTS

OPEN THE BACK of any camera you are considering, hold the unit to the light, and depress the shutter. Check to see that everything works smoothly and easily. Check the operation at different time settings.

How to buy a good used camera

■ LOOKING FOR A WAY to upgrade the quality of your photography equipment? A very good way to do it inexpensively is to buy used equipment—notably cameras. By shopping carefully, you can own the best camera of its type at a price you can afford.

The trick, of course, is in knowing how to judge the used camera you are buying. Here are some simple checks you can perform to help assure yourself of a good buy:

1. Know the kind of camera you want before you start to shop. Even make a decision as to the brand and model, if possible. Then visit several camera stores and make a cursory check. Is the camera you want available used? What is the price range? What is the general condition of the equipment?

This information should lead you to the dealer with the best stock and the best prices, and give you a "feel" of the market.

2. Select the most promising dealer and visit him to talk some serious business. Select the camera that seems to fit your situation both in price and in general condition. Now settle down with that camera and perform a thorough inspection.

3. First, the appearance. How does it look? Does it show signs of heavy wear? Look for

WITH THE BACK of an SLR camera open, depress the shutter and observe the action of the focal plane shutter. Cock the camera and look again.

RUN A ROLL of exposed or out of date film through the camera, noting the action. All parts should work smoothly with no binding.

TEST A BUILT-IN METER by taking a reading from a Kodak gray card. Place the card in a light place and note the reading given by the meter.

NEXT, TAKE A READING with a good light meter, using the same gray card and placing the meter in the same position as the camera. Readings should agree.

dents and other clues that it may have been dropped. Look for signs of corrosion, and for evidence of an accumulation of dirt—anything that tells you the camera didn't receive good care. Check the tiny screws that hold it together. If they are burred, suspect that an amateur tried to repair it.

Reject the camera if you suspect it was dropped, was badly cared for, or repaired by an amateur. A well-worn camera can be a good camera—but only if it was cared for.

4. Open the back. Check the serial number, and if it has been deleted, reject the camera. Is the interior clean, showing care? Snap the shutter and advance the film controls. Watch to see that all the controls function smoothly. Look to see that the shutter is absolutely undamaged.

5. Thread a roll of film into the camera to see that all the parts work smoothly. Most camera stores have an exposed roll you can use for this purpose. If not, bring your own, or even invest in a new roll. Remember, you are making a considerable investment.

6. Remove the lens, or, if the lens doesn't come off, open the back of the camera so you can look through it. Put the shutter on "bulb" and hold the lens toward the light. Look for nicks, scratches, discoloration or disfiguration. Ignore small air bubbles, since these appear in most lenses. While the lens is open, move the lens aperture to each of the f-stops. The iris blades should move in unison and form a symmetrical opening (usually hexagonal) at each stop, and each opening should be half (or double) the area of the one next to it.

7. Now, with the lens aperture wide open, close the shutter and run a similar test. With the camera toward the light, cock and fire the shutter at each of its speeds, up and down the scale. It should look and sound consistently faster or

REMOVE THE LENS from cameras with interchangeable lenses. Examine the lens threads for damage. Be sure all parts of lens mount are undented.

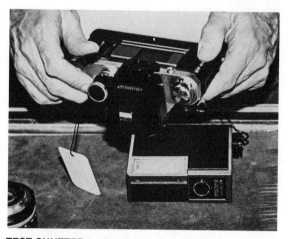

TEST SHUTTER by this test, using an electronic flash gun. Connect the gun to the camera, then place the gun so it fires directly into lens.

good used camera, continued

slower than the previous setting. If the blades on either the iris or the shutter stick—or in severe cases flop loose—reject the camera. On a camera with interchangeable lenses, make the shutter and aperture tests separately.

If examining an interchangeable lens, see that the threads are undamaged. Shake it and listen for loose elements. Move the turning rings with your fingers to be sure they move easily but at the same time are snugly in place. Reject the lens if the rings are loose and wobbly.

8. Check the accessories. For example, fit a flash gun into the hot shoe and fire the camera—to be sure the hot shoe contacts are good.

9. If the camera has a built-in exposure meter, check it by borrowing an Eastman gray card from the dealer (he has them in stock). Set the card up in a light place and look at it through the camera, taking a reading from the meter in the camera. Now borrow a good light meter (or bring your own) and make a reading, placing the meter at the same distance from the gray card as the camera was. The two readings should agree. Otherwise you can suspect trouble in the camera's built-in unit.

10. If the camera has a focal plane shutter (a flat cloth shutter which travels from one side to the other, visible when the back is off the camera) examine it to see that there are no holes. You can test it for timing and operation in the following manner: Borrow a small electronic flash unit. Place it on the counter, attached to the camera so that it will fire when you depress the shutter button (use a short connector cord). With

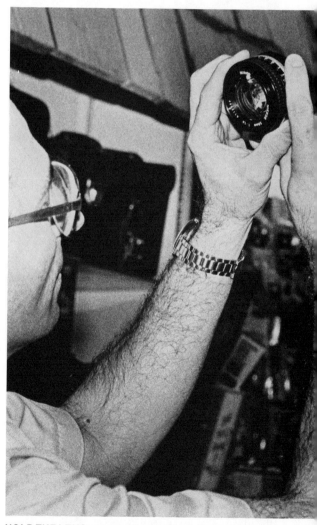

HOLD THE LENS up to the light and look through it. Look for scratches, discoloration and other damage. Ignore tiny bubbles, which are in many lenses. Shake the lens and listen for rattle.

WITH FLASH UNIT pointing into lens, place piece of paper over shutter. Set camera at 1/60-second, fire flash, and watch rectangle on paper.

FULL rectangular opening of shutter should be visible at 1/60 during flash. About half is visible at 1/125, and a quarter at 1/250 of a second.

the back off the camera so you can see the shutter, place the camera so the flash gun fires directly into the lens. (See accompanying photos.) Place a small sheet of white paper over the shutter and set the time on the camera for flash synchronization, usually 1/60 of a second.

Now keep your eye on the white paper and depress the shutter button. The gun will fire and you should be able to see the entire rectangular shutter opening outlined on the paper. Now set the timer at 1/125-second and repeat. The size of the rectangle you see should be smaller. Make the test at 1/250. By now, when the flash fires, you should be able to see only a small part of the rectangle. At 1/500, you should see none of the rectangle.

This is a good test to indicate whether the shutter timing is functioning and is more or less accurate.

11. Check the focus by looking at objects through the camera. Bring them into sharp focus. Then measure with a tape the distance from the camera to the object. The footage scale on the lens should agree with your measurements.

If these seem like too many tests to perform in a camera store, ask the dealer for a trial period. Most will allow you 10 days. Take the camera home and make the tests at your leisure. Also shoot some test rolls and have them processed. During the tests it is best to use a tripod to assure steady pictures. Otherwise, you may blame the camera for fuzziness when actually it was your own body motion that caused the problem. Shoot some detailed subjects, such as a brick

wall, from a distance of six feet. Make an enlargement of the resulting picture and examine it for sharpness of detail. Shoot a sequence of pictures of the same subject, using all the f-stops and a series of different times. Compare these pictures. Look for a sharp fall off of focus from the center to the edges of the pictures. And look for a steady progression of exposures in the series of time pictures.

Ask the dealer about his guarantee. Most good dealers will allow 30 to 90 days on used equipment, depending on the conditions, brand and price asked.

If the camera is in top shape, don't expect too low a price. You should save a fair amount, depending on the age of the unit, but if the price is too low, be suspicious. The camera may have a history of repairs and the dealer may be trying to dump it.

In general, stay away from antiques—cameras more than 15 years old—unless you are a collector. It is also a good idea to avoid off brands when buying used equipment. Don't be surprised if you find some very recent models available in the used market. Often a shutterbug overextends himself for a new camera, then finds he must sell it back to the dealer to get some ready cash. Cameras acquired under these conditions will have very little use, but will be priced close to the new camera figure.

When looking at any camera, use your nose. Check to see if it has a smell of mildew, and look to see if there is evidence that the camera may have been water soaked. If you see any such signs, pass it by.

A beautiful home for your holidays

'Super Camp'

■ NOT EVERYONE with a piece of land wants—or needs—a true vacation home. Young weekenders especially find themselves "camping-out" and enjoying it more than reveling in a spectacular summer-home showcase.

A "super camp" such as this may be the answer. It will keep you dry on rainy afternoons, keep the wind out at night and minimize the need to pack up your outing equipment and bring it home.

The shelter fulfills three important requirements—it can be locked securely to discourage pranksters and vandals; it provides over 400 sq. ft. of enclosed living area, and perhaps most

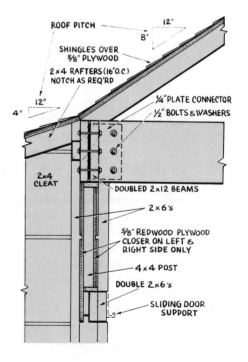

ROOF PITCH
12"
8"
SHINGLES OVER
5/8" PLYWOOD
2 x 4 RAFTERS (16"O.C.)
NOTCH AS REQ'RD
1/4" PLATE CONNECTOR
1/2" BOLTS & WASHERS
12"
4"
2x4
CLEAT
DOUBLED 2x12 BEAMS
2 x 6's
5/8" REDWOOD PLYWOOD
CLOSER ON LEFT &
RIGHT SIDE ONLY
4 x 4 POST
DOUBLE 2x6's
SLIDING DOOR
SUPPORT

SEE ALSO
Home buying . . . Home winterizing . . .
House additions . . . Insurance

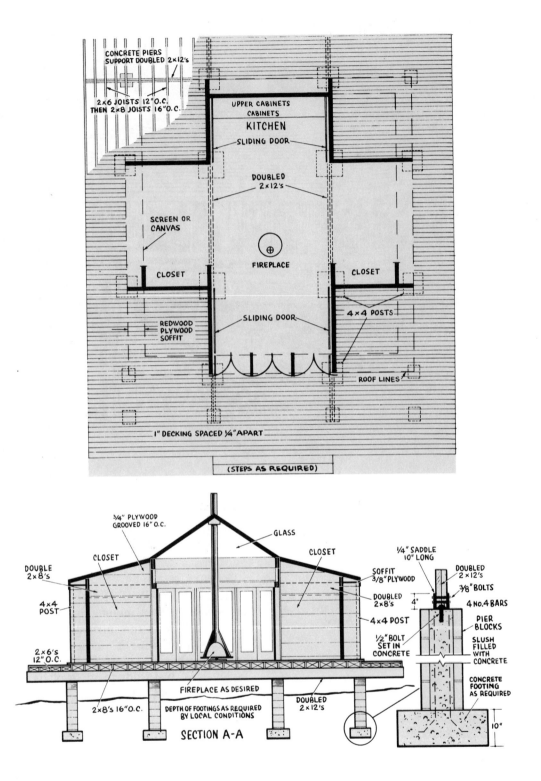

CONCRETE PIERS
SUPPORT DOUBLED 2×12's

2×6 JOISTS 12"O.C.
THEN 2×8 JOISTS 16"O.C.

UPPER CABINETS
CABINETS

KITCHEN

SLIDING DOOR

DOUBLED
2×12's

SCREEN OR
CANVAS

FIREPLACE

CLOSET   CLOSET

REDWOOD
PLYWOOD
SOFFIT

SLIDING DOOR   4×4 POSTS

ROOF LINES

1" DECKING SPACED ¼"APART

(STEPS AS REQUIRED)

¾" PLYWOOD
GROOVED 16"O.C.   GLASS

CLOSET   CLOSET   ¼" SADDLE
                                        10" LONG
DOUBLE   DOUBLED
2×8's   SOFFIT   2×12's
                                 ⅜"PLYWOOD
4×4   DOUBLED   ⅜"BOLTS
POST   2×8's   4 No.4 BARS

                                 4×4 POST   PIER
                                                    BLOCKS
2×6's   ½"BOLT   SLUSH
12"O.C.   SET IN   FILLED
                                 CONCRETE   WITH
                                                    CONCRETE

FIREPLACE AS DESIRED   CONCRETE
                                                    FOOTING
                                 DOUBLED   AS REQUIRED
2×8's 16"O.C.   DEPTH OF FOOTINGS AS REQUIRED 2×12's
                BY LOCAL CONDITIONS

SECTION A-A   10"

important, it is a stylish structure with a pleasing appearance.

The clerestory above the entrance dramatizes the roofline and also provides good interior illumination. Similarly, a prefabricated fireplace adds interest to the center of the shelter, while providing a source of heat. Functionally, the closets and kitchen cabinets make "roughing it" a bit easier, and the sliding doors allow you to lock up the "camp" in a matter of minutes.

On following pages you'll find plans for other vacation cabins.

Octagonal house—modern design with complete livability

■ THIS HIGH-STYLE HOME adapts easily to beach, lakeshore or mountainside to provide a panoramic view of the surrounding territory.

What's more, since the house is shown here in three different sizes, it can fit a variety of needs and lot sizes. Just study the floor plans and pick the one that suits you best.

The smallest version of the octagonal house is basically a comfortable combination of a living-sleeping-dining area with separate bath and kitchen divisions, all built into a 309-sq.-ft. area. The next largest plan has a similar layout, but increases the total area to 483 sq. ft.

The largest of the three plans offers 768 sq. ft. and can be built as either a one-bedroom or two-bedroom house.

A roomy deck edges five of the eight sides of the house, adding spaciousness and guaranteeing a place to sun any time of the day.

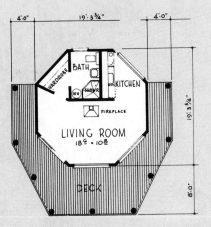

A BACHELOR with a small wooded site high in the mountains would be unlikely to find a better plan for a vacation home. It's comfortable and laid out for convenience, but has flair.

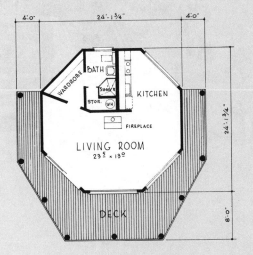

A LARGER VERSION of the octagonal design, this plan requires an additional five feet (in length and width) over the smaller version, yet has half again as much available living space.

"A HOME AWAY FROM HOME" best describes this one-bedroom version of the eight-sided design. Although the deck rings five of the eight sides, amount of deck can be increased or decreased.

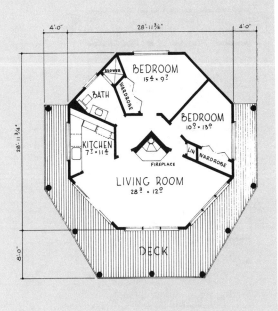

AS A YEAR-ROUND vacation home or a retreat solely for warm months, this two-bedroom version leaves little to be desired. Measurements shown in these plans are taken from extreme corners.

A-frame updated for comfort

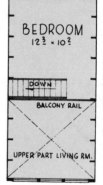

BEDROOM
12³⁄ × 10²⁄

DOWN

BALCONY RAIL

UPPER PART LIVING RM.

PRACTICAL layout of the A-frame is highly suitable for weekending the full year round. A front wall of glass allows full view of scenery and lets in plenty of daylight. Adding a rear door improves the traffic pattern.

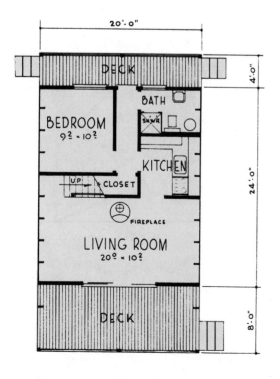

■ ONCE CONSIDERED a radical design innovation, the A-frame has become a classic among vacation home styles. The adaptability of the A-frame has much to do with its popularity, since it can be built on most any site and customized to reflect the owner's individuality.

The plan utilizes a large expanse of glass on the front to add spaciousness to the 645-sq.-ft. home (480 sq. ft. on lower floor, 165 sq. ft. on upper level), and includes an often-needed back door.

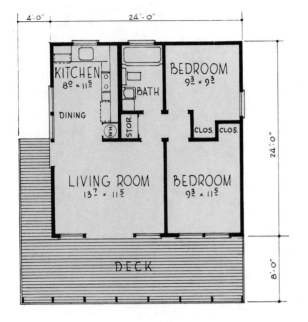

Sloping roof adds
eye appeal

■ THE WEATHER-WORTHY shed roof has proven itself to be strong, durable and highly practical—and too often, extremely ugly.

However, thoughtful planning in the design stage has made the shed roofline appear clean and contemporary in this plan. Modestly sized, the house offers 576 sq. ft. of enclosed living space, an additional 272 sq. ft. of deck space, and an exterior that's fronted with supporting posts angled to break both the vertical and horizontal lines of the structure.

Inside, both bedrooms have a separate closet, and provision for a hot-water heater is made at one end of the kitchen.

Attractive vacation-home plans

By LEONARD E. SABAL

■ SPORTSMAN, family man, banker man, thief—all need a hideaway to get away from it all. Only nowadays, it's got to be a hideout big enough for the rest of the gang.

And, when you consider that it also must be inexpensive, comfortable, trouble-free and adaptable to any location, the obvious solution is a vacation home—preferably one you can build with a minimum of time, skill and cash outlay.

With these points in mind, we took a good look at the vacation-home market, or as some prefer, the second-home industry. The result is this collection of five homes you can build *now* and enjoy later, while the last house is presented for what it is—a brand new idea in stylized retreats.

Complete plans for each of the five are available from the American Plywood Assn., 1119 A St., Tacoma, WA 98401. An important part of each set of plans is a detailed bill of materials listing plumbing and electrical supplies, as well as lumber, miscellaneous hardware and foundation materials.

SEE ALSO

Home buying . . . Home winterizing . . .
House additions . . . Insurance

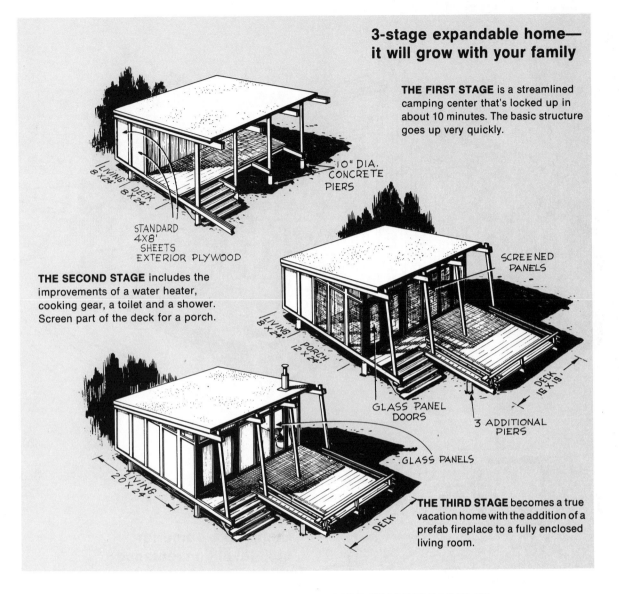

3-stage expandable home—
it will grow with your family

THE FIRST STAGE is a streamlined camping center that's locked up in about 10 minutes. The basic structure goes up very quickly.

THE SECOND STAGE includes the improvements of a water heater, cooking gear, a toilet and a shower. Screen part of the deck for a porch.

THE THIRD STAGE becomes a true vacation home with the addition of a prefab fireplace to a fully enclosed living room.

THIRD STAGE FLOOR PLAN

The first home, as shown on these two pages, is a three-stage affair that can be built quickly in first-stage form, then expanded as the need arises. You could, however, complete all three stages at once, because the house is designed around the 4x8-ft. modular concept, and therefore requires a minimum of cutting during the actual construction.

The first stage basically is a simple shelter that doubles as a camping center. Add a cooking unit, water heater, shower, toilet and more deck area to convert the basic module into an easy-to-live-in cabin. To complete the third stage, enclose the living area, install a prefab fireplace, insulate if desired, and add those personal touches that makes a home.

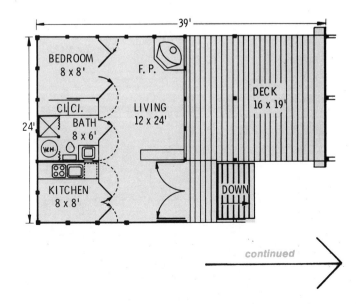

continued

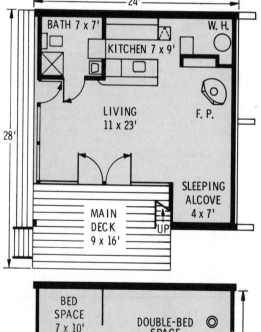

BATH 7 x 7'

KITCHEN 7 x 9'

W. H.

24'

28'

LIVING
11 x 23'

F. P.

SLEEPING
ALCOVE
4 x 7'

MAIN
DECK
9 x 16'

UP

BED
SPACE
7 x 10'

DOUBLE-BED
SPACE
10 x 16'

13'

UPPER DECK
7 x 16'

CLOSET
4 x 7'

DN.

8'

Stepped A-frame for split-level convenience

■ WELL-PROPORTIONED and inviting, this double-deck A-frame integrates the desirable features of upstairs bedrooms with spacious living areas to provide the privacy and appeal of a split-level home.

The dual-deck arrangement also contributes to this split-level effect while simultaneously providing a natural borderline for the upper and lower walls of windows and doors. The end result is an interior that's always bright, airy and cheerful.

Should the upper bedrooms prove large enough for the members of your family, the lower sleeping alcove can easily be converted to a convenient 4x7-ft. closet like that on the upper level.

The structure rests on nine concrete pilings, while panels of Texture 1-11 act as both roof and walls to provide the lateral rigidity required for an A-frame.

Rigid-frame cabin for remote homesites

■ THIS CABIN would make an ideal vacation home for your family or, if you are a hunter, a hunting lodge for you and some friends.

Its rigid-frame construction offers two distinct advantages. First, the cabin goes up in a hurry because all the framing members are identical and, thus, can be prefabricated before the actual erection. Second, the absence of load-bearing interior walls means the floor plan can be varied to suit any requirements without affecting the strength and rigidity of the cabin.

Although normal spacing of frame members is 2 ft. on centers, you could double up on each and space them 4 ft. o.c. for larger sidewall openings. Inside the cabin, the large frames can be left uncovered for a handsome "exposed beam" look. However, if you're already planning on next season's hunting, you can add insulation between the frames and then panel the interior with decorative plywood.

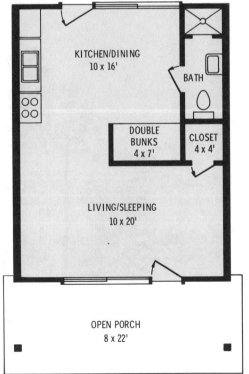

KITCHEN/DINING
10 x 16'

BATH

DOUBLE BUNKS
4 x 7'

CLOSET
4 x 4'

LIVING/SLEEPING
10 x 20'

OPEN PORCH
8 x 22'

please turn the page →

Palatial hideaway for peaceful afternoons

■ DESIGNED for easy building on remote sites, this luxurious retreat can be put together in a week, using preframed plywood panels and precut lumber.

When you're through, you have a vacation palace—a true second home—with 770 sq. ft. of enclosed living space and another 700 sq. ft. of outdoor deck space.

The attractive clerestory arrangement in the roof not only adds to the appearance of the house, but it also serves a utilitarian purpose by flooding the interior with light, even on cloudy days.

Another unusual feature is found in the living room, where hinged privacy panels drop from the ceiling to create three separate sleeping areas for weekend guests. Yet even when the panels are lowered, there's still plenty of space remaining around the fireplace for informal entertaining and relaxing. Using sliding doors throughout also adds a touch of casual elegance.

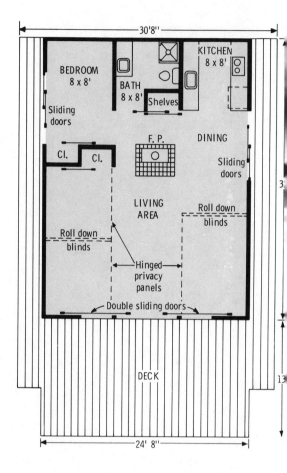

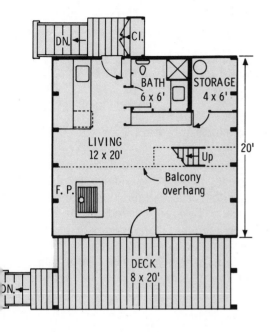

Spartan A-frame for rugged vacationers

◼ NESTED ATOP a rocky mountain, this striking A-frame withstands gusting winter winds as well as sudden summer storms to make it an ideal weekend refuge.

To relieve the bare A-frame lines, an extra pair of frames and a canvas canopy extend over the deck to form a shelter from sun, rain and snow. Inside, a neat plastic skylight provides natural illumination, while the front wall of windows and door takes full advantage of the view.

The living room contains 240 sq. ft. of space with a prefabricated corner fireplace that's perfect for warming up after a hard day's skiing. The 144 sq.-ft. sleeping balcony overlooks the living area and is accessible via a shiptype stairway. The rear of the A-frame has a second entry (into the kitchen) on the lower level, while cool summer night breezes can enter the balcony area through a pair of swinging windows.

As with all the homes designed for the American Plywood Assn., it's best to lay the foundation *in strict accordance with the plans* before the delivery of the other construction materials.

How to close up your vacation home

A vacation home can be a lot of fun, but there's also work involved. Here are some tips to help you prepare your home for the winter months

■ WHEN THE END of summer approaches the time comes to think about "battening down the hatches" at a vacation home which will be unattended during the winter months.

Many of the closing-down chores are things you've done year after year, and most of the items listed on these pages are simply common sense. But, if you make up a list and assign each member of your family specific tasks, the closing-down will go a lot faster—without a chance of missing any important items.

You can usually hire a local resident who, for a nominal fee, will keep an eye on your place during your absence. To avoid misunderstandings, agree upon his fee and what services he is expected to perform.

Finally, check your homeowner's insurance policy to see if any conditions must be met to assure your policy remains in full force during your absence.

Start with inspection of house exterior and grounds. Look for, and remove, broken or dead tree limbs or trees which may be leaning dangerously toward your house. Your "check-list" tour should include the following:
1. Clean out gutters and leaders.
2. Repair any loose roof shingles.
3. Point up any loose chimney bricks.
4. Clear *all* accumulation from the crawl-space area.
5. See that garbage cans have properly fitting covers. Scrub the cans with disinfectant and soap and water. When dry, store them out of the weather. Throw out damaged and uncovered cans.
6. Keep out vermin by covering chimney flues with a galvanized sheet-metal cap, securely fastened. *Immediately, upon fastening flue cover,* go inside and put a *big sign* on the fireplace to assure you *uncover flues* prior to use next season.

If possible, your boat should be drydocked. This may be: 1) at the local marina, 2) at your year-round home after a trailer tow or 3) stored on your vacation-home property. Items 1 and 2 simplify your task considerably. If you elect to do your own storing, follow these simple guidelines: Pick an area near the house on the opposite side from prevailing winds. A small boat can be inverted and stored on sawhorses; just make certain it is lashed down securely with a stout cord. With boat stowed, check your dock, mooring lines and accessories for any loose gear which may be stored in and lashed to the boat.

Grounds, dock and boat check

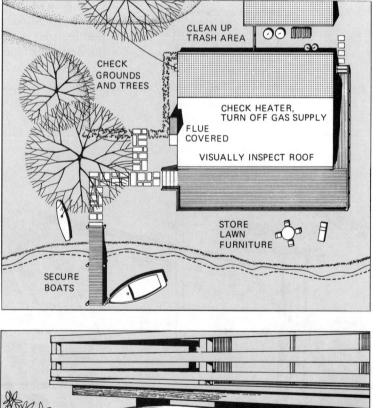

CLEAN UP TRASH AREA

CHECK GROUNDS AND TREES

CHECK HEATER, TURN OFF GAS SUPPLY

FLUE COVERED

VISUALLY INSPECT ROOF

STORE LAWN FURNITURE

SECURE BOATS

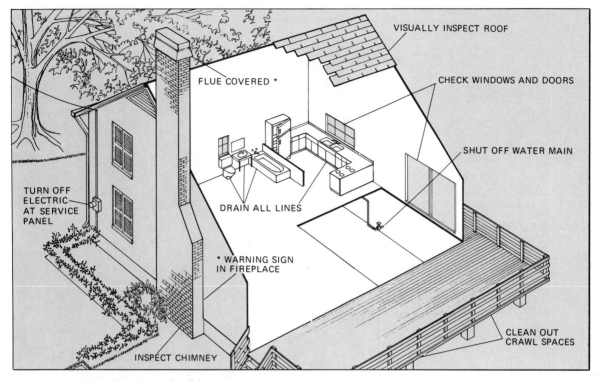

VISUALLY INSPECT ROOF

CHECK WINDOWS AND DOORS

FLUE COVERED *

SHUT OFF WATER MAIN

TURN OFF
ELECTRIC
AT SERVICE
PANEL

DRAIN ALL LINES

* WARNING SIGN
IN FIREPLACE

CLEAN OUT
CRAWL SPACES

INSPECT CHIMNEY

There's work to be done inside too

Scatter a liberal number of mothballs around the house, in each room. Mothballs will be easier to gather than flakes next spring. Also place mothballs between mattresses and springs. Since camphor evaporates when exposed to air, you may wish to have your "caretaker" replenish the supply every six weeks or so. *Do not set rodent traps.* Decomposition over the winter can cause an odor that will be difficult to eliminate. A strong camphor odor will deter most rodents from entering the house.

Clean out all foodstuffs. Food packed in cardboard containers (cereals, flour and the like) will attract rodents and other vermin. Foods packaged in cans and bottles may be subject to below-freezing temperatures and stand a good chance of exploding. At best, they will probably outlive their shelf lives if left behind. Your best bet is to remove all food from your vacation home before leaving. For economy, of course, bring home what you can. Add what you decide isn't worth packing to the pile of trash that is to be hauled to the dump.

Before locking the front door, make a final check to assure that all combustible materials—paints, solvents, cleaning fluids, matches and the like—are removed from the house. Turn the heater switch to off, shut off the gas supply at the main and pull the main electric fuse (or trip the breaker). Finally, check screens, windows and doors to make certain they are firmly secured.

Shut off water-supply main and drain *all* water-supply lines. Open valves on fixtures, drain fittings at their lowest points and leave valves open. A small amount of water

may remain in the valves. To remove it, rig a section of hose to the pressure side (outlet) of your vacuum cleaner and blow out the fixtures. If your summer home is closed while the climate is still moderate, small amounts of water remaining in valves and lines left open will evaporate prior to freezing weather. Drain or siphon water from the toilet-bowl tank and remove the last bit with a sponge. Pour about a cup of permanent-type antifreeze in every trap. (Don't forget, the bathtub drain has a trap too.) Pour *two* cups of antifreeze in the toilet bowl. Waterpump and well-point systems vary depending upon the type installation. Here, it is best to have your plumber show you what to do the first-time around. Write down what he tells you for use next year. (You may have a foot-valve type point, a flexible submersible point, or other: "Breaking" the vacuum by needless loosening of fittings can shorten the life of the fitting.)

Final points: Make certain your washed-down refrigerator is propped open. Also, it is worth the few dollars more your caretaker will charge to have him clear the driveway after each snowfall. In the event that fire should break out while the house is closed, a clear access could spell the difference between minimal damage and total loss.

SEE ALSO
Boat storage . . . Caulking . . . Home winterizing . . . Insulation . . . Plumbing . . . Roofs

By BILL McKEOWN

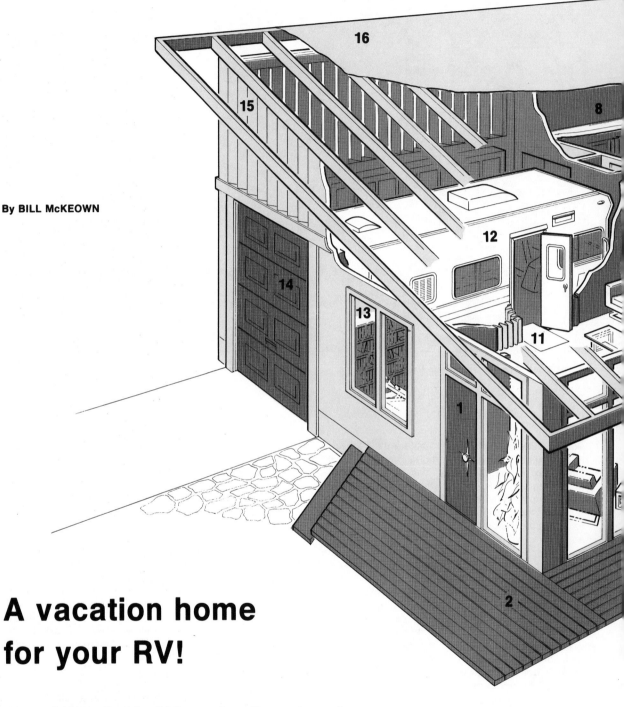

A vacation home for your RV!

A recreational vehicle can form the nucleus of a
more spacious and comfortable permanent vacation home. Rudimentary
at first, the shelter can be developed gradually over the years
until it contains all the comforts of a regular house

SEE ALSO
**Campers . . . Home buying . . . House additions . . .
Recreational vehicles . . . Trailers . . . Trailers, tent**

RV COTTAGE built around motor home and its utilities has: (1) door opening from (2) deck into basic (3) living area. Added room divisions can include (4) bar/breakfast counter with pass-through space to (5) kitchen. The plumbing and sewer connections allow addition of (6) bathroom. Shutting off back of two-car garage makes (7) bedroom with (8) storage over. (9) Utilities room with furnace and central airconditioner plus (10) laundry room are refinements. (11) Level ramp leads to (12) motor home. (13) Workshop. (14) Garage door. Garage enclosure has louvered (15) front, side ventilation under the roof (16).

■ A RECREATIONAL VEHICLE FAMILY in Toledo built a spacious one-room summer camp on its lakeside lot in Upper Michigan—and used its motor home parked alongside as bedroom, bathroom and kitchen. A fishing club in Maine, two mountain-climbing couples in Seattle, a family of six in Denver and a water-skiing group from Houston—all RV owners—are among many groups that have set up similar arrangements. So have several RV retirees in New Mexico.

One Winnipeg couple had more specific needs: "We were going to retire in two years," they wrote, "and had bought some land in central Florida. Like many undeveloped spots, it had no gas, electricity or water, but that was no problem since we could live in our motor home. Next to it we put up a simple one-room cottage in which we could store some of our things from our house up North, once we sold it. Eventually we expanded and fixed up the cottage to accommodate our children and grandchildren when they came to visit. Now, part of the year, we shut up the cottage and take to RV touring again.''

The shelter shown here was designed with the needs of such people in mind. The building starts with an enclosure and carport. Check local building codes and restrictions, plus insurance requirements, before getting started. Since some communities don't like the appearance of an RV, we have enclosed the carport with a garage door but louvered the top for ventilation so that the generator, airconditioner or furnace can be employed. For extensive use, exhaust hose extension or chimney connection may be installed.

The floor level of the camp cottage is planned at a height equal to the RV interior with a walkway leading in and accordion walls and ceiling fitting snugly around the RV door. Initially the room can be a simple screened-in shelter—with windows, walls, plumbing, room divisions, kitchen and bath, furnace and airconditioning, separate bedroom and outer decking added later. Storm shutters can close up the house completely when the owners drive off on tour. With sleeping accommodations in the vehicle and a fold-out sofa in the living area, back-bedroom space may be kept as a garage extension for a second car.

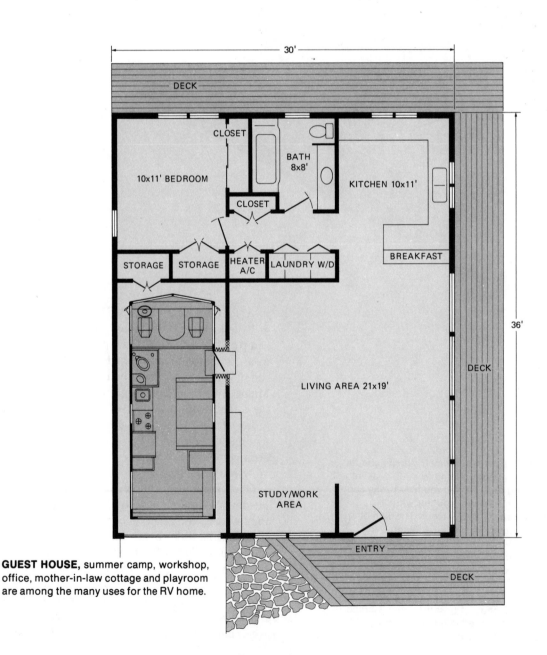

GUEST HOUSE, summer camp, workshop, office, mother-in-law cottage and playroom are among the many uses for the RV home.

Resticking cove base

A section of cove base in my bathroom has come loose and won't restick, though I've tried this twice with the recommended cement. Do you have a suggestion?—Ray Cameron, Atlanta.

Probably dust and other debris have collected in back of the cove to prevent the cement from bonding. This dirt must be removed completely by light scraping and thorough washing with a mild detergent or soapy solution. Make sure that the surface is clean and dry before you apply the new cement, then devise some temporary means of exerting pressure on the cove across the width and length until the cement has cured.

Snow blows in attic louvers

Last winter snow blew through our attic louvers dampening, but not ruining, plaster in the room below. I'm told to close the louvers in winter, also not to close them. What do I do?—Ralph Larsen, Rochester, Minn.

There's a difference of opinion. I favor leaving the louvers open, principally because ventilation tends to keep frost from forming in the attic. This is fairly common, especially in ranch-type houses having low-pitched roofs. You can close the louvers against snow by stretching a burlap cloth over the screen on the inside, tacking the cloth in place. Since this does reduce air circulation I'd suggest that you watch that frost does not form anywhere in the attic. If it does, open louvers to allow free air circulation.

Table leaf warps seasonally

I have a rather old drop-leaf table. One leaf warps slightly, but straightens in winter when the heat's on. It appears to be a replacement. How can I prevent it from warping?—F.M. Wales, Philadelphia.

If the leaf is a replacement, it may stabilize in time. Thus, I'd let well enough alone for a time. But if it remains warped, you can usually correct this by cutting several ¾-in.-wide dadoes crosswise on the underside to a depth about half the thickness of the wood. Space dadoes about 10 in. apart and don't extend them all the way across if the edges are decorative. Fasten strips of the same stock in the grooves, using glue and screws.

Preventing 'bubbles' in varnish

Recently I varnished a tabletop and ended up with what appear to be tiny bubbles on the surface. Steel-wooling doesn't take out the imperfections. What did I do wrong?—H. Stanley, Los Angeles.

If the top is of hardwood, did you remember to apply a filler before staining and varnishing? Possibly you stirred the varnish or shook the can before application. Though some modern clear finishes do require stirring or agitating, varnish doesn't. Or, the bubbles could be particles of dust which were on the surface or in the brush at time of application.

Always clean a brush with compatible solvent and wipe the surface to be finished before you apply *any* finish.

Think twice

When my home was built, 4 in. of insulation was poured between the attic floor joists. I have access to Styrofoam sheets used as packing. Could I use these between joists, or would it be better to add blow-in insulation, and how much more?—Royce Watson, Bryan, Tex.

I would add, say, 3 in. of poured insulation for a total depth of about 7 in. In time, this should return its cost in fuel savings. Be leery about using the styrene foam sheets. Styrene insulation is used in home construction but the variety used for packing may not have the fire-retardant qualities or insulating rating that you need. Be sure you know what you have before you use it.

Changing laminate color

Is it possible or practical to change the color of plastic laminate to a lighter shade by painting? The present color is a gold which seems rather dark and unattractive.—Mrs. F.T. Bruce, Arcade, N.Y.

Paints do not bond readily to smooth, hard laminate surfaces, and no air-drying finish can match the durability of the laminate itself. You could try roughening the surface with a medium-coarse steel wool to provide a "tooth" for paint, but don't be surprised if the coating doesn't hold up well.

Paint over wallpaper?

What type of paint should I apply over wallpaper?—Mrs. Jack Loomis, Detroit, Mich.

Think of the job of getting the paper off after you paint it—even one coat! I *never* suggest this procedure. In rare instances there may be a good reason for painting over paper; otherwise, no! Why not remove the old paper, even if it is several layers thick, and begin anew with the attractive and easily applied interior paints that are now available? You'll be pleased in the end.

by W. Clyde Lammey

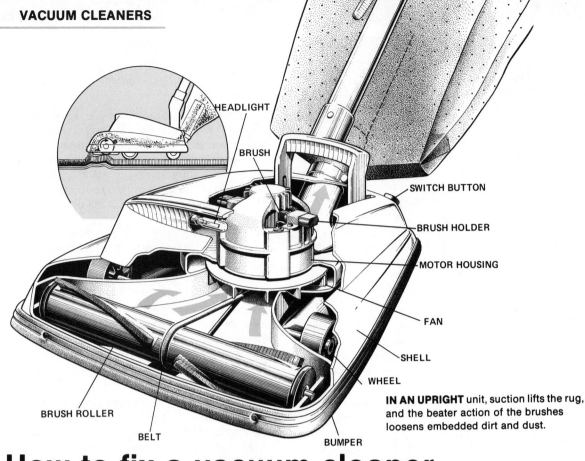

HEADLIGHT

BRUSH

SWITCH BUTTON

BRUSH HOLDER

MOTOR HOUSING

FAN

SHELL

WHEEL

BRUSH ROLLER

BELT

BUMPER

IN AN UPRIGHT unit, suction lifts the rug, and the beater action of the brushes loosens embedded dirt and dust.

How to fix a vacuum cleaner

By ED FRANZESE

■ A VACUUM CLEANER is a simple appliance; with the aid of trouble-shooting charts on the following pages, you should be able to deal with most of its common problems. The machine is basically a motor-driven fan with a nozzle attached, either directly or with a hose, to its low-pressure end. Atmospheric pressure forces air into the nozzle and dirt is carried with it and on through into the bag.

There are two types: the upright and the tank or canister. The upright usually, and the tank sometimes, has a motor-driven brush to loosen embedded dirt.

Nearly all vacuum cleaners use universal motors with replaceable carbon brushes. These bear under spring pressure on the commutator; they are eventually consumed and when worn, can cause problems. Many vacuum-cleaner designs offer direct access to brushes.

SEE ALSO
Electrical wiring . . . Testers, continuity

You can test the suction of a hose-equipped cleaner with a vacuum gauge, available through most heating and refrigeration-supply houses; it simply plugs into the hose. Vacuum is expressed in terms of water lift—how many inches above its normal level a column of water is pulled—and between 50 and 70 in. is normal for most cleaners.

When motor armature and fan both turn freely, a malfunctioning vacuum cleaner's trouble is probably electrical. Tests are outlined on the next page. If the ohmmeter reading for the entire circuit is higher than 2-4 ohms, it may indicate poor connections; no reading (infinite resistance) may indicate an open or shorted circuit. You can also check the circuit for grounds by placing one lead of the ohmmeter or continuity tester on one plug prong and the other on any *metal* part of the cleaner, then doing the same with the other prong. There should be no readings. Most cleaners have one or more capacitors across the circuit to eliminate radio interference; if a short or ground is indicated, remove the capacitor and retest. If the short or ground disappears, replace the capacitor with one of exactly the same value.

Motor will not run

POSSIBLE CAUSES	WHAT TO TRY
1. Fuse blown or circuit breaker tripped.	Replace fuse or reset circuit breaker. If blowing or tripping is repeated, disconnect power and check for shorts.
2. Line cord defective.	Inspect cord for breaks or fraying. Check for continuity by removing cord at terminals; placing one lead of tester on plug prong, other on corresponding terminal wire, flex cord. There should be an uninterrupted reading. Repeat for other prong, wire. Replace cord if there is no reading or flexing cord interrupts reading.
3. Switch defective.	Place continuity-tester leads on switch terminals; turn switch on. There should be a reading. Turn switch off. There should be no reading. Replace switch if there is variation.
4. Connection loose at terminal block.	Check all terminal-block connections; tighten any found loose.
5. Motor brushes worn or sticking.	Check lengths of brushes. Replace them if ¼ in. or shorter. Check for free brush movement in holder. If tight, sand brushes just enough to make them slide easily.
6. Armature shorted or open.	Place ohmmeter test leads on brush holders, rotate armature manually. Resistance reading should remain fairly constant. Sharp decrease indicates short, infinite reading indicates open. Replace armature in either case; new motor may be required.
7. Fan jammed.	Check for obstructions, clear. Replace fan if bent or damaged.
8. Motor bearings frozen.	Disassemble motor, clean and lubricate bearings. Replace bearings if worn.
9. Motor defective.	Disconnect both motor leads; direct test with 110-v. jumpers. Replace motor if defective.

Motor stops and starts

POSSIBLE CAUSES	WHAT TO TRY
1. Intermittent break in line cord.	Shake cord while vacuum is running; inspect for wear. Test continuity as explained above.
2. Loose connection.	Check entire circuit; tighten all connections.
3. Switch defective.	Test switch as explained above.
4. Wiring shorted.	Locate short, repair, insulate with electrical tape.

Motor runs too slowly

POSSIBLE CAUSES	WHAT TO TRY
1. Bearings tight or misaligned.	Disassemble motor; check, realign and lubricate bearings. Replace bearings if worn.
2. Fan jammed.	See chart, "Motor will not run" (above).
3. Brush contact poor.	Check brush length as in chart, "Motor will not run." If length is okay, stretch brush springs slightly.

Straight-suction upright

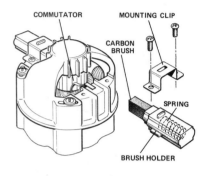

Typical brush assembly

COMMUTATOR   MOUNTING CLIP

CARBON BRUSH

SPRING

BRUSH HOLDER

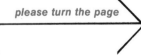

please turn the page

Typical tank-type cleaner

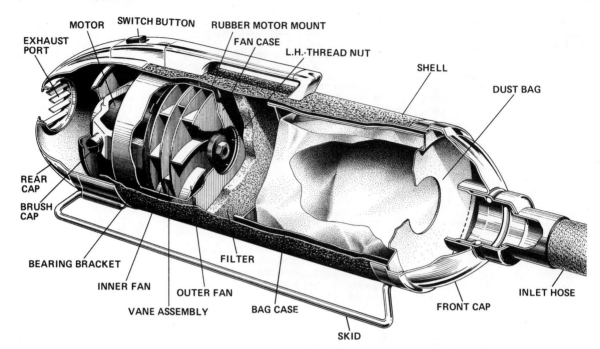

Motor runs too fast

POSSIBLE CAUSES	WHAT TO TRY
1. Fan loose.	Check and tighten fan.
2. Armature shorted.	See chart, "Motor will not run."
3. Dust bag overloaded.	Replace or clean bag.

Motor sparks

POSSIBLE CAUSES	WHAT TO TRY
1. Commutator dirty.	Clean thoroughly with trichlorethylene, sand with 2/0 or finer sandcloth.
2. Brushes worn.	See chart, "Motor will not run."
3. Brushes new.	Normal. Sparking will diminish when new brushes wear to shape of armature.
4. Armature wire open.	See chart, "Motor will not run."

Motor is noisy

POSSIBLE CAUSES	WHAT TO TRY
1. Foreign matter.	Clean out motor.
2. Brushes new.	Normal. Noise will diminish when new brushes wear.
3. Armature obstructed.	Check armature bearings for misalignment or wear; realign or replace.
4. Fan bent or loose.	Check fan, tighten on shaft. Replace fan if blades are bent.

Suction is weak

POSSIBLE CAUSES	WHAT TO TRY
1. Attachment or hose connection loose.	Check hose, attachments to make sure connections are tight.
2. Obstruction in hose or attachment.	Check for large pieces of paper, pins, wads of lint, and clear.
3. Cover loose.	Check for correct insertion of bag. Adjust and reclose cover.
4. Bag overloaded.	Replace or clean bag.
5. Hose leaking.	Check entire length of hose for cracks, holes. Replace hose if any are found. Also check for tight connections between hose, tank and attachments.
6. Exhaust port clogged.	Clear exhaust port.
7. Belt broken.	(Upright models.) Replace belt.
8. Agitator brush jammed.	(Upright models.) Clear brush of all foreign matter—brush should turn freely.
9. Nozzle setting wrong.	Check nozzle setting according to manufacturer's instructions for type of cleaning being done.

Dust leaks into room

POSSIBLE CAUSES	WHAT TO TRY
1. Holes in dust bag.	Replace bag.
2. Bag installed incorrectly.	Check manufacturer's instructions for correct installation of bag.
3. Sealing gasket defective or leaking.	Check gasket, replace if worn or broken. Also check gasket alignment where cleaner opens for insertion and removal of bag.
4. Bag overloaded.	Replace or clean bag.

Electrical tests

Place test leads across: 1. A and G to test entire circuit (should be 2-4 ohms); 2. A and B, G and H to test line cord (there should be continuity in each leg); 3. C and D to test switch; 4. E and F, I and J to test field coils (there should be continuity in each); 5. I or E and motor case to test for shorts (there should be no continuity); 6. F and J to test armature, turning it by hand (resistance reading should be constant). Tests 1 and 6 require ohmmeter; rest can be done with continuity tester. Power must be disconnected for *all* tests.

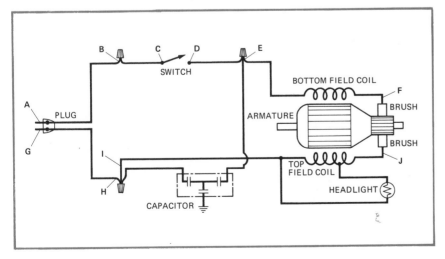

Canister variations

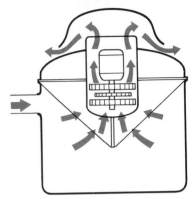

TOP-MOUNTED MOTOR (SHOP VACUUMS)

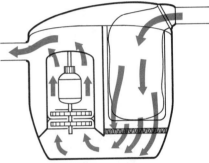

SIDE-MOUNTED MOTOR

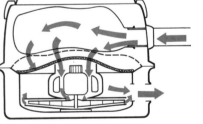

BOTTOM-MOUNTED MOTOR

AIR CUSHION

Build an elegant vanity

By HARRY WICKS

■ BECAUSE IT IS GENERALLY surrounded by lights, mirrors and medicine cabinet, the vanity often becomes the focal point in the bathroom. Design consultant Roger Wothe of Environments, Inc., Edina, Minn., took advantage of this fact when he remodeled his home. He gave great attention to the elegant version shown at right.

Construction consists of putting together a basic box with a pair of partitions installed inside. The vanity's beauty is enhanced when an oak plastic laminate by Formica Corp. is bonded to the box's exterior and the final touches—masculine hardwood moldings, and legs created from store-bought spindles—are applied. The finished product is a fine piece of bathroom furniture—durable, functional and attractive. Designed with a strong Mediterranean accent, its styling will suit almost any decor.

SEE ALSO

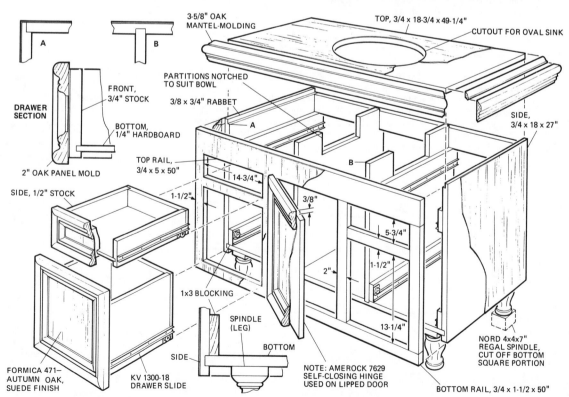

Velvetizing adds a soft and colorful touch

By WAYNE C. LECKEY

■ IF YOU CAN PICTURE a deep-pile coating of velvet being sprayed from a gun, you can begin to understand how a unique decorating system called VelveTouch works. However, you don't use a regular spray gun, and the velvet fibers are not really sprayed—they're applied by a special gun called a wand and the fibers are actually pulled from the wand, not blown.

The velvet fibers transform commonplace items into unusual ones, and you can velvetize practically anything whether it's made of wood, metal, plastic, glass, leather or fabric. A partial list of objects you can velvetize includes decoupage boxes, ceramic items, picture frames, bottles, lamp bases and shades, wall switch plates, glasses, T-shirts, plaques, lunch boxes, trinket-chest drawers, old toys, toilet seats, trays, Easter eggs, Christmas gifts—and countless others. You have a choice of 16 colors and three different kinds of fibers called velvet, glow and sparkle.

Application is unique, child-safe and magically done by static electricity. The electrically charged, adhesive-coated surface attracts the velvet fibers like a magnet attracts steel filings, bedding and packing them perfectly erect in the adhesive to produce a thick-pile texture which looks and feels just like velvet.

When I first tried velvetizing I was fascinated watching the fibers sail mysteriously from the wand and bombard the adhesive-coated surface, and I was also surprised to find the technique so easy. As the instructions explain, the trick is to learn to spend two minutes or so more in wand work than your eye tells you since the electro-

SEE ALSO
**Bottle craft . . . Boxes, trinket . . .
Christmas decorations . . . Frames, art . . .
Gifts, Christmas . . . Jewelry**

GROUNDED WAND applicator is hand-held about 3 in. from object and rotated back and forth as it's aimed at adhesive-coated surface. Electrostatic action causes fibers to bombard surface and stand erect in adhesive, producing deep-pile texture which feels like velvet. It does not matter what position the wand is in; it velvetizes whether you hold it up, down or sideways.

static action can build an astonishingly dense nap as long as the adhesive remains "wet."

Basically, the technique is simple: You first brush a colored adhesive on the object to be velvetized, fill the wand with fibers of the desired color, flip a switch and gently rotate the wand back and forth as you aim it at the surface. As a final step, the surface is "combed" with the wand for bringing it very close to the surface without touching.

When the velvetized object is left untouched and the adhesive has been allowed to dry thoroughly (usually overnight), the velvet coating is exceptionally durable, even scrubbable.

There are three kinds of adhesive—multipurpose, super and fabric—and the one you want is dictated by the size of the object and fibers being used. Fabric adhesive creates a soft glue bed without stiffness. Multipurpose provides a relatively short working period of 20 minutes, a period in which the adhesive effectively accepts the fibers and assures good coverage. The slower-drying super (epoxy) adhesive provides 90 minutes of working time and is used where the area to be covered is extensive and thus requires more time to velvetize before the adhesive dries.

All adhesives are clear and, except for the fabric adhesive, require the addition of a color-

TYPICAL SPRAY SETUP

TO WORK PROPERLY, the system must be well grounded: Plug power unit into a grounded receptacle and also attach grounding clips to a water pipe and to adhesive coating. The latter is done by lining cardboard booth with aluminum foil and attaching clip to it as indicated in diagram at left.

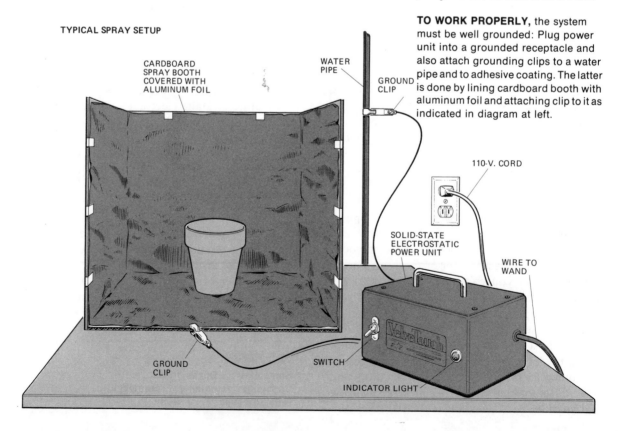

CARDBOARD SPRAY BOOTH COVERED WITH ALUMINUM FOIL

WATER PIPE

GROUND CLIP

110-V. CORD

SOLID-STATE ELECTROSTATIC POWER UNIT

WIRE TO WAND

GROUND CLIP

SWITCH

INDICATOR LIGHT

BASIC HOBBY MODEL includes a solid-state power unit (7) and wand applicator (4). Materials (not part of basic unit) include solvents (1, 2) for adhesives (5, 6) and fibers (3) available in 16 different colors. Colorant, enough to color a 7-fl.-oz. jar of adhesive, is bagged with fibers. Unit is ideal for school use and as way to earn extra income at home. Power unit and applicator wand can be rented from some hobby stores.

A 1-OZ. JAR OF COLORANT, packed with each 3½-oz. bag of fibers, is used to color the adhesive.

ADHESIVE is applied liberally with a brush to create a deep bed for fibers. Avoid thin spots.

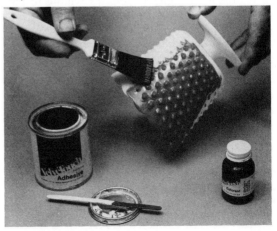

ant in order to tone them to the approximate shade of the fibers to assure good hiding.

There are several ways to establish a ground for the electrostatic process. A metal-top table makes a good surface to work on. If you are working with a cardboard booth, you can make a good grounding surface by lining the walls and floor of it with aluminum foil.

If the object should be made of a material that resists grounding such as unfinished wood or some plastics, you may ground directly into the wet adhesive by inserting a needle or hat pin and attaching the ground-wire clip to it. The pin is moved around during application.

Some small objects may be grounded for velvetizing simply by holding them in your hand and lightly touching a thumb or a fingertip to the wet adhesive.

For additional information about Velve-Touch, write American Art Clay Co., Inc., Box 68163, Indianapolis, IN 46268.

THIS BRAZILIAN ROSEWOOD veneer is laid out so that the beautiful figure of the wood can be matched.

All about furniture veneering

By LEN HILTS

Take an ordinary table or chest and perform the magic of applying a rare-wood veneer. Presto! You have a beautiful collectors' item for your home. The process is easy and the cost is low

■ WANT THE RARE BEAUTY of a Brazilian rosewood table to set off the decor in your living room? Or the richness of an ebony or teak desk to highlight the den? If you are willing to pay premium prices, you can find these pieces at fine furniture stores.

Or you can produce them yourself—by learning how to veneer.

Take an old table, desk, secretary or chest of drawers. Maybe you already have it, or can find one at a garage sale. Apply a veneer of exotic wood. Give the veneered piece a rich polyure-

thane varnish finish. The result can be a showpiece that becomes a focal point in any room.

Today, many rare woods are so scarce that they are available only in thin veneer sheets. These veneers are used by fine furniture makers to produce the very best furniture now being made. You can buy these veneer sheets—more than 100 exotic varieties are available—from specialty suppliers and woodworking supply houses at prices ranging from 30¢ to $1.15 a square foot.

Apply them yourself and make your own rare pieces. You can veneer a small table top for less than $10, and the price includes the tools and cement. Brazilian rosewood, a lovely red wood figured in black, was used to transform the gateleg table shown on these pages. It cost $19.

Veneers are applied to flat surfaces—table

tops, drawer fronts, cabinet sides. You can't veneer legs, turnings and oddly shaped parts, but you can stain these parts to match or blend with the veneer you use on the large areas.

A veneer is a paper-thin sheet of wood, usually $1/28$-in., shaved from a log with a veneering knife. When you apply veneer, you cement this thin wood to the core material with contact cement. The job is fairly simple when you know a few tricks and methods.

Some of the tricks depend on the veneer you buy. Very rare woods often are available only in sheets 4 in. wide and 36 or 48 in. long. Others may be available in sheets up to 18 in. or more in width. The rosewood we used came in 4 x 36-in. sheets.

If your veneer comes in sheets large enough to cover the area in one piece, the veneering job is simple. First cut the veneer sheet slightly larger than the area you intend to cover. Then sand the bottom surface of the veneer and the surface to which it is to be bonded, to remove irregularities, bumps and outstanding grain marks.

Because the veneer is so thin, any bump on the under surface will show through and perhaps give you problems in the final finishing operation.

Clean the sanded surface thoroughly with a tack rag. Now brush a coat of contact cement on the underside of the veneer sheet and also one to the surface to which it will be bonded. Make sure both surfaces are evenly and adequately coated.

Allow both surfaces to dry completely. Drying times vary with the brands of cement. To test for dryness, place a sheet of brown kraft paper on the cemented surface. If it can be touched to the surface without sticking, then the cement is ready.

Now place two sheets of brown kraft paper on the surface to which the veneer will be bonded. Each piece of paper should cover about half of the surface, and the two pieces should overlap 1 in. or more at the center. Position the veneer sheet, cement side down, on top of the kraft paper.

Move the veneer around until it is located exactly where you want it. You can do this because the kraft paper prevents contact between the two cement-coated surfaces.

When the veneer is positioned correctly, hold it firmly in place by pressing your hand near the center of one of the pieces of brown paper. Then, with your other hand, pull the other piece of brown paper out from between the veneer and the surface. The two cemented surfaces will then bond on contact.

There is no room for error here. Once the surfaces have bonded, they are permanently bonded. You can't pull them apart and start over. Now gently press the veneer to improve the bond. Then pull the paper from the other end.

Use a veneer roller (same as a wallpaper roller) over the entire surface to assure firm, even contact. Spend a lot of time rolling to be sure you cover every square inch. Any veneer which doesn't make good contact will show up as a bubble in the surface later.

When the veneer has been thoroughly rolled, trim the excess veneer from the edges. The best way is to turn the table upside down, with the veneer against a hardwood surface, and trim from the bottom side with a veneer saw (an inex-

SOME OF THE VENEER you buy may arrive as stiff, crinkled sheets. Before you can use it for veneering, it must be flattened. Do this by spraying a fine water mist over the veneer sheets—enough to thoroughly dampen them—and then place them between two heavy, flat sheets for 24 hours or more. These particle board sink-cutouts are ideal for the job.

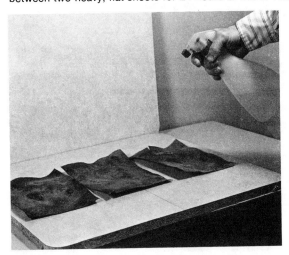

TO MATCH THE EDGES of small sheets of veneer, pick up the sheets to be matched so the edges are together, as shown. In the trade, this process is known as book matching.

pensive sawtoothed blade with an offset handle).

Cut with gentle, long strokes, taking care to keep the saw against the table edge so as to cut the veneer flush with it. If you are sawing across the grain of the veneer, reverse the saw stroke when working near the end of the cut, to prevent the veneer from splintering at the edge.

If you are doing a table top with a square edge, you can also veneer the edge. For the best job, veneer the edges first, then do the top of the table, which will then lap the top of the edges.

If you must match veneer sheets to cover a large surface—as we did with the pictured gateleg table—the first step is to lay the veneer sheets on the table top and arrange them so the color and pattern of the wood figure are most pleasing. Then you must "book" the edges.

The problem to be solved is this: The edges of veneer sheets are never true and straight, so you must cut them so they match perfectly.

TAPE THE SHEETS together with masking tape, being careful to align the edges. Then tape sandwich to a straightedge.

USE A VENEER SAW to trim the edges after clamping the straightedge firmly. Use long, smooth strokes.

PIN THE VENEER sheets to a flat surface with the trimmed edges butted together, and join them with masking tape.

POSITION the cement-coated veneer sheet on the kraft paper exactly as you want it. Then press with your hand.

WITH YOUR other hand, pull out one of the paper sheets. Press the veneer against the table top, then pull out other paper.

NOW USE the veneer roller to thoroughly roll the entire surface. It is vital to roll enough to get complete contact.

Study the photographs on these pages to see how this is done. You first pick up two sheets of veneer so that the matching edges are together. Square up these sheets and tape them together with veneering tape or masking tape. Put this taped sandwich between two long pieces of hardwood which you use as a straight edge. (The hardwood should be straight and true for this purpose.) Clamp the two pieces of hardwood together, allowing a small edge, perhaps ¼ in. of the veneer sandwich, to protrude.

Trim this protruding edge with the veneer saw. When you have finished, both sheets of veneer will have identical edges which fit together. Remove them from the hardwood and pin them to a flat surface with the edges butted tight together. Lay a wide piece of tape down across the butt joint to hold the pieces together.

Follow this same process to match the edges of all the veneer sheets. You will end up with a sheet of veneer large enough to cover the table top, made up of carefully joined and taped smaller pieces.

To finish this process, turn this veneer sheet over. Open each joint by folding it back, using the tape as a hinge. Run a thin bead of white (polyvinyl) glue on the edges of the veneer sheets, then fold them flat again. When you have finished applying the glue, tape the joints on the untaped side and set the sheet aside to dry.

The next morning, peel off the tape on the underside of the veneer sheet, and then apply the sheet to the table top with contact cement, as described earlier. Be sure to sand the underside before applying the contact cement. After the veneer has made contact with the table top, roll it, and roll it, and roll it some more to assure a good bond. Then strip off the masking tape on the surface, trim the edges, and proceed with a final finish.

NOW FOLD the joint open as shown and lay a bead of white glue in it. Then fold it closed, tape it, and allow the glue to dry.

WHEN THE VENEER has been joined, apply contact cement to both the table top and to the bottom side of the veneer sheet.

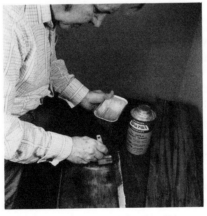

WHEN THE CEMENT has dried, place two sheets of brown kraft paper on the table, overlapping in the middle about an inch,

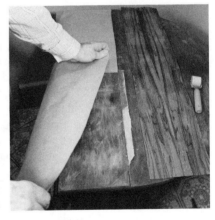

PULL off the tape which has held the two sheets together. Use your veneer saw to trim excess veneer from the edges.

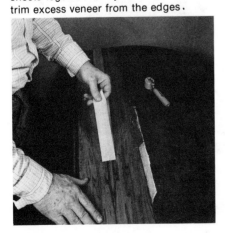

SHEETS OF VENEER have been matched, taped and glued and are ready for cementing to this table top.

THE ROSEWOOD veneer has now been cemented to the tabletop. The edges should be sanded.

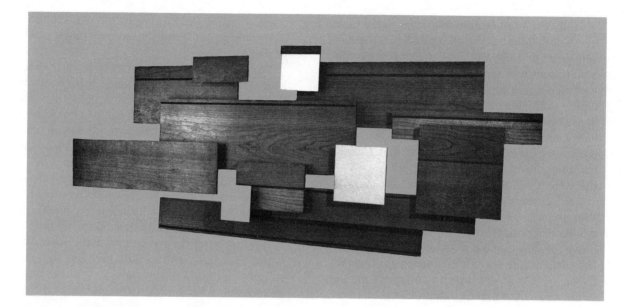

Decorate your walls with bits of paneling

By HARRY WICKS

■ A RECURRING QUESTION every time you panel a room is "What can I do with leftover ¼-in. plywood?" Since cutouts from window and door openings can, and usually do, represent considerable square footage, if you're an economy-minded do-it-yourselfer you automatically convert that square footage into dollars and cents to see what it cost you. Then, if you feel as I do, the scrap is stored in the shop for future use as drawer bottoms and cabinet backs.

One good and practical use for that scrap is to make wall plaques as pictured. Simply arrange pieces of wood paneling in layers to give an attractive three-dimensional appeal to wall decoration. Though we've selected two designs to show as a springboard for ideas, your plaques can be made to run the decorating gamut from Early American to traditional, Mediterranean and contemporary. And since the popular approach to home furnishing today is to draw from several sources, each design travels easily from one decor to another.

SEE ALSO

The plaques can be assembled from one type of paneling, or, if you have some of the recently evolved tinted panelings available, spots of color can be added to create a Mondrian-like design to the display. If you lack a variety of paneling, colors or materials in the room can be emphasized by painting several plaque elements or covering them with a fabric.

The beauty of the two designs shown is that if you have no scrap ¼-in. paneling, each arrangement can be made from less than a standard 4x8-ft. sheet of plywood. Thus, it is only necessary to purchase one sheet and the plaques still provide an elegant-looking wall treatment.

smooth all edges

After cutting the plywood pieces to size, and before assembling, shave any "whiskers" on the edges with a block plane and fine sandpaper wrapped around a block of wood.

Spacers. The various elements in the design can be placed in a variety of vertical planes by varying the thickness of the spacers. Whether you elect to use ¾, 1⅛ or 1⅝-in. stock, minimize any chance of splashing paint on the plywood's finished surface by painting the spacers before assembly. Though flat black enamel is recommended for spacers and plywood edges alike, color judiciously selected to blend with the room could be substituted if desired.

Designing your own plaques. You can turn your imagination loose and dream up one of your own plaque designs or refer to an art book for ideas. Impressionistic and pop art, in particular, are well suited for adaptation to a three-dimensional "painting." To start, lay out the arrangement on scaled graph paper. When satisfied with its looks, determine the size of each part and key it with a number. Working from the drawing, lay out the full-size pieces on the back of the plywood. Then, as you cut each piece on the table saw, a quick glance at the back will tell you what size to cut the scrap. Reference to the drawing also speeds up assembly.

Caution: In addition to white glue, be sure to use an ample number of brads to insure tight joints. And, to minimize the chance of the ¼-in. material warping on large panels, use an adequate number of spacers to keep unsupported areas small.

You can use standard picture hangers (the serrated type) or picture wire and screw eyes to hang the plaques. Just bear in mind that a sizable plaque will have considerable weight and require a hefty hook installed in a wall stud.

TO PREVENT flexible paneling from sagging under a fence, cut a piece of 2x4 stock to fit between the extension arms and clamp it to the fence bottom.

SPACERS ARE STAINED, then fastened to plywood using glue and ¾-in. brads through the plywood. Glue alone doesn't bond well to prefinished paneling.

WALL HANGERS are located equidistant from both ends and fastened in place. The panel edges are finished with a single coat of flat black enamel.

A handsome whatnot shelf

By RICHARD C. STICKLER

SEE ALSO

**Bandsaws . . . Gifts, Christmas . . . Routers . . .
Sabre saws . . . Shelves . . . Table saws . . .
Wood-lathe techniques**

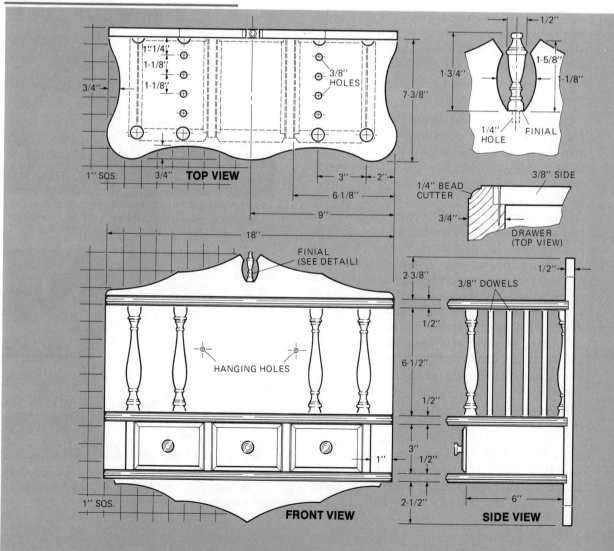

TOP VIEW

1" SQS.   3/4"

1"1/4"
1-1/8"
1-1/8"
3/4"
3/8" HOLES
7-3/8"

3"   2"
6-1/8"
9"

1/2"
1-3/4"
1-5/8"
1-1/8"
1/4" HOLE   FINIAL

1/4" BEAD CUTTER   3/8" SIDE
3/4"
DRAWER (TOP VIEW)

FRONT VIEW

18"
FINIAL (SEE DETAIL)
HANGING HOLES
1"
1" SQS.

SIDE VIEW

2-3/8"
1/2"
6-1/2"
1/2"
3"
1/2"
2-1/2"

3/8" DOWELS
1/2"
6"

■ **IF YOU ENJOY** the challenge of producing a fine piece of cabinetry, you'll be eager to try your hand at making this handsome whatnot shelf with its graceful turnings and pleasing scroll-cut shelves.

The original was made of solid walnut. However, to save gluing up several pieces to cut the 15⅞ x 18-in. back, walnut-faced plywood can be used. It also could be used for making the three scroll-cut shelves.

To make the whatnot, you'll need a bandsaw (or sabre saw) to cut the shelves and back, a router to shape the edges, a table saw to form the shelf grooves in the back and a lathe to produce the six turnings.

Patterns are needed for the back and shelves, but before you cut the back you must make the dadoes in it for the three shelves. The latter are identical, and the three can be bandsawed at one time. The blind holes for the turnings and dowels are identically spaced in mating surfaces with the aid of a template. All 12 holes are bored ¼ in. deep.

Two turnings make the four split ones. These are turned from blanks that consist of two pieces glued together with paper between. The paper permits the completed turning to be split apart neatly at the joint with a thin-bladed knife.

The drawer compartments are formed by gluing four dividers between the bottom and middle shelves. The shelves, dividers and turnings must be assembled as a single unit and then glued to the back. The four split turnings can be glued in place before or after the back section is added.

The three drawers are made to fit their respective compartments. The fronts are ¾ in. thick, the sides and backs ⅜ in. and the bottoms ¼ in. A small cove is shaped around the fronts and suitable metal knobs attached. The finial can be turned of wood or brass to complement the drawer knobs.

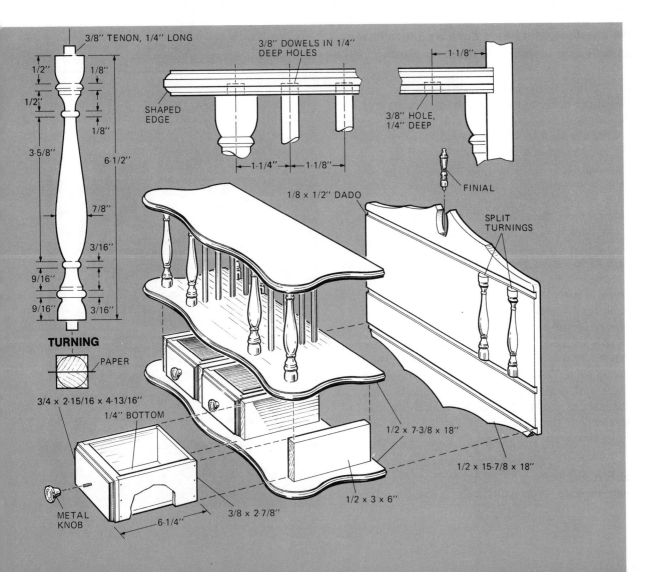

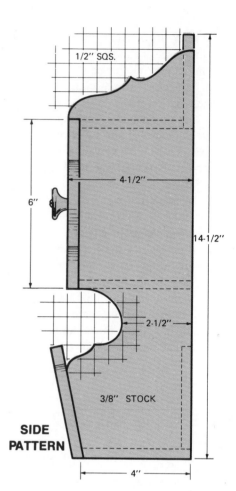

4-1/2"

1/2" SQS.

6"

14-1/2"

2-1/2"

3/8" STOCK

SIDE PATTERN

4"

An early American minishelf

By DON SHINER

This classic wall cabinet has a built-in picture frame as well as a planter and room for storing small items

■ THIS SMALL wall cabinet blends well with any decor because the picture-frame door is used to display favorite greeting-card scenes, which can be changed periodically to reflect the season. Behind the door, there is room for storing small personal and household items such as pens, pencils and pads. The tray below can be utilized as a planter for artificial or live greenery. If the latter is used, the tray must be fitted with a water-proof liner.

The 6 x 8-in. picture frame used was bought at a variety store; remaining measurements were determined by its size. For a larger or smaller frame simply adjust dimensions to suit. The cabinet looks best if made of a hardwood such as cherry or walnut. If you use pine, try to select boards with small, tight knots. The cutouts are sanded, glued and assembled as shown on the facing page. You can leave the piece natural and finish with a semigloss varnish or antique using the stain of your choice. To hang, turn two eye-screws into the underside of the top shelf and drive two screws through them.

SEE ALSO
Finishes, wood . . . Gifts, Christmas . . . Shelves

CABINET width is determined by the picture frame. Check width carefully, then glue up assembly.

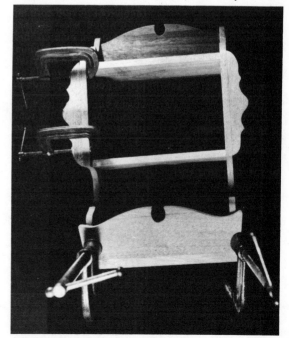

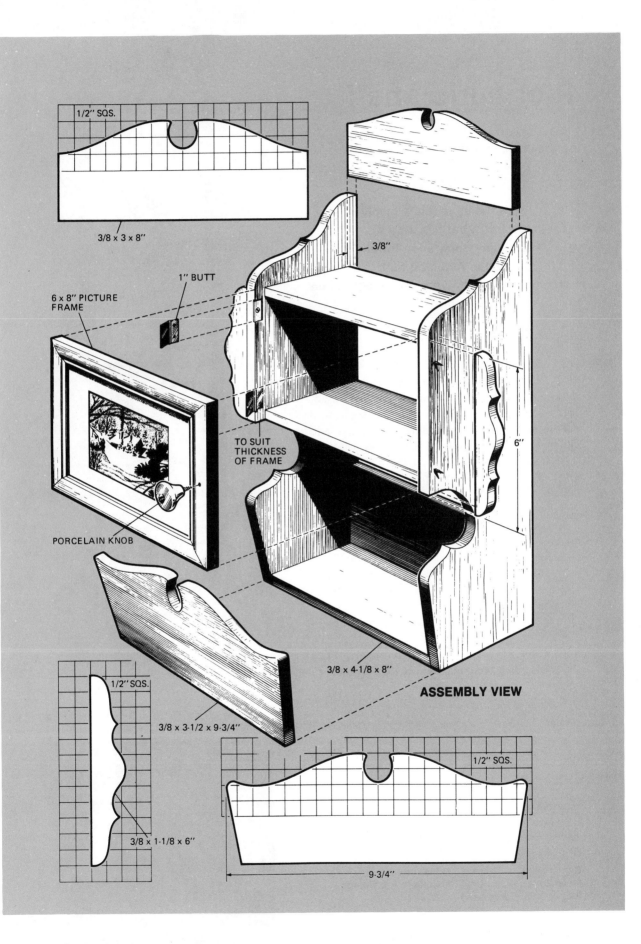

1/2" SQS.

3/8 x 3 x 8"

6 x 8" PICTURE
FRAME

1" BUTT

3/8"

TO SUIT
THICKNESS
OF FRAME

6"

PORCELAIN KNOB

3/8 x 4-1/8 x 8"

ASSEMBLY VIEW

1/2" SQS.

3/8 x 3-1/2 x 9-3/4"

3/8 x 1-1/8 x 6"

1/2" SQS.

9-3/4"

Pier curio shelf

By ROSARIO CAPOTOSTO

**Not only is this a display
cabinet for your curios, but it is also a
handsome decoration for any wall
in your home. It can be built
of common pine for a very reasonable price**

■ THIS CHARMING curio shelf will do wonders in showing off your most prized pieces of bric-a-brac, as well as making a handsome wall decoration itself. It is not difficult to make and can be fashioned from wood that is easy to obtain at a reasonable price. It cost me about $5 for 14 ft. of ½ x 8-in. common pine, a short length of cove molding, a piece of ⅛-in. hardboard and a wooden drawer knob.

Construction starts with the side panels. For an easy way to make the cutouts, bore a 2¼-in.-diameter hole as indicated in the drawing. Then, using a smooth-cutting blade, make two parallel internal cuts on the bench saw by lowering the blade below the saw table and then carefully positioning the board over it. Lock the rip fence in place, turn on the saw, then slowly raise the blade until it cuts through the top of the board. Feed the work along the fence until the cut is made to

FILLER BLOCKS are glued to the ends of each of the dadoes to conceal (make blind) the exposed grooves.

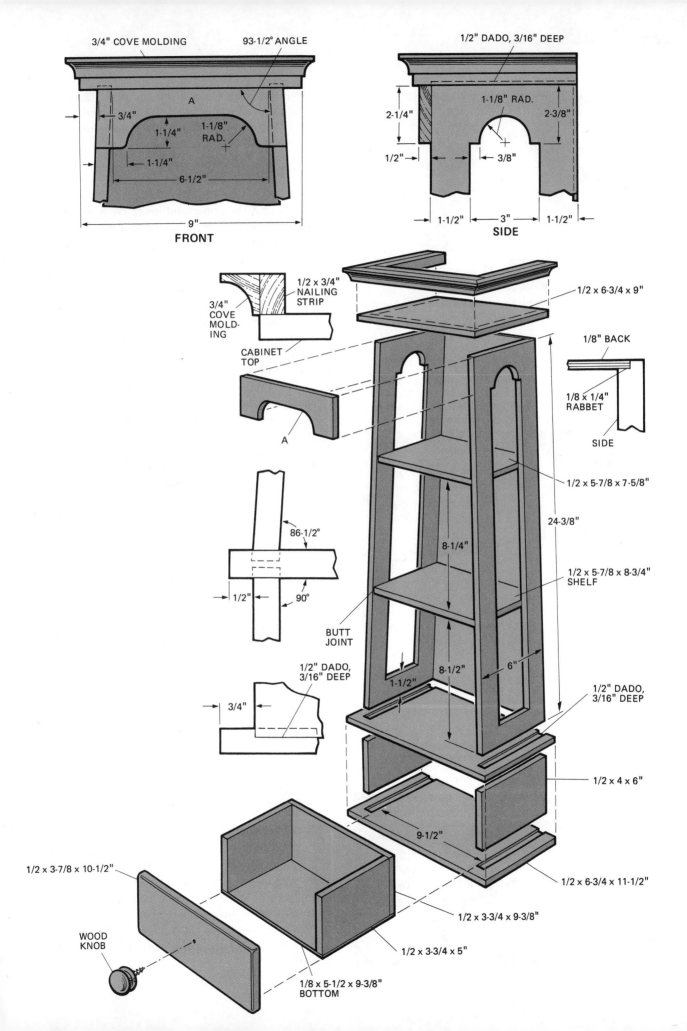

3/4" COVE MOLDING

93-1/2° ANGLE

1/2" DADO, 3/16" DEEP

A

3/4"

1-1/4"

1-1/8" RAD.

1-1/4"

6-1/2"

9"

FRONT

2-1/4"

1-1/8" RAD.

2-3/8"

1/2"

3/8"

1-1/2"

3"

1-1/2"

SIDE

1/2 x 3/4"
NAILING
STRIP

3/4"
COVE
MOLD-
ING

CABINET
TOP

A

1/2 x 6-3/4 x 9"

1/8" BACK

1/8 x 1/4"
RABBET

SIDE

1/2 x 5-7/8 x 7-5/8"

86-1/2°

1/2"

90°

24-3/8"

8-1/4"

1/2 x 5-7/8 x 8-3/4"
SHELF

BUTT
JOINT

1/2" DADO,
3/16" DEEP

3/4"

1-1/2"

8-1/2"

6"

1/2" DADO,
3/16" DEEP

1/2 x 4 x 6"

9-1/2"

1/2 x 6-3/4 x 11-1/2"

1/2 x 3-7/8 x 10-1/2"

WOOD
KNOB

1/2 x 3-3/4 x 9-3/8"

1/2 x 3-3/4 x 5"

1/8 x 5-1/2 x 9-3/8"
BOTTOM

A HOLE SAW is used in your drill press to make a circular cut at the top of the side panels.

WASTE is removed by raising the rotating blade and pushing the stock forward or backward.

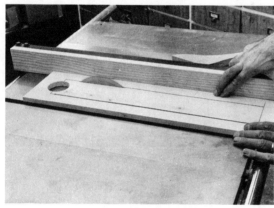

A SABRE SAW is used to complete the parallel cuts to the very corners to drop out the remaining waste.

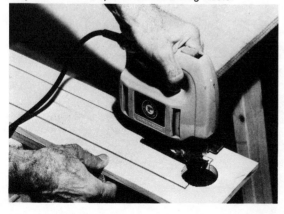

the length required. Cut off the power and wait until the blade comes to a full stop before taking the board away. Make the final corner cuts with a sabre saw to drop out the waste.

dado for side panels

Angled dado cuts are required to seat the side panels into the upper and lower cross members. Tilt the dado blade to a 86½° angle for these cuts. Blind dadoes are not necessary in any of the joints. Run the cuts through, then simply cut filler blocks and glue them into the exposed ends to fill the voids. This method will prove simpler and quicker than making blind dadoes. A ⅛ x ¼-in. rabbet is required at the rear of the side panels and the top and lowermost members to form a recess for the hardboard back panel. Sand all parts before you begin to assemble the shelf.

The two open shelves need not be set into dadoes as the other parts. Simple butt joints will do the job here. Carefully cut them to the exact length with the appropriate bevel so they will fit snugly against the sides. They can be secured by using finishing nails and glue. The top trim of the shelf looks like fancy router work, but is simply molding. Cove molding, ¾-in., is used for this trim work. Since its profile does not permit direct nailing to the top, small nailing strips are added to the back of the molding. Cut 45° miters to join the molding.

The finish is optional depending on your personal preferences. You can use stain, shellac, clear varnish or paint, or you may want to try a woodgraining finish. For the last, use a latex-based woodgraining or antiquing kit of the desired tone for quick results. Coat the surfaces with the latex-base coat and allow to dry (this usually takes about one hour). Then apply the glaze coat, working one main section at a time. Run a dry brush over the still wet glaze to produce the "grain." If the result is not quite what you want, simply wipe off the glaze and try again (you can't fail). If you want to highlight the corners, as was done here, run a dry rag pad over them before the glaze dries.

install back panel last

The hardboard back panel should be installed after finishing for an easier, neater job. Instead of graining the back panel, you may consider applying only the base coat to it. This will produce a neutral background which will allow your curios to stand out more clearly. Bore a hole near the top of the back panel for hanging on a screw.

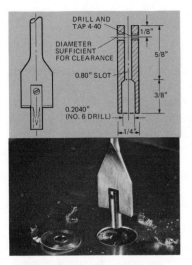

A SPADE BIT, used with the pilot shown, cuts holes in materials like aluminum and brass and does counterboring. Drill a ¼-inch hole through metal and backup, then use the bit at low speed.—*Hallan E. Goldstine, Port Jefferson, NY.*

THE SAFEST, easiest way to enlarge existing holes in thin sheet metal is with a tapered reamer, not a drill. It leaves the holes round and smooth; the slight taper of the hole is usually not noticeable.—*Federico Strasser, Santiago, Chile.*

A 2x2-FT. SQUARE of perforated hardboard, lashed with wire to the legs of a card table used as a drawing table, will accept hooks and shelves on both sides. Three sides could receive this treatment.—*Grace B. Weinstein, Los Angeles, CA.*

WOODEN TONGS can be handy in the shop. They're quickly and cheaply made from Popsicle-type sticks, glued to a block (four thicknesses of the same stock) and tapered slightly to the rear.—*Burt Web, Skokie, IL.*

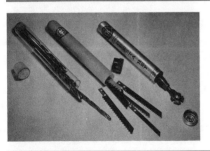

CIGAR TUBES make excellent storage for small tools such as drill bits and sabre-saw blades. In glass ones, put a cork or felt pad in the bottom to protect against breakage.—*W. B. May, Oak Park, IL.*

TO HELP in pulling nails with a hammer, a "four-thickness" block can be glued up from squares of scrap plywood. The block shown is 5½ in. square with ¼-in.-thick steps.—*Walter E. Burton, Akron, OH.*

How to hang wallpaper

■ THANKS TO the many "fabric"-backed wall coverings now available, wallpapering is easier than ever. Since these newer materials come in a wide variety of attractive patterns, they are especially desirable for a first venture.

There are several good reasons. First, these wall coverings are easier to work with than ordinary wallpaper. You can correct mistakes by peeling off strips already in place, without fear of ripping the material. Ordinary wallpaper, once pasted in place, usually cannot be reused. Sec-

ond, any adhesive on the surface can safely be washed off after the covering is in place.

Finally, wall coverings of the cloth type can be moved in position on the wall until they match perfectly with strips already in place. This maneuverability is extremely limited with ordinary wallpaper.

SEE ALSO
Bricks, simulated . . . Painting, interior . . . Remodeling . . . Tile, wall . . . Wall decorations . . . Wall shelves

Tools needed

Carpenter's square

Spirit level

Cutting board, ¾ x 24 x 72-in.

Clean sponge

Yardstick

Stepladder

Plumb line and chalk

Large scissors or shears

Two plastic buckets (one for paste and one for washing)

4-in. brush for applying paste (for unpasted wall covering)

Plastic water tray (for prepasted wall covering)

12-in. smoothing brush

Wall covering trimmer, utility knife or single-edge razor blades

Dropcloth

Corner and seam rollers

All tools required for wallpapering are available at well-stocked paint and wall-covering stores.

How to measure

A standard wall-covering roll contains 35 sq. ft.—narrow rolls are longer than wide ones. To allow for waste and matching, figure on covering 30 sq. ft. with each roll.

1. Measure the distance around room at baseboard.

2. Measure wall height from baseboard to ceiling.

3. Find number of rolls you need in chart (right). For example, if room is 8x12x16 ft. with a door and window (as sketched above):

4. Add room dimensions around baseboard: 12+12+16+16=56 ft.

5. Find 56 in first column of chart.

6. Find number opposite 56 in applicable wall-height column (8 ft.): 14 rolls are needed.

7. Compute square feet of window-door openings and trim, deduct proportionate number of rolls; in this case, deduct one roll for door and window—13 rolls are needed to cover the walls.

8. Before you paper a ceiling, use column at far right to estimate the number of rolls needed—eight in this case.

Around Room (ft.)	Rolls for Walls in Room With Height of			Border (yds.)	Ceiling (rolls)
	8′	9′	10′		
28	8	8	10	11	2
30	8	8	10	11	2
32	8	10	10	12	2
34	10	10	12	13	4
36	10	10	12	13	4
38	10	12	12	14	4
40	10	12	12	15	4
42	12	12	14	15	4
44	12	12	14	15	4
46	12	14	14	17	6
48	14	14	16	17	6
50	14	14	16	18	6
52	14	14	16	19	6
54	14	16	18	19	6
56	14	16	18	20	8
58	16	16	18	21	8
60	16	18	20	21	8
62	16	18	20	22	8
64	16	18	20	23	8
66	18	20	20	23	10
68	18	20	22	24	10
70	18	20	22	25	10
72	18	20	22	25	12
74	20	22	22	26	12
76	20	22	24	27	12
78	20	22	24	27	14
80	20	22	26	28	14
82	22	24	26	29	14
84	22	24	26	30	16
86	22	24	26	30	16
88	24	26	28	31	16
90	24	26	28	32	18

ROOM ESTIMATING CHART

Types of wall coverings and adhesives

Prepasted wall coverings are popular with do-it-yourselfers because they save time and create considerably less mess. They are available in most of the same designs as unpasted wall coverings.

Unpasted wall coverings offer a slightly greater selection of patterns and finishes, including both flocked and foil coverings. Different types of unpasted wall coverings require different types of adhesive. Use the chart at the right to determine the kind you need.

It is important to mix wheat paste or stainless paste at least one hour before you use it. Allowance for this setup time makes it easier to eliminate dry lumps. Properly mixed, the paste will be lump-free and have the consistency of heavy cream.

ADHESIVES CHART

	Wheat Paste or Stainless Paste	Liquid Strippable or Wheat Paste	Vinyl Adhesive	Stainless Paste
Regular wallpaper	X			
Strippable wallpaper		X		
Vinyl wall covering			X	
Foils			X	
Burlap with backing			X	
Burlap (porous)	X			
Cork with backing			X	
Silks and fabrics				X
Flocks, murals, hand prints, borders	Use adhesive appropriate for wall covering's backing			

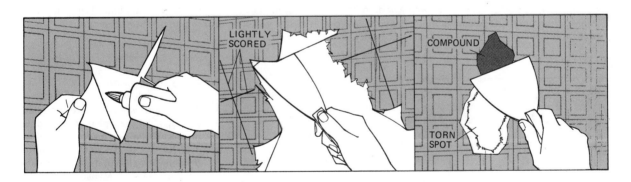

Dealing with old wallpaper

Don't underestimate the importance of properly preparing the walls to be covered. A professional generally removes an existing covering as there is always the possibility that it may work loose and ruin the new job. If you do cover existing wallpaper, make sure it's tight and smooth.

Cut an X in any air bubble and glue the paper back with white glue. Corners should be cut from floor to ceiling and reglued. Uneven spaces—where paper has pulled off the wall in spots, for example—should be filled with spackling compound and sanded. Check the joints of existing paper, fill with spackling compound and sand smooth where necessary—otherwise they may show through a new covering.

If there are two or more layers of paper on the walls,

remove them. The best way is to rent a steamer. It's easy to use and you will have no trouble if you follow instructions. Another way to remove paper is by sponging the walls with hot water and using a scraper. Keep in mind that the wetter the paper is, the faster it will come off. When removing paper from drywall, take care not to get under its layer of finish by mistake.

Some extra tips to make the job easier: Before starting the soaking operation, spread many layers of newspaper on the floor—remember that the paper that comes off the wall will have softened glue on the back, which can adhere to the floor, necessitating another soaking and scraping. Lightly score crosshatch marks over the paper with a utility knife (carefully so you don't damage the wall beneath); this will break the surface so that hot water will dissolve the old paste faster.

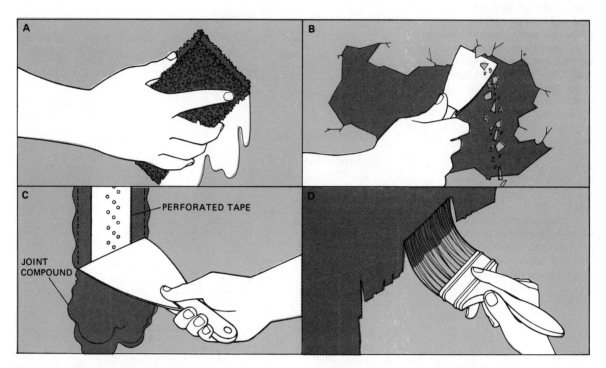

Preparing plaster and drywall surfaces

On unpainted plaster, make any needed repairs, scrape out loose cracks and fill with spackling compound (joint compound). Then apply a coat of wall size. Painted plaster should be thoroughly washed with detergent and water, rinsed with clear cold water. Make sure no soapy residue is left to dry on the surface. If necessary, remove peeling, chipped or cracked paint with a wide putty or joint knife and sand the surface smooth. Repair cracks or holes with spackling compound, sanding when dry. Dull a gloss or semigloss finish on existing paint with a strong soda solution or coarse-grit sandpaper; slick walls will not satisfactorily accept wall covering adhesives. On new plasterboard, tape seams and apply compound according to maker's directions. Set nailheads without breaking paper (dimple with hammer), cover with compound. Sand surfaces smooth when dry. Use two coats if necessary. Prime walls with oil, alkyd or latex primer-sealer; with latex, be sure to allow curing time. Sizing surfaces lets you slide covering in position, assures better adhesion.

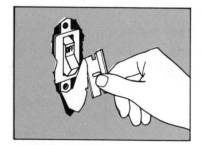

Switches, fixtures

Before wall covering is applied, all switch plates and outlet covers should be removed and wall fixtures loosened and pulled away from the wall. Remove fixture wall brackets *after turning off power at service panel* and then disconnecting wires. When the wall covering is in place, cut an area slightly smaller than wall plate so that plate covers cutout completely.

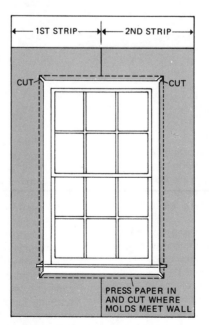

Papering around windows, doors

Doors and windows are handled exactly alike, except that a window means extra wall to be covered below it. Make a rough cutout by measuring from the last strip to the window casing and add ½ in. Measure the same way from ceiling and baseboard to trim. Remove the cutout before applying paste. Hang the strip, press in around casing and roll the joint with the seam roller, trim excess paper. Measure cutout size for the second strip as for the first and hang it, butting the first strip, in the same manner. Press and roll at joint with casing, trim. If you have taken care in cutting strips, pattern-matching at doors and windows will present no problem.

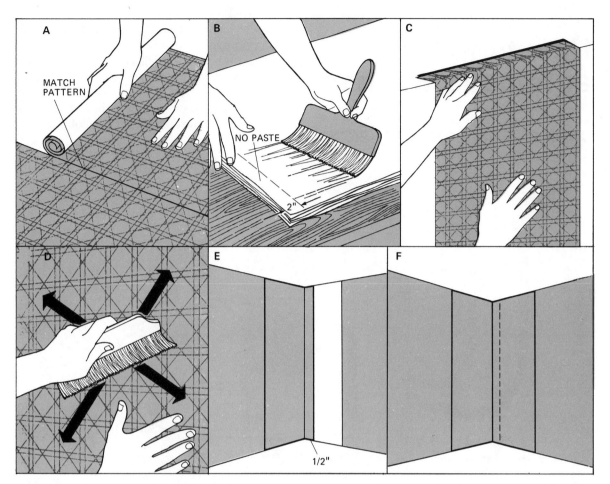

Preparing and hanging the wall covering

Two rules of thumb: If you plan to paper all the way around the room, hang the first strip along the edge of a door or window. If there is a fireplace in the room, center the first strip over it and work in both directions from there.

On an ample-sized table—a 2x6-ft. piece of ¾-in. plywood on sawhorses is fine—unroll the wall covering and lay it face up. Measure out wall height and add 6 in. allowance for trim. Lay the second strip next to the first, match the pattern and cut it to the same length. Lay the second strip on top of the first and continue matching and cutting strips in this manner.

When all strips are cut, turn over the stack of paper. Apply adhesive evenly with a large paste brush. Start at the center and brush toward the bottom. For easier handling, leave a 1-in. strip at the bottom unpasted. Allow about three minutes for the paper to expand before you handle it. Now fold the bottom half of the strip toward the center, paste to paste, without creasing the paper. Stop short of the center so that the fold you later make from the top will be slightly longer than the bottom one. Align the edges carefully. Apply paste to the top half of the strip as to the bottom, wait for paper to expand, and fold the top over to the center. The 1 in. unpasted strip at the top should overlap the bottom edge folded up to the center.

To hang the paper, unfold the top section and place the strip high on the wall, overlapping the ceiling-wall joint by approximately 2 in., and aligning its edge with a vertical snapped with your chalked plumb line. Give the upper section a couple of strokes with your smoothing brush to hold it to the wall. Then open the lower section. When you are satisfied with the paper's alignment, brush the entire strip smooth. Always brush from the center toward edges to get rid of air bubbles. Trim off excess paper at baseboard and ceiling joint and around doors and windows.

To hang the second strip, use the first as a guide, matching the pattern and butting—not overlapping—the seams. Repeat the smoothing procedure, then roll the seam with the seam roller. On flocked or embossed wall covering, seams should not be rolled—instead, tap along the seam with the tips of the smoothing-brush bristles. Clean strips with a damp sponge immediately to remove any paste on the surface, ceiling or baseboard. Hang remaining strips the same way.

To prepare a corner, measure from the last strip to the corner at ceiling level, midpoint and baseboard. Add ½ in. to the widest measurement, cut a strip to this width, and hang it in the usual manner; it will overlap the corner by ½ in. Snap a plumb chalkline over this overlap for use as a guide in hanging the first strip on the other wall of the corner. This technique will give you a true vertical even if the corner is not perfectly straight.

How to fix an automatic washer

COMMON WASHER COMPONENTS

■ A MALFUNCTION in your automatic washer usually affects a basic function: fill, wash (agitation), drain or spin.

The troubleshooting charts on these pages will help you pinpoint a problem and correct it. To determine what the common components look like and their location, refer to the large illustration. It's a composite that's typical of most machines.

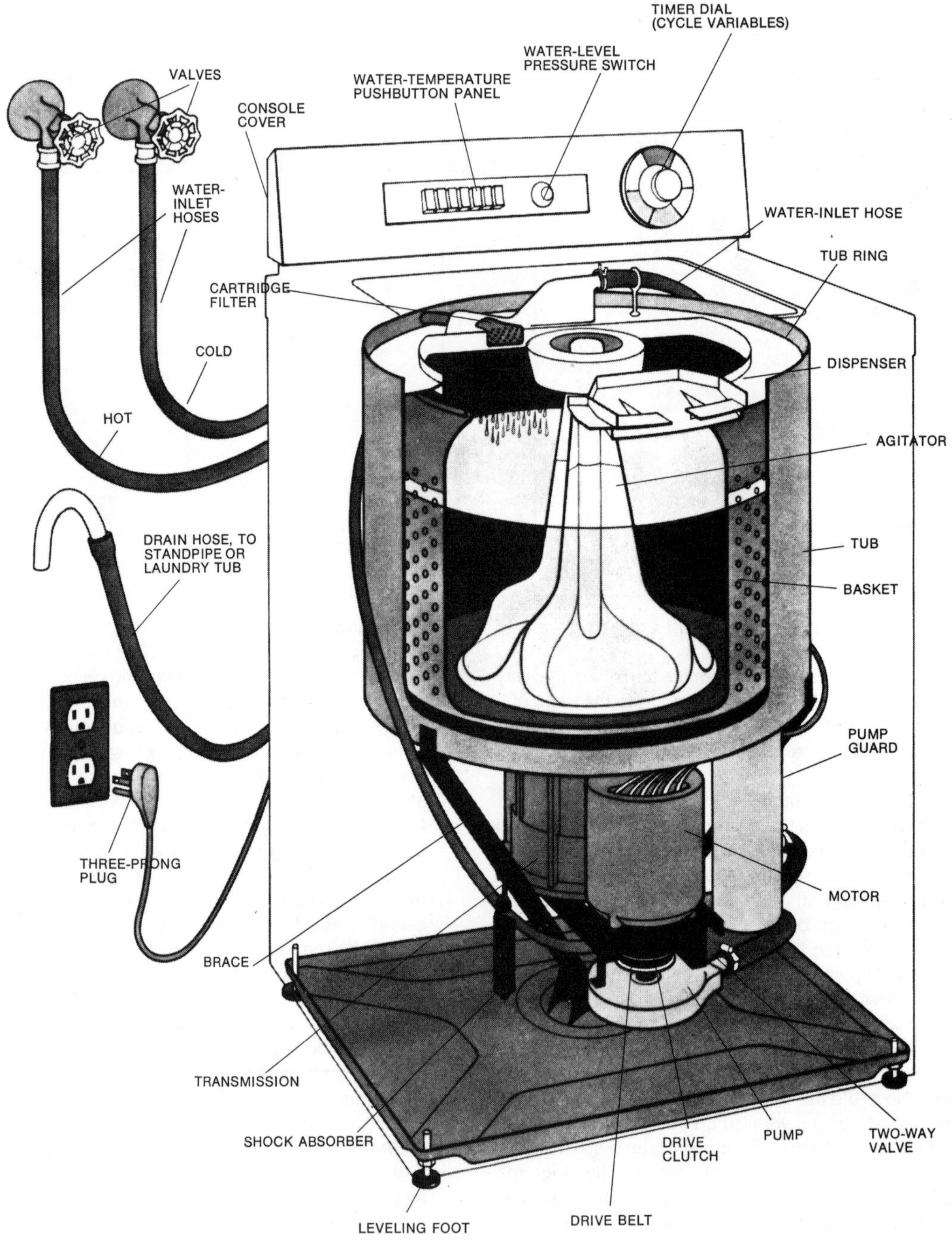

VALVES
CONSOLE COVER
WATER-INLET HOSES
WATER-TEMPERATURE PUSHBUTTON PANEL
WATER-LEVEL PRESSURE SWITCH
TIMER DIAL (CYCLE VARIABLES)
WATER-INLET HOSE
TUB RING
DISPENSER
AGITATOR
TUB
BASKET
CARTRIDGE FILTER
COLD
HOT
DRAIN HOSE, TO STANDPIPE OR LAUNDRY TUB
THREE-PRONG PLUG
PUMP GUARD
MOTOR
BRACE
TRANSMISSION
SHOCK ABSORBER
LEVELING FOOT
DRIVE BELT
DRIVE CLUTCH
PUMP
TWO-WAY VALVE

SEE ALSO
Appliance centers . . . Clothes dryers . . .
Heaters, water . . . Irons . . . Laundry counters

When testing electrical components, consult your machine's wiring diagram, which is glued on the back of, or inside, the machine. The chart with this article will help you interpret the electrical symbols.

To test the timer, turn the control knob slowly from the "Off" position before the regular cycle to the spot in the cycle where the machine isn't working properly as you count the number of increments (clicks). Count the corresponding increments on the timer cam chart and determine which terminals should be closed. Timer contact terminals are marked on the timer and timer cam chart by a letter or numerical code. Connect a 115-v. test light to the terminals and turn on the machine. If the test light fails to light, the timer is faulty in that model and should be replaced.

Washer doesn't fill

CAUSE	ACTION TO TAKE*
1. Water faucet(s) closed.	Open faucet(s).
2. Water inlet hoses kinked.	Straighten hoses.
3. Clogged water valve screens.	Remove screens and flush out sediment.
4. Damaged water valve solenoid.	Remove leads and connect a 115-v. test light across terminals, turn on electricity and move control knob to "Fill." No light signifies a bad solenoid. Replace.
5. Defective timer.	Test as described in text above.
6. Defective water temperature switch.	Remove leads and connect a 115-v. test light across terminals, turn on electricity and move control knob to "Fill." No light signifies a bad solenoid. Replace.
7. Defective water-level pressure switch.	The switch normally has three terminals. With switch in "Fill" position there is contact between two of the terminals with the third terminal "open." Make sure you connect a 115-v. test light across the terminals affecting "Fill." Consult the wiring diagram. Turn on electricity and move control knob to "Fill." No light signifies a bad solenoid. Replace.
8. Water valve internal malfunction.	Disassemble water valve and check each part for damage, paying particular attention to the guide assembly and diaphragm. Replace the bad part, if possible. If not, replace the whole valve.
9. Open circuit.	Using the wiring diagram as a guide, probe each wire connection with a 115-v. test light to determine if defective wiring or a loose connection is causing the problem. Be sure control knob is at "Fill" position.

*After taking each "action," reconnect power and test operation, but be sure to pull plug from wall receptacle before continuing.

Washer doesn't drain

CAUSE	ACTION TO TAKE
1. Kinked drain hose; clogged drain.	Straighten hose; clear drain.
2. Broken or slipping drive belt.	Replace or tighten.
3. Defective pump.	Usually pump is clogged or impeller goes bad. Pump may be taken apart for cleaning or replacement of defective parts, or it may be replaced as a unit.
4. Defective timer and open circuit.	If the motor doesn't kick into "Drain," test timer as described in text above. Also check for open circuit. Be sure the control knob is set to "Drain" position.

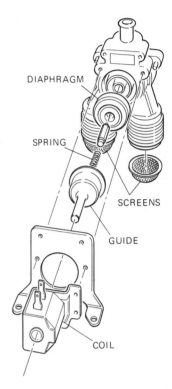

WATER VALVE

DIAPHRAGM

SPRING

SCREENS

GUIDE

COIL

WATER PUMP

HOUSING

LARGE IMPELLER

PLATE

SMALL IMPELLER

GASKET

COVER

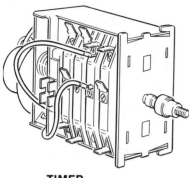

TIMER

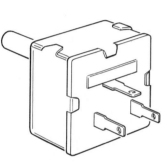

**WATER-
TEMPERATURE
SWITCH**

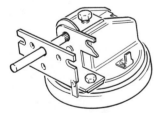

**WATER-LEVEL
PRESSURE
SWITCH**

Washer doesn't agitate (wash)

CAUSE	ACTION TO TAKE*
1. Broken or slipping drive belt.	Replace or tighten.
2. Defective drive clutch.	Remove the drive belt and turn the clutch by hand with the control knob in the "Wash" (agitate) position. If there is no "grab," the clutch is defective and should be replaced.
3. Defective transmission.	With the drive belt off, manually rotate the transmission pulley in agitate direction (usually clockwise) with control knob in "Wash" (agitate) position. If this doesn't drive the agitator, the problem is in the transmission.
4. Defective timer.	Test as described in text.
5. Faulty water-level pressure.	When water has filled the tub, contact reverts to the third terminal of this switch and to one of the other two terminals. The remaining terminal reverts to "Open" position. Make sure to connect a 115-v. test light across the terminals affecting "Filled." Consult the wiring diagram. Turn on the electricity and move the control knob to "Wash." No light signifies that you have a bad switch.
6. Open circuit.	Using the wiring diagram as a guide, probe each wire connection with a 115-v. test light to determine if either defective wiring or a loose connection is causing the problem. Make certain that the control knob is set at the "Wash" position.

*After taking each "action," reconnect power and test operation, but be sure to pull plug from wall receptacle before continuing.

Washer doesn't spin or spins slowly

CAUSE	ACTION TO TAKE
1. Broken or slipping drive belt.	Replace or tighten.
2. Loose motor pulley.	Tighten pulley.
3. Defective drive clutch.	Test as described under "Washer doesn't agitate," Cause 2 (above); be sure control knob is in "Spin" position.
4. Spin brake doesn't release or transmission is frozen.	The brake is not part of the transmission, but since they are attached and work together, they are checked as a unit. Set control knob in "Spin" position and remove drive belt. Turn brake stator; it should move freely. If not, the brake assembly or transmission is defective. Both units can be repaired.
5. Defective timer or open circuit.	If motor doesn't kick into "Spin," test timer as in text. Also check for open circuit. Be sure the control knob is set to the "Spin" position.

Abide by the following precautions:

• Be sure that electricity is turned off before handling components.
• Turn off water when working on water-handling components, such as the water valve.

• Before replacing an electrical component you believe is faulty, make certain that a loose connection isn't causing the problem.

• After replacing an electrical component, tighten connections.

• Before reconnecting your electrical service, see to it that ground wires are tightly attached.
• Make sure that water connections are secure.
• Install replacement parts that meet factory specification. You can't go wrong using parts made by the manufacturer of the washer.

Motor doesn't run

CAUSE	ACTION TO TAKE*
1. Electrical service cord isn't plugged in; blown fuse or a tripped circuit breaker; possible malfunction in branch circuit.	Be sure that plug is connected and fuse or circuit breaker is okay. If there is no power at the wall receptacle, check the circuit.
2. Defective timer.	Test as described in text.
3. Defective lid switch.	Many models have a switch in the lid which automatically turns the washer off if door is open during cycling. If the machine refuses to operate with the lid closed, connect a test light across the lid switch. No light indicates a faulty switch. Replace.
4. Defective motor.	Most motors are protected by an internal overload circuit breaker that stops operation if the motor overheats. If this protective device halts motor operation, but the motor can be started again after about 30 minutes, consider the following conditions:

(a)
If the motor trips off when the machine goes into the spin cycle, the cause of trouble may be in the clutch, brake or transmission—not the motor. To find out, remove transmission drive belts and let the motor operate. If it doesn't trip off now, there is no motor problem.

(b)
If the motor operates in agitate position, but won't operate in spin position or vice versa, check timer and lid switch, and look for broken wire before condemning the motor.

CAUSE	ACTION TO TAKE*
5. Open circuit.	This possibility always exists, so before you rip the motor out of the machine conduct continuity tests with your test light at each wire connection.

*After taking each "action," reconnect power and test operation, but be sure to pull plug from wall receptacle before continuing.

TRANSMISSION PULLEY

SPIN PULLEY

1/2"

1/2"

1/2"

PUMP PULLEY

PROPER belt tension is reached when you can deflect it ½ in. Minimum belt tension after extended use should be 15 pounds. To check this, hook spring scale at mid-point and note what force is required to deflect the belt 1 in.

Symbols found in wiring diagrams

ITEM	OLD	NEW	ITEM	OLD	NEW	ITEM	OLD	NEW
Ballast			Terminal			Double-throw thermostat		
Adj. Thermostat			Timer motor			Internal conductor		
Thermocouple			Plug connector			Harness wire		
Neon light	None		Starter (automatic)			Permanent connection		
Transformer	None		Light (incandescent)			3-prong plug		
Thermistor	None		Pressure sw.			Timer sw.		
Transistor	None		Fluorescent			Automatic sw.		
Diode (rectifier)	None		Coil			Manual sw.		
Rectifier (controlled)	None		Capacitor			Double throw		
Coil and switches			Resistor	500	500 Ω	Crossover		
Motor, single speed			Centrifugal sw.			Heater (wattage shown)	2800	2800w.
Motor, multispeed	1725 1140	1725 1140	Thermostat			Ground		

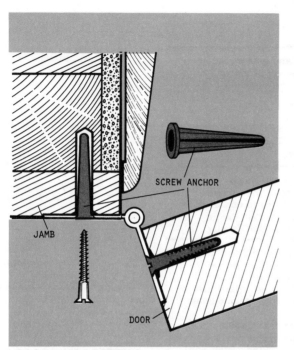

LOOSE HINGE SCREWS can be tightened quickly by using plastic drywall anchors. Just choose anchors sized to suit the screws and screw holes and drive them in the oversize holes.—*Leo Niemi, Warren, OH.*

PLANING A DOOR when you have no helper to hold it steady will be easier if you use bar clamps and a block of wood as shown. Then you can hold the plane with both hands.—*Abe Contreras, Azusa, CA.*

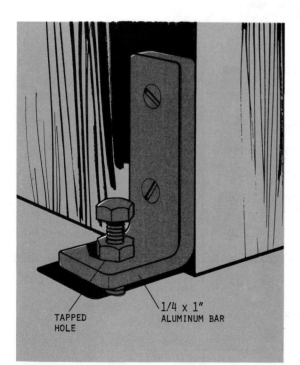

A WOBBLE PROBLEM with a bench-saw cabinet or other toolstand can be eliminated with this leveler. Drill and tap one end of an L-shaped bar. —*Doug Blodgett, St. Charles, MO.*

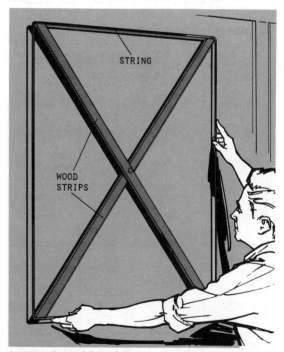

GETTING AN OPINION as to the right spot to hang a heavy mirror wears out your arms less if you hold up a dummy mirror made to the same size from lattice strips .—*Fred Rittenbusch, Elsinore, CA.*

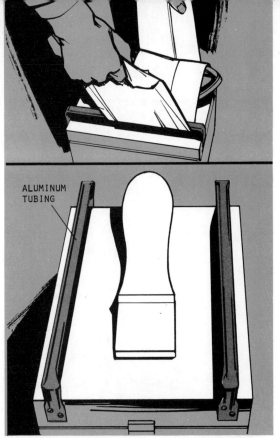

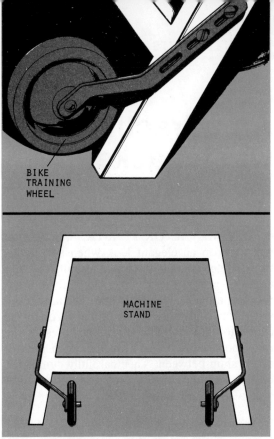

POLISHING YOUR SHOES will be easier and you'll also get a better shine if you add tubing to each side of the shoeshine box so the cloth can be pulled up instead of down.—*George Walker, Nutley, NJ.*

TRAINING WHEELS no longer needed on a kid's bike will make it easy for you to roll a heavy bench saw around your shop when they're bolted to a pair of legs on the machine stand.—*P. R. Bliss, Atlanta, MI.*

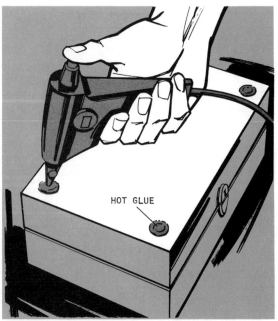

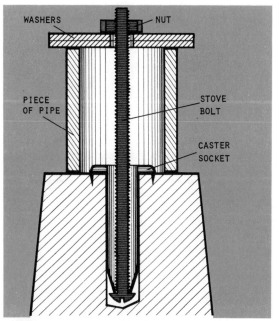

IMPROVISED "FEET" for a trinket box can be mere dabs of hot-melt glue. You apply them at each corner of the base and in 20 seconds you can have nonslip, legs.—*Joel Amkraut, Palo Alto, CA.*

REMOVE A CASTER SOCKET by driving in a stovebolt until its head hooks the top of the socket. Then, using a spacer, turn a nut on the bolt and pull out.—*James Forney, Nutley, NJ.*

An attractive wastebasket

By KENNETH WELLS

■ ANY METAL OR PLASTIC wastebasket will take on an elegant look when set in this three-legged stand of brass and walnut. The legs are simple cutouts joined together by three brass rods radiating from a center hub. The latter consists of two plywood discs drilled through the center for a ¼-in. bolt. To drill the holes for the rods, bolt the two discs together with a cardboard shim between. Then carefully center the bit so it straddles the joint and drill to the center hole. Cardboard is discarded.

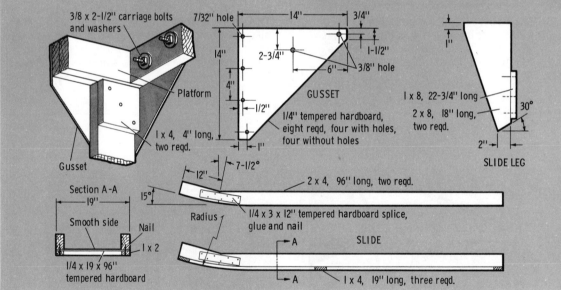

3/8 x 2-1/2" carriage bolts and washers

Platform

Gusset

1 x 4, 4" long, two reqd.

7/32" hole

14"

14"

4"

1/2"

1"

2-3/4"

6"

3/4"

1-1/2"

3/8" hole

GUSSET

1/4" tempered hardboard, eight reqd., four with holes, four without holes

1"

1 x 8, 22-3/4" long
2 x 8, 18" long, two reqd.

30°

2"

SLIDE LEG

Section A-A

19"

Smooth side

Nail

1 x 2

1/4 x 19 x 96" tempered hardboard

15°

7-1/2°

12"

Radius

1/4 x 3 x 12" tempered hardboard splice, glue and nail

2 x 4, 96" long, two reqd.

SLIDE

A

A

1 x 4, 19" long, three reqd.

"SPLIT" PLYWOOD washers lock brass leg braces together at center as you tighten bolt through center.

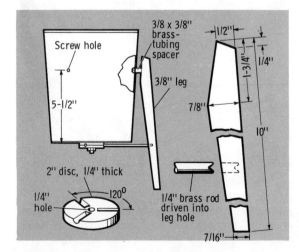

Screw hole

5-1/2"

3/8 x 3/8" brass-tubing spacer

3/8" leg

1/2"

1-3/4"

1/4"

7/8"

10"

2" disc, 1/4" thick

1/4" hole

120°

1/4" brass rod driven into leg hole

7/16"

METRIC CONVERSION

Conversion factors can be carried so far they become impractical. In cases below where an entry is exact it is followed by an asterisk (*). Where considerable rounding off has taken place, the entry is followed by a + or a − sign.

CUSTOMARY TO METRIC

Linear Measure

inches	millimeters
1/16	1.5875*
1/8	3.2
3/16	4.8
1/4	6.35*
5/16	7.9
3/8	9.5
7/16	11.1
1/2	12.7*
9/16	14.3
5/8	15.9
11/16	17.5
3/4	19.05*
13/16	20.6
7/8	22.2
15/16	23.8
1	25.4*

inches	centimeters
1	2.54*
2	5.1
3	7.6
4	10.2
5	12.7*
6	15.2
7	17.8
8	20.3
9	22.9
10	25.4*
11	27.9
12	30.5

feet	centimeters	meters
1	30.48*	.3048*
2	61	.61
3	91	.91
4	122	1.22
5	152	1.52
6	183	1.83
7	213	2.13
8	244	2.44
9	274	2.74
10	305	3.05
50	1524*	15.24*
100	3048*	30.48*

1 yard =
   .9144* meters
1 rod =
   5.0292* meters
1 mile =
   1.6 kilometers
1 nautical mile =
   1.852* kilometers

Fluid Measure

(Milliliters [ml] and cubic centimeters [cc or cu cm] are equivalent, but it is customary to use milliliters for liquids.)

1 cu in = 16.39 ml
1 fl oz = 29.6 ml
1 cup = 237 ml
1 pint = 473 ml
1 quart = 946 ml
          = .946 liters
1 gallon = 3785 ml
          = 3.785 liters
Formula (exact):
fluid ounces × 29.573 529 562 5*
   = milliliters

Weights

ounces	grams
1	28.3
2	56.7
3	85
4	113
5	142
6	170
7	198
8	227
9	255
10	283
11	312
12	340
13	369
14	397
15	425
16	454

Formula (exact):
   ounces × 28.349 523 125* = grams

pounds	kilograms
1	.45
2	.9
3	1.4
4	1.8
5	2.3
6	2.7
7	3.2
8	3.6
9	4.1
10	4.5

1 short ton (2000 lbs) =
   907 kilograms (kg)
Formula (exact):
   pounds × .453 592 37* =
   kilograms

Volume

1 cu in = 16.39 cubic centimeters (cc)
1 cu ft = 28 316.7 cc
1 bushel = 35 239.1 cc
1 peck = 8 809.8 cc

Area

1 sq in = 6.45 sq cm
1 sq ft = 929 sq cm
        = .093 sq meters
1 sq yd = .84 sq meters
1 acre = 4 046.9 sq meters
       = .404 7 hectares
1 sq mile = 2 589 988 sq meters
          = 259 hectares
          = 2.589 9 sq kilometers

Kitchen Measure

1 teaspoon = 4.93 milliliters (ml)
1 Tablespoon = 14.79 milliliters (ml)

Miscellaneous

1 British thermal unit (Btu) (mean)
   = 1 055.9 joules
1 calorie (mean) = 4.19 joules
1 horsepower = 745.7 watts
             = .75 kilowatts
caliber (diameter of a firearm's bore in hundredths of an inch)
   = .254 millimeters (mm)
1 atmosphere pressure = 101 325* pascals (newtons per sq meter)
1 pound per square inch (psi) =
   6 895 pascals
1 pound per square foot =
   47.9 pascals
1 knot = 1.85 kilometers per hour
25 miles per hour = 40.2 kilometers per hour
50 miles per hour = 80.5 kilometers per hour
75 miles per hour = 120.7 kilometers per hour

PIPE FITTINGS

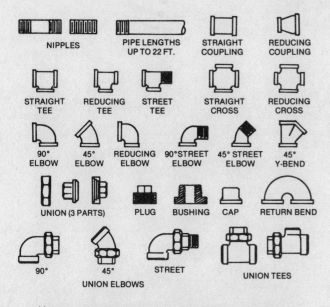

NIPPLES • PIPE LENGTHS UP TO 22 FT. • STRAIGHT COUPLING • REDUCING COUPLING

STRAIGHT TEE • REDUCING TEE • STREET TEE • STRAIGHT CROSS • REDUCING CROSS

90° ELBOW • 45° ELBOW • REDUCING ELBOW • 90° STREET ELBOW • 45° STREET ELBOW • 45° Y-BEND

UNION (3 PARTS) • PLUG • BUSHING • CAP • RETURN BEND

90° • 45° UNION ELBOWS • STREET • UNION TEES

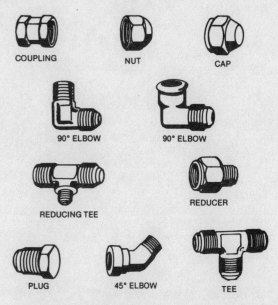

COUPLING • NUT • CAP

90° ELBOW • 90° ELBOW

REDUCING TEE • REDUCER

PLUG • 45° ELBOW • TEE

Here are the common steel pipe fittings. Nipples are simply short lengths of pipe threaded on both ends. Reducing fittings join two different sizes of pipe.

Compression fittings of the flared-tube type are the easiest for the novice to handle when working with copper tubing.

STANDARD STEEL PIPE
(All Dimensions in Inches)

Nominal Size	Outside Diameter	Inside Diameter	Nominal Size	Outside Diameter	Inside Diameter
⅛	0.405	0.269	1	1.315	1.049
¼	0.540	0.364	1¼	1.660	1.380
⅜	0.675	0.493	1½	1.900	1.610
½	0.840	0.622	2	2.375	2.067
¾	1.050	0.824	2½	2.875	2.469

SQUARE MEASURE
144 sq in = 1 sq ft
9 sq ft = 1 sq yd
272.25 sq ft = 1 sq rod
160 sq rods = 1 acre

VOLUME MEASURE
1728 cu in = 1 cu ft
27 cu ft = 1 cu yd

MEASURES OF CAPACITY
1 cup = 8 fl oz
2 cups = 1 pint
2 pints = 1 quart
4 quarts = 1 gallon
2 gallons = 1 peck
4 pecks = 1 bushel

WOOD SCREWS

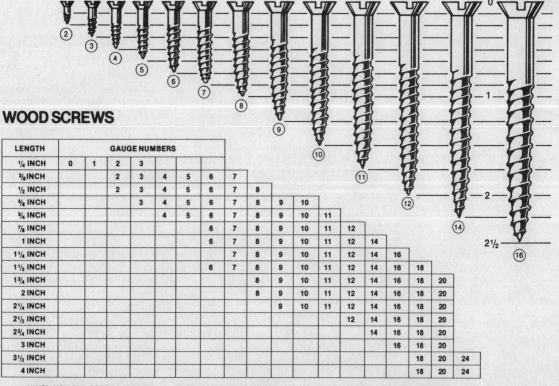

LENGTH	GAUGE NUMBERS													
¼ INCH	0	1	2	3										
⅜ INCH			2	3	4	5	6	7						
½ INCH			2	3	4	5	6	7	8					
⅝ INCH				3	4	5	6	7	8	9	10			
¾ INCH					4	5	6	7	8	9	10	11		
⅞ INCH							6	7	8	9	10	11	12	
1 INCH							6	7	8	9	10	11	12	14
1¼ INCH								7	8	9	10	11	12	14	16
1½ INCH							6	7	8	9	10	11	12	14	16	18
1¾ INCH									8	9	10	11	12	14	16	18	20
2 INCH								8	9	10	11	12	14	16	18	20
2¼ INCH									9	10	11	12	14	16	18	20
2½ INCH												12	14	16	18	20
2¾ INCH													14	16	18	20
3 INCH														16	18	20
3½ INCH															18	20	24
4 INCH															18	20	24

WHEN YOU BUY SCREWS, SPECIFY (1) LENGTH, (2) GAUGE NUMBER, (3) TYPE OF HEAD—FLAT, ROUND, OR OVAL, (4) MATERIAL—STEEL, BRASS, BRONZE, ETC., (5) FINISH—BRIGHT, STEEL BLUED, CADMIUM, NICKEL, OR CHROMIUM PLATED.